COMPUTER TEST BANK
QUESTION MANUAL

MERRILL

BIOLOGY

AN EVERYDAY EXPERIENCE

Glencoe/McGraw-Hill

A Division of The **McGraw·Hill** Companies

New York, New York   Columbus, Ohio   Woodland Hills, California   Peoria, Illinois

A MERRILL BIOLOGY PROGRAM

Biology: An Everyday Experience, *Student Edition*
Biology: An Everyday Experience, *Teacher Edition*
Biology: An Everyday Experience, *Teacher Resource Package*
Biology: An Everyday Experience, *Study Guide*
Biology: An Everyday Experience, *Transparency Package*
Biology: An Everyday Experience, *Laboratory Manual, Student Edition*
Biology: An Everyday Experience, *Laboratory Manual, Teacher Edition*
Biology: An Everyday Experience, *Computer Test Bank*
Biology: An Everyday Experience, *Cooperative Learning*
Biology: An Everyday Experience, *Spanish Resources*
Biology: An Everyday Experience, *Videodisc Correlations*
Biology: An Everyday Experience, *Lesson Plans*
Biology: An Everyday Experience, *Tech Prep Applications*

Glencoe/McGraw-Hill

A Division of The McGraw-Hill Companies

Send all inquiries to:
Glencoe/McGraw-Hill
936 Eastwind Drive
Westerville, OH 43081

Printed in the United States of America.
ISBN: 0-02-825699-9

3 4 5 6 7 8 9 10 069 05 04 03 02 01 00 99

CONTENTS

TO THE TEACHER

This test bank contains true/false, multiple choice, matching, completion, problem, and short answer questions covering all 32 chapters in the *Glencoe Biology: An Everyday Experience* text. The questions are grouped by cognitive type within each chapter. These questions have been prepared to assist you in developing objective-based tests for your students.

LEARNING OBJECTIVES

Learning objectives are suggested outcomes of what your students may be capable of achieving during or after your teaching. The objectives for each chapter (the same ones found in the Student Edition and Teacher Wraparound Edition) are listed before the questions in this manual. Each objective is covered by at least two questions.

LEVELS OF DIFFICULTY

In addition to being correlated to the objectives, each test question is designated with one of two levels of difficulty. Most questions are ranked "B" for *Basic* level of difficulty. These questions ask the student to understand or to review the material studied. Some questions are ranked "A" for *Advanced* level of difficulty. These questions require a deeper understanding of the material, and students are asked to apply concepts or to think critically. At the end of each question is a code that gives you both the objective number and the level of difficulty for that question. Use this information when you select questions to help you tailor your test to the exact needs and abilities of your students.

COMPONENTS

- *Glencoe Biology: An Everyday Experience* Test Bank Question Manual
- Glencoe Test Generator User's Manual (Windows)
- Glencoe Test Generator User's Manual (Macintosh)
- Diskettes (Windows/Macintosh)

The *Glencoe Biology: An Everyday Experience* Test Bank consists of a Question Manual and a set of diskettes (the program disk, the test bank data disks, and a set of disks containing graphics that may accompany some questions). The *User's Guide* contains instructions for the setup and use of the software. Be sure to use the correct booklet for your system (Windows or Macintosh). The program disk contains a program that lets you retrieve the questions you want and print tests. It also lets you edit and add questions as needed.

The Question Manual contains a printed listing of all the questions in the test bank. Use this manual to preview the available questions and to make your choices for inclusion on tests; or, if you prefer, you may view and select questions on-screen using the included computer program.

SITE LICENSE

Your adoption of Glencoe's 1999 edition of *Biology: An Everyday Experience* entitles you to site-license duplication rights for all components of this test bank with the restriction that all copies must be used within the adopting schools. This license shall run for the life of the adoption of the accompanying text.

USING THE TEST BANK

Before you begin, follow the directions in the *User's Guide* to make backup copies of all the disks. Then, set up your computer and printer and configure the software, following the instructions. The *User's Guide* contains all the instructions on how to use the software. Refer to this Question Manual as needed to preview and select questions for your tests.

Some questions require the student to examine a drawing or chart. If you have a compatible printer, the program can print the graphic with the questions. The Question Manual also contains blackline masters of all the figures and solutions referenced by the test questions. These figures are grouped by chapter to simplify the process of copying and collating them with the copies of your tests if you do not have a compatible printer.

SOFTWARE SUPPORT HOTLINE

Should you encounter any difficulty when setting up or running the programs, contact the Software Support Center at Glencoe Publishing between 8:30 a.m. and 6:00 p.m. Eastern Time. The toll-free number is 1-800-437-3715. You can also send an E-mail to the following address: epgtech@mcgraw-hill.com

---

WINDOWS TEST GENERATOR INTRODUCTION

This package includes a test generator program called *ExamView*–an application that enables you to quickly and easily create tests, enter your own questions, and customize the appearance of the tests you create. The *ExamView* test generator program offers many unique features. Using the QuickTest wizard, for example, you are guided step-by-step through the process of building a test. Numerous options are included that allow you to customize the content and appearance of the tests you create.

As you work with the *ExamView* test generator, you may use the following features:

- an "interview" mode or a "wizard" to guide you through the steps to create a test in less than five minutes
- five methods to select test questions
  - from a list
  - random selection
  - by criteria (difficulty code or objective–if available)
  - while viewing questions
  - all questions
- the capability to edit questions or to add an unlimited number of questions
- a sophisticated word processor
  - streamlined question entry
  - toolbar
  - cut, copy, paste, undo
  - tabs (center, left, right, decimal, leaders)
  - fonts and text styles (bold, underline, color, etc.)
  - support for symbols and foreign characters
  - tables
  - borders and shading
  - paragraph formatting (justification, spacing, hanging indent, etc.)
  - pictures or other graphics within a question, answer, or narrative
  - find/replace commands
- numerous test layout and printing options
  - scramble the choices in multiple choice questions
  - organize matching questions in a one- or two-column format
  - print multiple versions of the same test with corresponding answer keys
  - print an answer key strip for easier test grading
  - change the order of questions
  - print a test with or without space for students to record their answers
  - specify the layout of a test to conserve paper
  - print a comprehensive answer sheet
- the ability to link groups of questions to common narratives
- password protection
- extensive help system

INSTALLATION AND STARTUP INSTRUCTIONS

The *ExamView* test generator software is provided on one or more floppy disks or on a CD-ROM depending on the size of the question bank. The disks include the program and all of the questions for the corresponding textbook. Before you can use the test generator software, you must install it on your hard drive or network. The system requirements, installation instructions, and startup procedures are provided below.

SYSTEM REQUIREMENTS

To use the *ExamView* test generator, your computer must meet or exceed these minimum hardware requirements:

- 486, 50 MHz computer
- Windows 3.1, Windows 95, Windows 98, or Windows NT
- color monitor (VGA-compatible)
- high-density floppy disk drive
- hard drive with at least 5 MB space available
- 8 MB available memory *(16 MB memory recommended)*
- mouse
- printer

INSTALLATION INSTRUCTIONS

Follow these steps to install the *ExamView* test generator software on a hard drive or network. The setup program will automatically install everything you need to use the *ExamView* test generator software.

Step 1
Turn on your computer.

Step 2
Insert the *ExamView* installation disk into Drive A. If the program is provided on a CD-ROM, insert the disc into your CD-ROM drive.

Step 3
Windows 3.1: While in the Program Manager, choose *Run* from the **File** menu.
Windows 95/98: Click the **Start** button on the *Taskbar* and choose the *Run* option.

Step 4
If you are installing the software from floppy disks, type **a:\setup** and press **Enter** to run the installation program. If the *ExamView* software is provided on a CD-ROM, use the drive letter that corresponds to the CD-ROM drive on your computer (e.g., **e:\setup**).

   Note: The installation program is configured to copy the software to *c:\examview* on your hard drive. You can, however, change this location. For example, you can select a location on your network server.

Step 5
Follow the prompts on the screen to complete the installation process. If the software and question banks are provided on more than one disk, you will be prompted to insert the appropriate disk when it is needed.

Step 6
Remove the installation disk from the disk drive when you finish.

GETTING STARTED

After you have completed the installation process, follow these instructions to start the *ExamView* software. This section also explains the options used to create a test and edit a question bank.

Startup Instructions

Step 1
Turn on the computer.

Step 2
Windows 3.1: Locate the *ExamView* program icon. Double-click the program icon to start the test generator software.
Windows 95/98: Click the **Start** button on the *Taskbar.* Highlight the **Programs** menu and locate the *ExamView* folder. Select the *ExamView* option to start the software.

Step 3
The first time you run the software you will be prompted to enter your name, school/institution name, and city/state. You are now ready to begin using the *ExamView* software.

Step 4
Each time you start *ExamView,* the **Startup** menu appears. As shown in Figure 1, choose one of the following options:

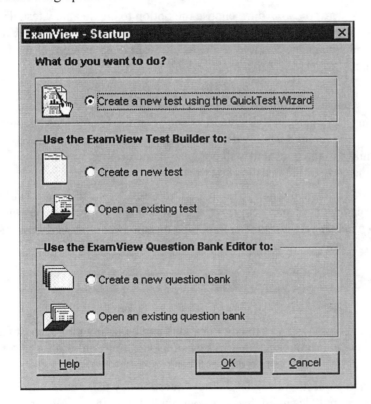

Figure 1 – ExamView Startup Menu

Step 5
Use *ExamView* to create a test or edit questions in a question bank.

The *ExamView* program is divided into two components: Test Builder and Question Bank Editor. The **Test Builder** includes options to create, edit, print, and save tests. The **Question Bank Editor** lets you create or edit existing question banks. Both the Test Builder and the Question Bank Editor have unique menus and options to work with tests and question banks.

As you work with *ExamView*, you can easily switch between these components using the *Switch to...* option in the **File** menu. Be sure to save your work before you switch between components.

Important: Whenever you need assistance using *ExamView,* access the extensive help system. Click the **Help** button or choose an option from the **Help** menu to access step-by-step instructions and detailed descriptions of the features of *ExamView.* If you experience any difficulties while you are working with the software, you may want to review the troubleshooting tips in the user-friendly help system.

Test Builder

The Test Builder will empower you to create tests using the QuickTest Wizard or you can create a new test on your own.

- *If you want ExamView to choose questions randomly from one or more question banks,* choose the QuickTest Wizard option to create a new test. Then, follow the step-by-step instructions to (1) enter a test title, (2) choose the question bank from which to select questions, and (3) identify how many questions you want on the test. The QuickTest Wizard will automatically create a new test and use the Test Builder to display the test on screen. You can print the test as is, remove questions, add new questions, or edit any questions.

- *If you want to create a new test on your own,* choose the option to create a new test. Then identify a question bank from which to choose questions by using the *Question Bank* option in the **Select** menu. You may then add questions to the test by using one or more of the following question selection options: *Randomly, From a List, While Viewing, By Criteria,* or *All Questions.*

After you create a test, you can customize the appearance of the test by changing the order of the questions, editing test instructions, specifying the font and style for selected test elements, and choosing whether to leave space for students to write their answers directly on the test. The customizing changes you make to the questions will not change the original question bank; your changes are made only to the copy of the questions on the test you just created.

When you have finalized the content and appearance of your test, you can print it and/or save it. To print a test, you may choose how many copies of the test you want, whether you want all the copies to be the same, and whether you want to scramble the questions and the multiple choice options. If you scramble the questions, *ExamView* will print a custom answer sheet for each variation of the test.

Question Bank Editor

The Question Bank Editor will empower you to edit questions in an existing publisher-supplied question bank or to create new question banks. Always use the Question Bank Editor if you want to change a question permanently in an existing question bank.

You may edit questions in a question bank or add new questions by using the built-in word processor. The word processor includes many features commonly found in commercially available word processing applications. These features include the following: fonts, styles, tables, paragraph formatting, ruler controls, tabs, indents, and justification.

A question bank may include up to 250 questions in a variety of formats including multiple choice, true/false, modified true/false, completion, yes/no, matching, problem, essay, short answer, case, and numeric response. You can assign a difficulty code, a page reference, and two objectives to each question.

WINDOWS USER'S GUIDE

SOFTWARE SUPPORT

Glencoe provides toll-free telephone assistance for instructors who experience difficulty while using *ExamView*. Before calling for assistance, please check the following:

- Is your computer working properly? Try some other software, which you know is working, on the same computer.
- Are you certain the software is working properly? Try the software on another computer.
- Can you repeat the problem? Does the problem occur at the same point each time?

In order for the Support Center to help you as quickly as possible, before calling for assistance have the following at hand:

- exact title and ISBN number from the disk label or package.
- brand, model, and configuration of the computer you are using.
- system version (Windows 3.1, Windows 95, or Windows 98) installed on your computer.
- the exact wording of any error message.

The Glencoe Support Center toll-free number is **800-437-3715**. The Support Center is available from 8:00 A.M. to 6:00 P.M. Eastern Time. You can also send an E-mail to the following address **epgtech@mcgraw-hill.com** to contact the Support Center.

WINDOWS USER'S GUIDE

MACINTOSH TEST GENERATOR
INTRODUCTION

With the *Glencoe Test Generator* you can quickly and easily create tests, enter your own questions, and customize the test layout to meet your needs. The *Glencoe Test Generator* program offers many features not found in other test generators. Using the *QuickTest* option, for example, the software guides you step-by-step through the process of building a test. For the more advanced user, the software includes numerous options that give you complete control over the content and appearance of the tests you create.

As you work with the *Glencoe Test Generator*, you will use these features:

- an "interview" mode to guide you through the process of having the software create a test

- five methods to select test questions yourself
  - from a list
  - random selection
  - by criteria (difficulty code, objective, or topic)
  - while viewing questions
  - all questions

- the capability to edit or add an unlimited number of test questions

- a word processor with many distinctive features
  - text manipulation functions (undo, cut, copy, paste, clear, and select all)
  - tabs (center, left, right, decimal)
  - text styles (bold, underline, italic, subscript, superscript, and condensed) and sizes
  - extended character support («» ½ ¼ α β Γ π Σ σ μ τ ϕ θ Ω ÷ $\approx$ ° $\cdots\sqrt{}$ ^{n} ...) using fonts
  - find/replace (within a question or the entire question bank)
  - include graphic images within a question, answer, or narrative

- numerous test formatting options
  - scramble the choices in multiple choice questions
  - print an answer strip
  - modify printing order for the question types
  - select the printing order based on difficulty, objective, or topic
  - provide space on the test for students to write their answers or remove all answer areas for tests completed on scanner sheets
  - specify layout for multiple choice questions (traditional or alternative to conserve paper)
  - print a comprehensive answer sheet (answer, topic, objective, etc.) or just the answer

- the ability to link groups of questions to common narratives

- password protection

- extensive on-line help

SECTION 1–INSTALLATION & STARTUP

WHAT'S ON THE DISK

The *Glencoe Test Generator* software is provided on one or more disks depending on the test bank. If the test bank is on one disk, it contains both the program and the question banks. When supplied on multiple disks, Disk 1 is the test generator program and the other disk(s) contain the question banks corresponding to your textbook.

WHAT YOU NEED

To use the *Glencoe Test Generator* software, you need the following equipment:
- Any Macintosh computer with at least 2Mb of memory
- System 6.0.5 or higher
- A hard drive or two floppy drives

INSTALLATION

Follow these steps to install the program and the question bank files on your hard drive. Although you can run the program from floppy drives, installing the software on your hard drive is recommended.

Step 1
Switch your computer on (if it's not already on).

Step 2
When the Desktop appears, insert the program disk (Disk 1) into a drive.

Step 3
Drag the disk icon to your hard drive to create a new folder and copy the test generator.

Step 4
Eject the disk from the drive.

Step 5
If the test bank is provided on more than one disk, insert the next disk into a drive. Drag the files to the test generator folder to copy the question banks to your hard drive.

Step 6
Eject the question bank disk. (Repeat Step 5 for each additional question bank disk.)

GETTING STARTED

If you installed the software on your hard drive, double-click the test generator folder at this time. If you are running the software from a floppy drive, insert the program disk into a drive.

Step 1

Double-click the test generator icon.

   The *Glencoe Test Generator* software starts and the opening screen appears. If the opening screen does not appear, check the Troubleshooting section of this manual (pp. M-25 to M-26).

Step 2

Click the mouse button to display the **Main** menu.

The Main menu, shown in Figure 1-1, appears on your screen. The software is divided into three parts: *QuickTest, Build/Print Test,* and *Edit Question Banks.* A brief description of each of the parts is given below.

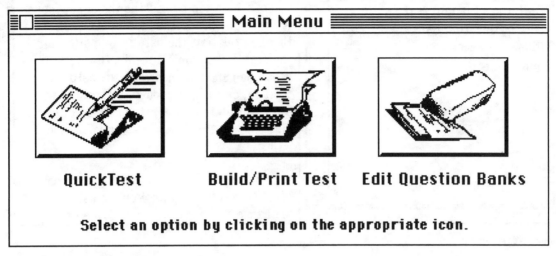

Figure 1-1 Main Menu

QuickTest

If you want the software to select the questions randomly, then *QuickTest* is just the thing for you! With *QuickTest,* you can build a test containing up to 250 questions from as many as thirty question banks in less than one minute.

Build/Print Test

Although *QuickTest* provides a quick and simple way to create tests, many times you will want to create a test with specific questions or questions that match specific criteria. The *Glencoe Test Generator* allows you to do just that. Using the *Build/Print Test* option, there are five different ways to select questions. You are also given a way to change the question type order, change the test layout options, edit headers and instructions, and edit questions even after they have been included in your test. Once tests have been built, you have the option of saving them to disk and retrieving them at a later time.

Edit Question Banks

In addition to using the supplied question banks, you also have the option of creating your own. The *Glencoe Test Generator* contains a powerful word processor with many distinctive features that allows you to add questions to existing question banks or create entirely new question banks. Question banks can contain up to 250 questions from a variety of question types. Each question can be assigned an objective, a page reference, a difficulty index, and a topic. Questions can include a picture (graphic) and/or be linked to a narrative (specialized instruction).

HELP

Context-sensitive help is available from anywhere within the software by choosing *Help* from the **Apple** () menu. A window appears on your screen as shown in Figure 1-2.

A list of help topics appears in the window. The software attempts to determine the most likely topic based on where you are in the program. Use the up and down arrow keys or the mouse to highlight the topic about which you want more information.

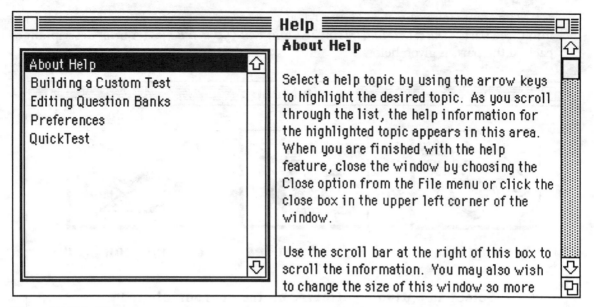

Figure 1-2 Help Window

As you move through the list of help topics, the program displays the help information in a box on the right side of the help window. If the help text is too long to fit on the screen at one time, you can use the mouse to scroll through the remainder of the information. When you are through reviewing the help information, close the window.

PREFERENCES

Choose *Preferences* from the **Edit** menu. The software lets you set the default font and size for all new questions, headers, instructions, and question numbers. The supplied question banks are in Courier 12. Unless you need to change the question banks to a different font, there is no need to change the default font and size.

If you enter a password in the Password field, each time you start the software you will be prompted to enter the password. Make sure that if you enter a password, you record it in a safe place.

If you want the software to select the questions randomly, then *QuickTest* is just the thing for you! With *QuickTest*, you can build a test containing up to 250 questions from many question banks in less than a minute.

When you choose the *QuickTest* option, the software leads you step-by-step through the process of building a test. Extensive prompt messages tell you exactly what to do and which buttons to press. There is no need to choose anything from the menus.

To begin *QuickTest*, start the software and choose *QuickTest* from the **Main** menu.

CHOOSING QUESTION BANKS

The dialog box shown in Figure 2-1 appears on your screen.

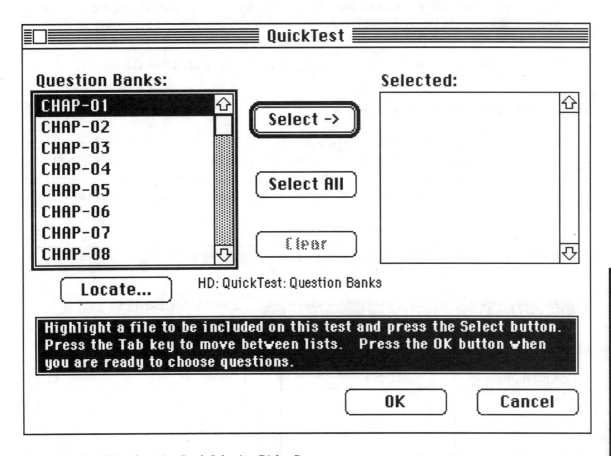

Figure 2-1 QuickTest Question Bank Selection Dialog Box

Step 1

A list showing question bank files appears at the left. Depending on whether you are working on a floppy drive system or a hard drive, follow the appropriate steps below:

Floppy Drives   Make sure the disk containing the question banks is in a drive. If the question banks are on separate disks, insert a question bank disk into another drive. Click the **Locate** button, select the question bank disk, and then click the **Done** button. The question banks on that disk will appear in the list. If, after selecting question banks from this disk, you decide that you want to select questions from another question bank disk, simply click the **Locate** button again, eject the disk, and insert the new disk in the drive.

Hard Drive When you installed the question banks on the hard drive, you placed them in the test generator folder. Click the **Locate** button, double-click the folder name, and click **Done**. The question bank names appear in the list.

Step 2

Use the up and down arrow keys or the mouse to highlight the first question bank file to include on your test. Once the bank name is highlighted, click the **Select** button. When you click the button, notice how *QuickTest* inserts the name of the question bank into the *Selected* list on the right of the screen. As a shortcut, you can simply double-click on a question bank name to select it.

Step 3

Select the other question banks to use for the test in the same manner. If you inadvertently select a question bank you do not want, simply highlight the question bank name you want to remove and click the **Remove** button.

Step 4

When you have selected all of the question banks you want, click the **OK** button.

SELECTING QUESTIONS

A list showing the types of questions in the selected banks (e.g., True/False, Multiple Choice, etc.) and the number of questions of each type that can be selected appears on the left of the dialog box (see Figure 2-2). A status area at the bottom of the dialog box shows the total number of questions on the test. Remember, you can select up to 250 questions for a test.

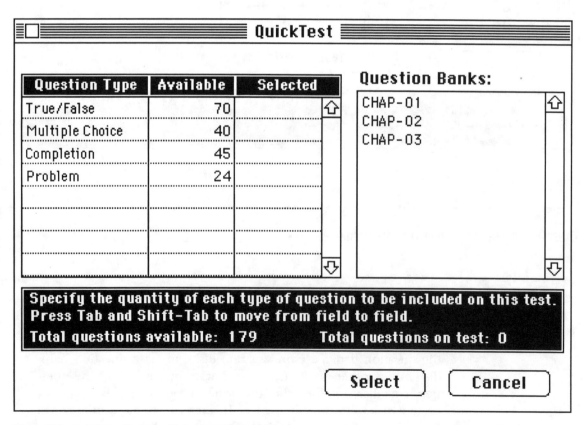

Figure 2-2 QuickTest Question Selection Dialog Box

If you notice that you forgot to include a question bank, simply click the **Cancel** button to return to the previous screen, select the question bank, and click **OK** again.

Step 1
In the spaces provided, key the number of questions of each type you want to include on your test. After you press **Return** for each entry, the status area is updated.

Step 2
When you are satisfied with the makeup of your test, click the **Select** button. The software will now automatically select the questions for your test.

QUICKTEST SUMMARY

Once the *Glencoe Test Generator* has completed the question selection process, the dialog box shown in Figure 2-3 appears on your screen. The summary shows you how many questions are on the test, which question banks were used in selecting questions, and how many questions of each question type have been selected. At this time, you can print the test, save it, change the test layout, or cancel the selections and begin again.

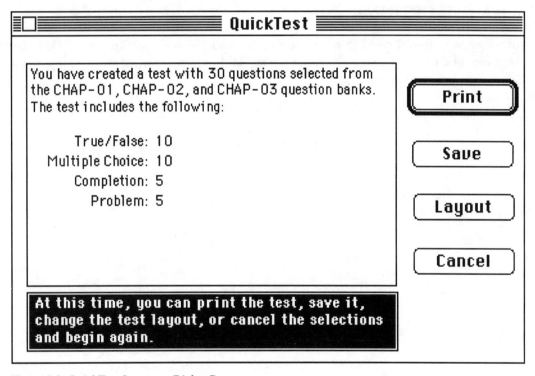

Figure 2-3 QuickTest Summary Dialog Box

Step 1
Review your selections.

Step 2
To continue, click the **Print** button. Once your test has been printed, the software returns you to the test summary screen.

Changing the Test Layout

If you prefer, you may change the test layout or print multiple variations of your test. The question order within each question type will be different for each variation. To print multiple variations, enter a number greater than one in the field using the *Layout* option.

Many test layout options, discussed in detail in Section 3–Build/Print Test, are available. To change any of the options, click the **Layout** button. Remember, you can get on-line help at any time by pressing ⌘+**H**. After changing the options, click the **OK** button to continue.

Saving Your Test

You may, if you like, choose to save your test to disk. Click the **Save** button. Use the controls to set the drive and/or folder on which to save. Key-enter a name for your test and click the **Save** button. Once a test has been saved, you can use the *Build/Print Test* option, discussed in Section 3, to retrieve the test from disk. The test can then be modified using the features discussed in that section.

EXIT TO MAIN MENU

At any time while working with *QuickTest*, you may choose to quit. To exit, simply press ⌘+**Q**. Return to the **Main** menu by choosing ⌘+**W** or by clicking the close box to close the QuickTest window. When the software asks if you want to select new questions from the current question banks, click the **No** button.

OTHER MENU OPTIONS

Although you do not need to access the menu options while working with *QuickTest*, you still can. The following menu options are available when creating a test: *Help, Close, Page Setup, Quit,* and *Preferences.*

SECTION 3–BUILD/PRINT TEST

Although *QuickTest* provides a quick and simple way to create tests, many times you will want to create a test with specific questions or questions that match specific criteria. The *Glencoe Test Generator* allows you to do just that. Using the *Build/Print Test* option, there are five different ways to select questions. You are also given a way to change the question type order, change the test layout options, edit headers and instructions, and edit questions even after they have been included in your test.

To begin building a new test, follow these steps:

Step 1
Start the *Glencoe Test Generator* software.

Step 2
From the **Main** menu, select the *Build/Print Test* option.

BUILDING A TEST

Once you have selected the *Build/Print Test* option, the "visual test" is displayed on your screen. If you do not want to build a new test, you can choose the *Open Test* option from the **File** menu to retrieve a previously saved test from disk.

The Visual Test

While you are building your test, the window shown in Figure 3-1 (referred to as the "visual test") will always reflect the current composition of the test. The program displays the first page header, instructions, narratives, and the questions in the order they will be printed on the test. Use the arrow keys or the mouse to scroll through the list of questions. A status line appears at the bottom of the window showing the current question bank name, current item highlighted [e.g., First Page Header, Instructions, TF (1 of 20), etc.], and the total number of questions on the test.

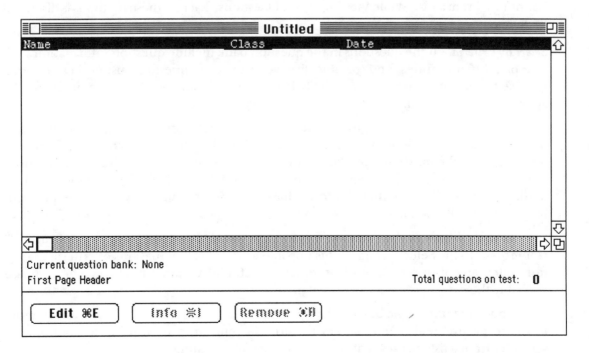

Figure 3-1 Visual Test Window

MACINTOSH USER'S GUIDE

Selecting a Question Bank

The first thing you will want to do when you begin a new test is select a question bank from which to select questions. Choose the *Question Bank* option from the **Select** menu. The dialog box shown in Figure 3-2 will appear. Use the controls shown to set the drive and/or folder where your question bank files are located. Select the desired question bank from the list. Click the **Open** button to open the selected question bank file.

Only one question bank file may be open at a time, although questions from many question banks may be contained on a single test. Select questions from one question bank, then open a different question bank and select additional questions.

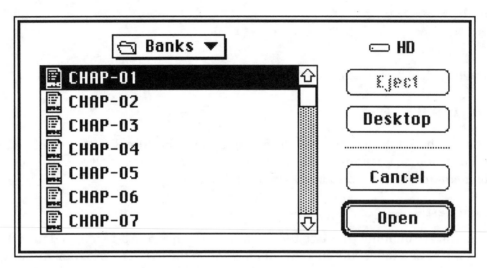

Figure 3-2 Question Bank Selection Dialog Box

Selecting Questions

Once you have selected a question bank, you are now ready to select questions for your test. As was mentioned above, you can select questions in five different ways: By Criteria, Randomly, From a List, While Viewing, or All Questions. Each of these methods is discussed in detail.

Select By Criteria. If the questions in the question bank include question information such as topic, difficulty index, and/or objective, you can select questions using these criteria. Choose the *By Criteria* option from the **Select** menu. The dialog box shown in Figure 3-3 appears on your screen.

To select questions on a given topic: (1) move to the Topic field, (2) click the **Topic** button, (3) select the desired topic from the list, (4) tab to the Select column, (5) enter a number up to the maximum available. Repeat these steps to select additional questions based on other criteria. Leave any column blank if you do not want to restrict the questions in that category. Click the **Done** button to have the software randomly select the questions based on the criteria set.

As you will notice when you use this feature, the MAX amount does not appear until you move into the Select column. It is possible to specify combinations of criteria that do not match any of the questions in the bank. If the MAX amount shows a zero, this is probably the case.

Notice that the **Topic** button changes to Difficulty, Objective, and Type as you move to the respective fields. You can key the criteria yourself without using the button, but selecting from a list ensures that you do not misspell anything.

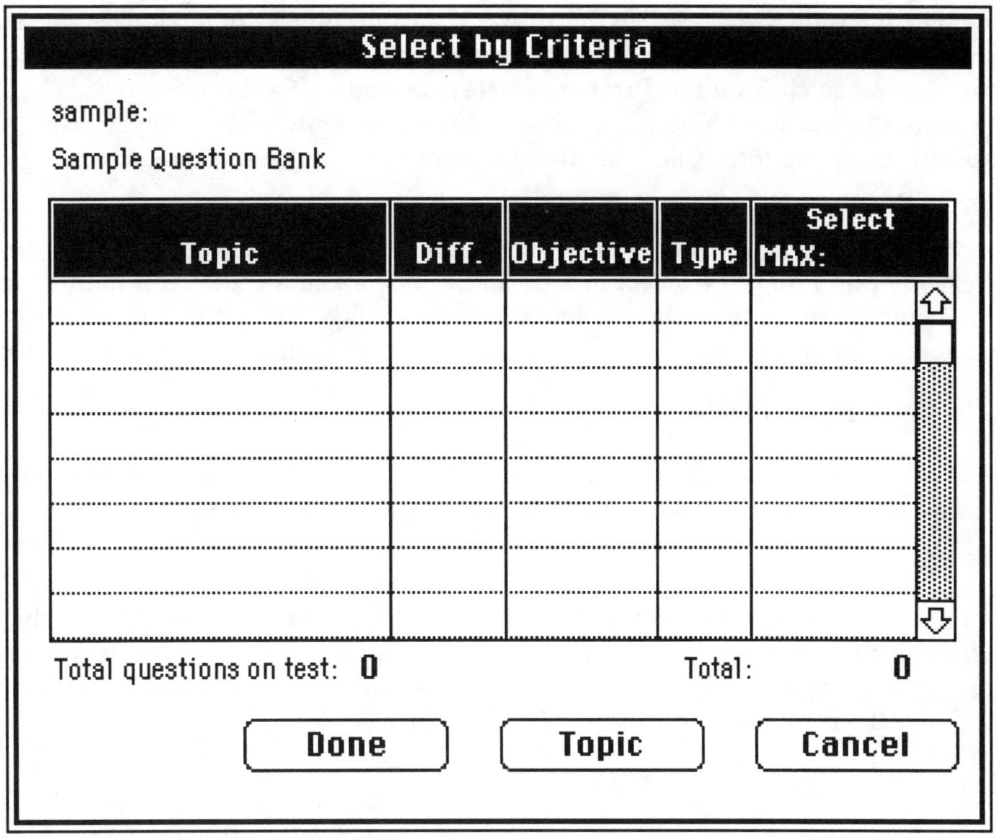

```
┌─────────────────────────────────────────────────────────┐
│                   Select by Criteria                      │
│ sample:                                                   │
│ Sample Question Bank                                      │
│                                              Select        │
│        Topic            Diff. Objective Type MAX:         │
│ ···································································· │
│                                                           │
│                                                           │
│                                                           │
│                                                           │
│                                                           │
│ Total questions on test:  0            Total:     0       │
│      ( Done )      ( Topic )      ( Cancel )              │
└─────────────────────────────────────────────────────────┘
```

Figure 3-3 Select by Criteria Dialog Box

Multiple groups of questions can be selected at any one time. For example, on the first line select three True/False questions with Topic 1 and difficulty index 2, and on the second line select five Multiple Choice questions with Topic 3 and difficulty index 4.

Note: This selection method is applicable only if the question banks include topics, objectives, or difficulty codes.

Select Randomly. Questions can also be selected randomly by question type, much as they were using *QuickTest.* Choose the *Randomly* option from the **Select** menu. For each question type, the number of questions available and the number already selected is shown. Enter the number of additional questions of each type that you want to add to the test. Click the **Done** button to have the software randomly select the questions.

Select From a List. Often, you will select questions while looking at a printout of the question bank. If you are selecting questions in this way, this is probably the best option for you to use. Choose the *From a List* option in the **Select** menu.

The software displays a list showing the question type, narrative number (if any), difficulty index, and topic for each of the questions in the bank. Click on a question to select it. A check mark appears to the left of the question information to indicate this question is now selected. To unselect a question, simply click on the line again. Click the **Done** button to have the software select the marked questions.

Select While Viewing. If you want to be able to see the questions before selecting them, then you will want to use the *While Viewing* option. Choose the *While Viewing* option from the **Select** menu.

The question text (as well as the answer if the question is not too long) appears in the viewing window. Move through the questions using the arrow keys. If you are using a mouse, you can click on the **Previous** or **Next** buttons. If a narrative is attached to the question, the **Narrative** button is enabled. While viewing the question you want to select, click the **Select** button. Click the **Done** button to have the software select the marked questions.

Select All Questions.   To include all of the questions from a question bank, choose the *All Questions* option from the **Select** menu. You will be asked whether you want to select all remaining questions from the particular question bank. Once the questions have been selected, an informational alert tells you how many additional questions were selected.

SAVING AND PRINTING

Once the questions have been selected, the *Glencoe Test Generator* allows you to save the test to disk. Review the selected questions by scrolling through the visual test.

Saving a Test

From the **File** menu, choose either *Save* or *Save As* to save your test to disk. Use the *Save As* option if you want to assign the test a new name. The Save As dialog box is very similar to the Open dialog box. Use the controls to set the drive and/or folder on which to save. Key-enter the file name and click the **Save** button.

Page Setup

Before you print a test for the first time, choose the *Page Setup* option from the **File** menu. Verify that the appropriate options are set.

Printing a Test

To print a test, choose the *Print Test* option from the **File** menu. Set the options and click the **Print** button.

Opening a Test

Choose the *Open Test* option from the **File** menu to open tests that have already been saved. In the Open Test dialog box, there are controls to change drives and folders to locate your tests. Choose a test by highlighting the name from the list and clicking the **Open** button. Files can also be opened by double-clicking on the file name.

MISCELLANEOUS FEATURES

In addition to those features already mentioned, the *Glencoe Test Generator* offers the following features while working with the *Build/Print Test* option. Use any or all of these features to customize your test.

Question Type Order

Questions on a test must be grouped by question type (True/False, Multiple Choice, etc.). The default order in which question types will appear on a test is as follows: True/False, Multiple Choice, Yes/No, Completion, Matching, Short Answer, Problem, and Other.

You can change the question type order for the current test only, or save the question type order for use with all new tests. Choose the *Question Type Order* option from the **Select** menu. Specify the order in which you want the question types to appear. To move a question type to another place in the list, drag it to its new location. Click the **OK** button to change the order for the current test only. Use the **Save** button to change all subsequent tests as well as the current test.

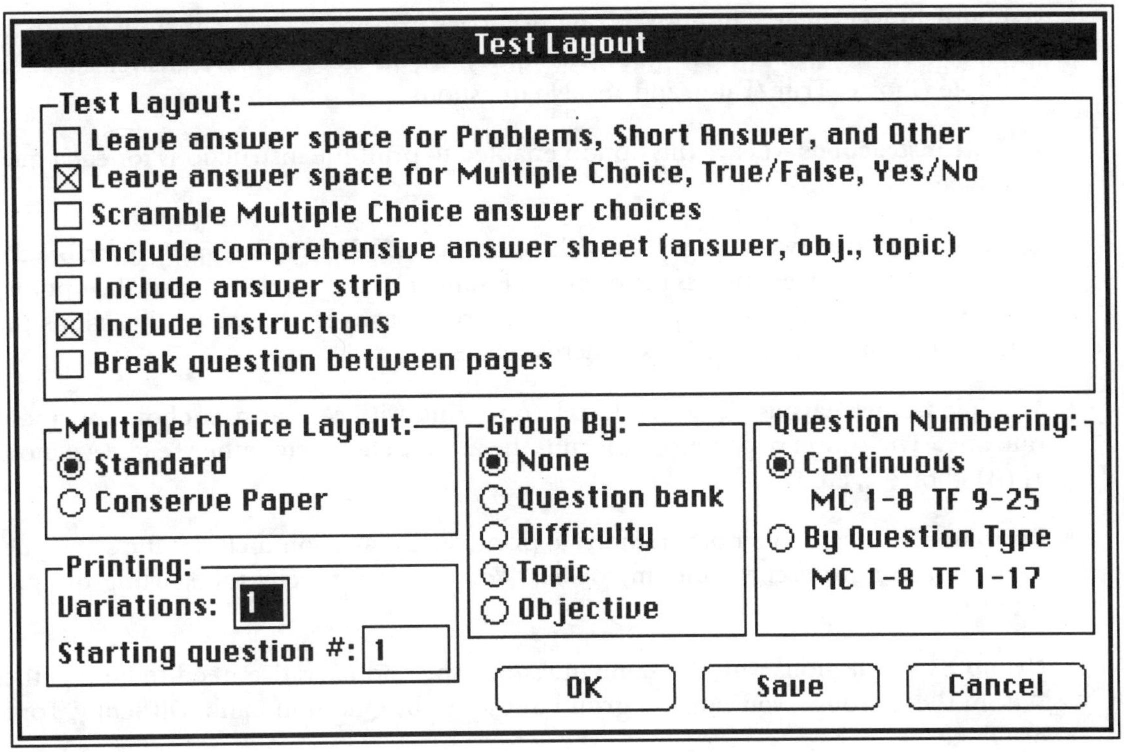

```
┌─────────────────────────────────────────────────────────────┐
│                        Test Layout                            │
│ ┌─Test Layout: ─────────────────────────────────────────────┐ │
│ │ ☐ Leave answer space for Problems, Short Answer, and Other│ │
│ │ ☒ Leave answer space for Multiple Choice, True/False, Yes/No│ │
│ │ ☐ Scramble Multiple Choice answer choices                 │ │
│ │ ☐ Include comprehensive answer sheet (answer, obj., topic)│ │
│ │ ☐ Include answer strip                                    │ │
│ │ ☒ Include instructions                                    │ │
│ │ ☐ Break question between pages                            │ │
│ └───────────────────────────────────────────────────────────┘ │
│ ┌─Multiple Choice Layout:─┐ ┌─Group By: ──┐ ┌─Question Numbering:─┐│
│ │ ⦿ Standard              │ │ ⦿ None      │ │ ⦿ Continuous        ││
│ │ ○ Conserve Paper        │ │ ○ Question bank│ │   MC 1-8  TF 9-25   ││
│ │                         │ │ ○ Difficulty│ │ ○ By Question Type  ││
│ │ ┌─Printing: ──────────┐ │ │ ○ Topic     │ │   MC 1-8  TF 1-17   ││
│ │ │ Variations: [1]     │ │ │ ○ Objective │ └─────────────────────┘│
│ │ │ Starting question #:[1]│ └─────────────┘ ┌────┐┌────┐┌──────┐ │
│ │ └─────────────────────┘ │                  │ OK ││Save││Cancel│ │
│ └─────────────────────────┘                  └────┘└────┘└──────┘ │
└─────────────────────────────────────────────────────────────┘
```

Figure 3-4 Test Layout Dialog Box

Clear All Selections

If you want to remove all of the questions from the test—not just those in the current question bank—select the *Clear All Selections* option from the **Select** menu. You will be asked if you want to clear all questions in the current test. Respond appropriately.

Test Layout

Numerous test layouts are available for customizing your test. Select the *Test Layout* option from the **Special** menu. A dialog box as shown in Figure 3-4 appears.

The options available are listed on pages M-13 and M-14.

- **Leave answer space for Problems, Short Answer, and Other** – Set this option to include space on the printed test for the students to write their answers. The blank space provided on the test will be slightly more than the amount of space that the correct answer requires.

- **Leave answer space for Multiple Choice, True/False, Yes/No** – Set this option to include a space to the left of the question for the students to write their answers.

- **Scramble Multiple Choice answer choices** – Set this option to scramble the answer choices for multiple choice questions when you print multiple variations of your test. Some answer choices should not be scrambled (e.g., **d. All of the above**). To prevent these choices from being scrambled on questions you create, insert the # symbol after the answer letter (e.g., **d.# All of the above**). This symbol will not be printed on the test.

- **Include comprehensive answer sheet** – Enable this option to print a comprehensive answer sheet including the answer, topic, objective, and difficulty code for each question.

- **Include answer strip** – Set this option to print an answer strip for True/False, Multiple Choice, and Yes/No questions. The software prints the answer strip in addition to the standard answer sheet. The answers on the answer strip are spaced so they align with the questions on the printed test. Use this option if you elect to leave answer space for Multiple Choice, True/False, and Yes/No questions.

- **Include instructions** – Leave this option enabled to print the instructions for each question type.

- **Break questions between pages** – If this option is off, the software will never break a question between pages unless the question is longer than a single page. If the option is set, the software will print a question on different pages if necessary. Questions that contain a picture will not be broken across pages.

- **Multiple Choice Layout** – The standard layout prints with each answer choice on a separate line. The conserve paper option runs the answer choices together [e.g., (A) choice 1, (B) choice 2, etc.].

- **Printing** – Set the number of variations to print. Each variation includes the same questions, but in a different (random) order. You can also specify the starting question number.

- **Group By** – Questions with the same question type and narrative need to be together. Within these groups, you can also group questions by Question bank, Difficulty, Topic, or Objective.

- **Question Numbering** – Choose to number questions continuously (MC 1-8 TF 9-25) or by question type (MC 1-8 TF 1-17).

Click the **OK** button to change the test layout options only for the current test. Use the **Save** button to save the test layout options for use with subsequent tests.

Headers

Each test contains two headers, one that prints at the top of the first page, and another for subsequent pages. Headers may be edited and saved with the current test only or saved to disk for use with all new tests. Choose the *Test Headers* option from the **Special** menu to edit the headers.

When editing the headers, you can use any of the features of the word processor. These features are discussed in Section 4–Edit Question Banks. Headers should be limited to about six lines.

The placeholder **[PG]** can be included in either of the headers. When this placeholder is encountered during printing, it will be replaced with the current page number (e.g., *Page [PG]* will be printed as *Page 1*).

Instructions

Default instructions are provided for each question type (e.g., True/False, Multiple Choice, etc.). Instructions may be edited and saved with the current test only or saved to disk for use with all new tests. Choose the *Instructions* option from the **Special** menu to edit the instructions.

For each question type, there are two sets of instructions–one that appears if you choose to leave space for the answers on the test, and one that appears if you do not. The instructions that you can edit depend on the current test layout settings.

When editing the instructions, you can use any of the features of the word processor. These features are discussed in Section 4–Edit Question Banks. Instructions should be limited to about six lines.

Summary

At any time while building a test, you can choose the *Summary* option from the **Special** menu. A test summary appears on your screen. The summary shows you how many questions are on the test, which question banks you used in selecting questions, and how many questions of each question type you selected.

Editing Questions

Usually, if you want to make changes to a question, you will make them using the *Edit Question Banks* option (see Section 4). From time to time, though, you may want to change a question for just one test.

To make changes to a question after you include it on a test, you first need to highlight the question on the visual test. Highlight the question and click the **Edit** button. Edit the question with the word processor. To edit the answer, click the **Answer** button. For a detailed description of all of the word processor options, refer to Section 4. After you make the desired changes, click the **OK** button.

Question Info

To view the question information for a particular question, you first need to highlight the question on the visual test. Once the question has been highlighted, click the **Info** button.

The Question Info dialog box includes question information such as question bank source (where you selected the question from), objective, page reference, difficulty index, topic, and narrative.

The question information cannot be changed at this point. To change the question information, you must edit the original question using the *Edit Question Banks* option.

SECTION 4–EDIT QUESTION BANKS

In addition to using the supplied question banks, you also have the option of creating your own. The *Glencoe Test Generator* contains a powerful word processor with many distinctive features that allows you to add questions to existing question banks or create entirely new question banks. Question banks can contain up to 250 questions from a variety of question types. Each question can be assigned an objective, a page reference, a difficulty index, and a topic. Questions can include a picture or be linked to a narrative (specialized instruction).

EDITING QUESTION BANKS

To begin editing question banks, follow these steps:

Step 1
Start the *Glencoe Test Generator* software.

Step 2
From the **Main** menu, select the *Edit Question Banks* option.

After you choose this option, the program displays the Open Question Bank dialog box.

Open Question Bank

Use the Open Question Bank dialog box to open an existing question bank. Choose a question bank by highlighting the name from the list and clicking the **Open** button. If you do not want to open a question bank, click the **Cancel** button.

Question Window

As you can see, the first question appears on the screen (see Figure 4-1). The bottom of the window indicates the current question number, the answer to the question (for True/False, Multiple Choice, Yes/No, and Completion questions), and the total questions currently in this bank. Buttons for editing the question, changing the answer, changing the question information (objective, page reference, narrative, etc.), and creating a new question appear at the bottom of the screen.

It is quite easy to move from question to question using the *Glencoe Test Generator*. To move between questions, simply press the up and down arrow keys or click the **Previous** or **Next** buttons. There are also options in the **Question** menu for moving between questions.

Previous (⌘+1)	Moves to the previous question in the question bank.
Next (⌘+2)	Moves to the next question in the question bank.
First (⌘+3)	Moves to the first question in the question bank.
Last (⌘+4)	Moves to the last question in the question bank.
Goto (⌘+G)	By choosing the *Goto...* option, you can go to any question in the question bank if you know the question type and question number. When this option is chosen, a dialog box appears on the screen. Select the appropriate question type from the pop-up menu, and enter the question number. Click the **OK** button to view the selected question.

You can also use the *Find* option from the **Edit** menu to locate a particular word or phrase in any question. See the "Find" section in this manual (p. M-20) for more information.

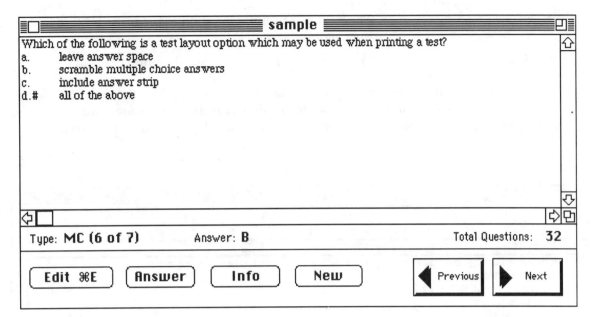

Figure 4-1 Question Window

Editing a Question

To edit a question, simply display the question in the main window and click the **Edit** button.

Creating a New Question

To create a new question, click the **New** button in the main window. The Add New Question dialog box appears. Use the pop-up menu to select the desired question type and click the **OK** button. The program adds the new question to the end of the group of questions with the same type. Key the question, answer, and information. Use the buttons provided to switch among these elements.

WORD PROCESSOR

The word processor for the *Glencoe Test Generator* appears on your screen as shown in Figure 4-2 when you edit an existing question or choose to add a new question. There are scroll bars for moving through the question. A ruler at the top of the screen indicates the margins, tab settings, spacing, and justification for the current paragraph.

Key your questions as you would with any word processor. Text will wrap when it reaches the right margin (as shown on the ruler). Questions should be limited to 100 lines in length, although most will be far less. At any time while keying, you can click the **Record** button to record your changes and return you to the main window. To make further changes to the question, simply click the **Edit** button from the main window.

Use the following keystrokes to move through the document if you have an extended keyboard.

Use This Key Command:	To Move to:
Home	The beginning of the question.
End	The end of the question.
Page Up	The previous page if the question requires more than one screen.

Page Down	The next screen if the question exceeds the bottom of the current screen.
Arrow keys	One character (or line) in any direction.

The mouse can also be used to position the cursor at any point in the question. Simply move the mouse pointer to the appropriate position, and click the mouse once. The scroll bar(s) can be used to move the viewing area but they do *not* move the current cursor position.

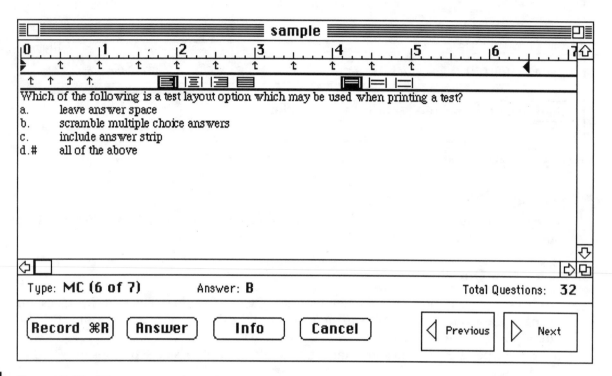

Figure 4-2 Word Processor

Selecting Text

Select a block of text when you want to perform an editing operation (Copy, Cut, Paste, or Clear). Selected text will be shown in a highlight color. Text can be selected in the following ways:

- Use any of the arrow keys while holding down the Shift key.

- Hold the mouse button down and *drag* the mouse pointer over the desired text.

- Highlight a word by double-clicking the mouse on it.

- Highlight a paragraph by triple-clicking (clicking the mouse three times quickly in the same location).

- Choose *Select All* from the **Edit** menu to select the entire question.

Once selected, you can use the following editing options (found on the **Edit** menu).

Cut (⌘+X)	Removes the highlighted text and copies it to the Clipboard.
Copy (⌘+C)	Leaves the highlighted text in place and copies it to the Clipboard.
Clear (Delete)	Removes the highlighted text without copying it to the Clipboard.

Also, if you press a key while text is highlighted, that character will replace the highlighted text. Any of the editing operations can be reversed by choosing *Undo* from the **Edit** menu. Once text has been copied to the Clipboard using either *Cut* or *Copy*, the cursor can be placed in a different position and the *Paste* option can be chosen to place the copied text in the new location.

To remove the highlight from the text, simply use the arrow keys to move the cursor, or click the mouse button once in the text.

Ruler Settings

As was mentioned earlier, the ruler shows the margins, tabs, indent position, and other format settings for the current paragraph. Each paragraph can have its own ruler, although this is not a requirement. Ruler settings can only be changed using the mouse.

Set Tab	Drag any one of the four tab types shown at the bottom left of the ruler to the desired position on the ruler.
Move Tab	Drag any of the current tab positions to the desired position on the ruler.
Delete Tab	Drag any of the current tab positions off the ruler.
Spacing	Highlight the selected paragraph and click the *Single Space, One and a Half,* or *Double Space* option.
Justification	Choose *Left Justify, Center Justify, Full Justify,* or *Right Justify.*
Set Margins	Drag any of the margin indicators to the desired position.

Note: It is recommended that you do not change either the left or right margin positions since extra space is required on each line when a question is printed.

To change the ruler settings for more than one paragraph, highlight all of the desired paragraphs and change the settings.

The **Format** menu includes several other options for working with rulers and formatting the question text.

Copy Ruler	Copies the ruler settings from the current ruler.
Apply Ruler	Applies the copied ruler settings to the selected paragraph(s).
Clear All Tabs	Removes all of the tabs from the current ruler. Affects all selected paragraphs.
Character Format	Displays a dialog box allowing you to change several attributes of the selected text at the same time (font, style, size, and color).
Paragraph	Displays a dialog box allowing you to set off an individual paragraph with lines on any side or entirely enclose the paragraph in a shadowed box.
Color	Displays a dialog box allowing you to set the color of the selected text. If you have a color printer, the *Glencoe Test Generator* software will print the question in color.
Show Codes	While editing a question, you may sometimes insert a carriage return or tab characters in places where you don't want them. Since these characters do not normally appear on your display, it can be frustrating trying to remove them. To make this easier, you can choose the *Show Codes* option. When you choose this option, hard carriage returns are displayed as "¶" and tabs appear as "→". To turn this option off, choose *Hide Codes.*

Fonts, Sizes, and Styles

The *Glencoe Test Generator* allows you to enter text in any font and in a wide variety of text styles (Plain, **Bold**, <u>Underline</u>, *Italic*, Outline, SHADOW) and sizes (9, 10, 12, 14, 18, 24, or any size from 8 to 72 points using the *Other Size* option). Other styles are available by choosing the *Other Style* option (Strikethru, Boxed, Dotted Underline, Double Underline, Superscript, and Subscript). Fonts, sizes, and styles may be changed while you are keying. For example, key "This text is going to be in <⌘+B>Bold<⌘+B>." Changes can also be applied to existing text by highlighting a block and choosing the appropriate font, size, and/or style from the menus. Format changes can be reversed by using the *Undo* option in the **Edit** menu.

Find

Sometimes when editing a longer question, you may want to find a word or phrase quickly. Choose the *Find* option from the **Edit** menu. The dialog box as shown in Figure 4-3 appears on your screen. Enter the text you want to find, set the other options, and click the **Find** button. If the text is found, it will be shown in the main window. If the text appears more than once and you want to search again, simply click the **Find** button again. Click the **Done** button to return to the editing window.

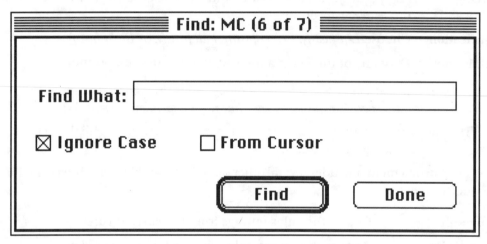

Figure 4-3 Find Dialog Box

Replace

To find and replace text while editing a question, choose the *Replace* option from the **Edit** menu. Enter the text you want to find and the text to replace it with. The software will either ask you before it replaces an occurrence of the text, or not, depending on the Confirm Replace check box setting. You can either elect to replace only the first occurrence (**Replace** button), or every occurrence in this question (**Replace All** button). When you are finished, click the **Done** button.

Replace Font

If you decide that you want to change the font and/or size for a question or all of the questions in a question bank, you can choose the *Replace Font* option. For example, to change the font for every question, answer, and narrative in a bank to Times, and the size to 14, follow these steps:

- Make sure that you are not in editing mode. If you are, the font and size will be changed for just that question.

- Choose the *Replace Font* option.

- Leave the "Replace" font and size set to "Any font" and "Any size" respectively.

- Set the "With" font and size to "Times" and "14" respectively.

- Click the **OK** button. You will be warned and given a chance to cancel the operation. It is important to be careful when using this option, since it cannot be undone.

WORKING WITH QUESTIONS

Once a question has been entered and recorded, the *Glencoe Test Generator* provides a variety of options to work with the questions in the question bank.

Changing an Answer

While viewing or editing a question, click the **Answer** button. If the question type is True/False, Multiple Choice, or Yes/No, a dialog box will appear with a pop-up menu containing valid answer choices. Simply press the letter of the answer (for example, **F** for false, **D** for choice D, **N** for no) and click the **OK** button.

For all other question types, edit the answer in much the same way as you would edit a question. Use any of the editing features mentioned earlier. When you are finished editing the answer, click the **Record** button.

Changing the Question Info

Although not required, each question can be assigned an objective, page reference, difficulty index, and topic. Questions can also be linked to narratives that will be automatically included in the test when printed. To change the question information, click the **Info** button while viewing a question.

The dialog box as shown in Figure 4-4 appears on your screen. Change any or all of the information. If you want to attach a narrative to a question, simply enter the narrative number in the corresponding field. See the "Narratives" section in this manual (p. M-22) for more information.

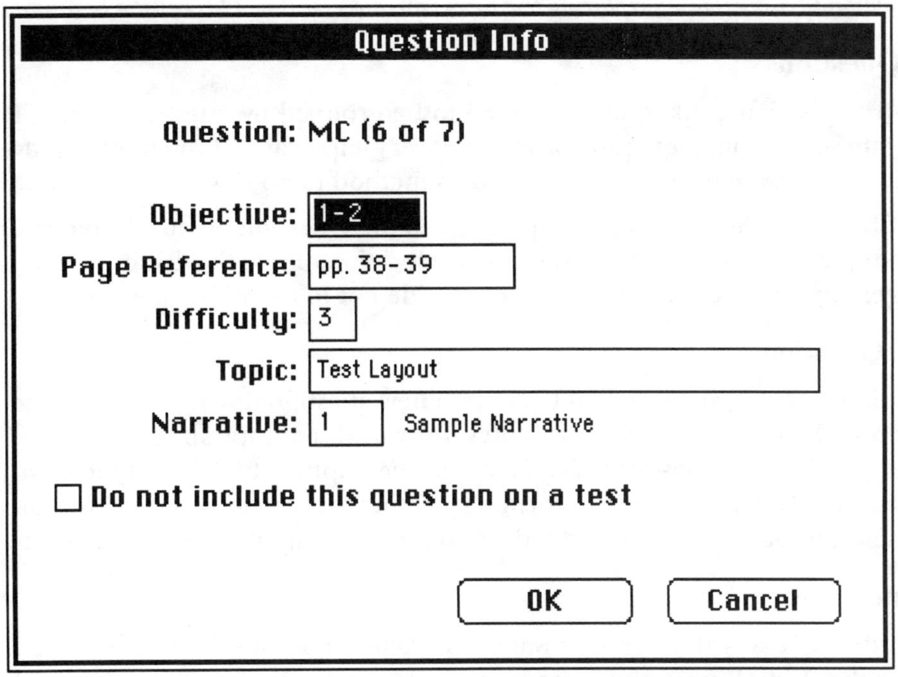

```
┌─────────────────────────────────────────────────┐
│                  Question Info                    │
│                                                   │
│                                                   │
│          Question: MC (6 of 7)                    │
│                                                   │
│          Objective: [1-2        ]                 │
│     Page Reference: [pp. 38-39      ]             │
│         Difficulty: [3  ]                          │
│              Topic: [Test Layout          ]       │
│          Narrative: [1    ]  Sample Narrative     │
│                                                   │
│     ☐ Do not include this question on a test      │
│                                                   │
│                                                   │
│                  ( OK )      ( Cancel )           │
│                                                   │
└─────────────────────────────────────────────────┘
```

Figure 4-4 Question Information Dialog Box

In the Question Info dialog box, there is also a check box stating "Do not include this question on a test." If this option is set, the *Glencoe Test Generator* will not select this question for a test when randomly selecting questions. You can use this option if you want to keep a question in the bank but, at least for the time being, do not want to include it on any test.

Narratives

Often, you will want to enter a group of questions that refer to the same descriptive paragraph (narrative) or specialized instruction. The *Glencoe Test Generator* provides an easy but powerful way to do just that. Choose the *Narratives* option from the **Question** menu.

Each narrative consists of a narrative number (1-20), a description (25 characters), and the narrative itself. Up to twenty narratives may be included in any one question bank.

It is important that the description you enter for each narrative be unique. When the software builds a test from selected questions, it uses the narrative description to decide whether or not a particular narrative has already been included in the test.

Once you have entered a narrative description, click the **Add** button to add a new narrative. Enter a narrative as you would enter a question. Click the **OK** button to record the narrative.

If you find that a narrative that was previously entered is no longer needed, use the **Delete** button. To edit an existing narrative, highlight the entry and then click the **Edit** button. Click the **Done** button when you are through working with this dialog box.

Find/Replace

The *Glencoe Test Generator* provides a way to find and/or replace text across multiple questions within a question bank. Use the same options you used when finding and/or replacing text within a question. The software will search through all of the questions in the question bank, displaying them if necessary when it finds the indicated text. To find/replace text across multiple questions, make sure that you are not editing a question when you choose the *Find* or *Replace* options from the **Edit** menu.

> Note: Be very careful when using the Replace All button with the Confirm Replace option turned off when replacing text across question banks. This cannot be undone.

Reorder Questions

Within a question bank, questions need to be grouped by question type (TF, MC, etc.). Inside these groupings, question order is not very important. If you want to move a question within a group, the software does provide a method to do this.

Choose the *Reorder Questions* option from the **Question** menu. To move a question to another place in the bank, drag it to its new location. Press the **OK** button to confirm the changes. Press the **Cancel** button if you decide not to move the question.

Duplicate Questions

From time to time, you may want to create a new question that is very similar to an existing question. To make this easier, the software provides an option to duplicate the current question. Simply choose the *Duplicate Question* option from the **Question** menu. An informational alert is displayed informing you that you are viewing the duplicated question. The new question can now be edited without disturbing the original question.

Delete Questions

If you decide that you no longer want a particular question in a question bank, you can choose the *Delete Question* option from the **Question** menu. A caution alert will be displayed asking you to confirm that you want to delete the question. Respond appropriately.

SAVING AND PRINTING

After you edit questions or create new ones, the *Glencoe Test Generator* allows you to save the question bank to disk. Also, you can print a question bank to be used as a reference sheet when selecting questions to build a test.

Saving a Question Bank

From the **File** menu, choose either the *Save* option or the *Save As* option to save your question bank to disk. Use the *Save As* option to assign a new file name or change the location of the file. Key-enter the name and click the **Save** button.

Printing a Question Bank

Printing a question bank is not the same as printing a test. A printed question bank is used more for a reference when building a test. To print a question bank, choose the *Print* option from the **File** menu. Print the entire question bank or the current question.

MISCELLANEOUS FEATURES

In addition to those features already mentioned, the *Glencoe Test Generator* offers the following features while working with the *Edit Question Banks* option. Review the information below.

Context-Sensitive Help

At any point while running the program, you can select the *Help* option from the **Apple** menu. Help can also be brought up using the help key (**⌘+H**). Close the window after viewing the help information.

Get Picture

Pictures (graphic images) can be included right in with the question, answer, or narrative using the *Glencoe Test Generator* software. To retrieve a picture (PICT file) from disk, choose the *Get Picture* option from the **Special** menu while you are in editing mode. Once loaded from disk, the picture will be automatically inserted into the question. To reposition the picture, click on it and drag it to the desired position. If the picture is positioned within a text block, the text will wrap around the picture on all sides.

To resize the picture, click on one of the resize handles as shown in Figure 4-5 and drag it until the picture is the desired size. To reduce the amount of white space surrounding a picture without changing the size of the picture frame, hold down the **Option** key while dragging one of the resize handles.

Pictures can also be cut, copied, or pasted to and from the Clipboard. You can also undo any editing operation on a picture.

New Question Bank

Choose this option (accessed from the **File** menu) to begin an entirely new question bank. Once this option is chosen, you will be prompted to enter the question bank title. Enter any name you want and click the **OK** button. The software displays the main window. Use the **New** button to add questions to the question bank.

Preferences

As in the other program modules, you can use the *Preferences* option from the **Edit** menu to change the software's password and/or the default font. If you do not want to use a password, simply leave the Password field blank.

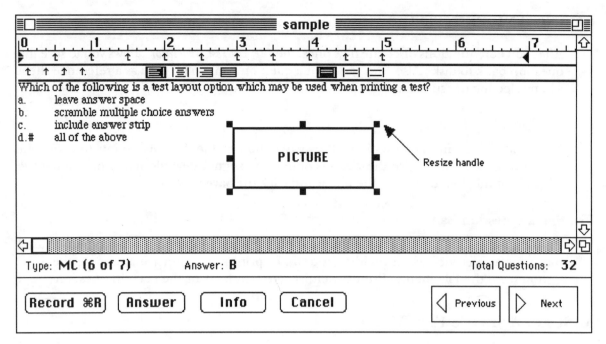

Figure 4-5 Get Picture

Bank Title

When the question bank was originally created, you were asked for a question bank title. If the title was entered incorrectly, or you just want to change it, use the *Bank Title* option from the **Special** menu.

SECTION 5–TROUBLESHOOTING

The following troubleshooting guidelines are provided to assist you if you have difficulty using the *Glencoe Test Generator*. If you need further assistance, the Software Support toll-free number is also provided.

COMMONLY ASKED QUESTIONS OR PROBLEMS

I can't locate the question banks or tests on disk.

Use the *Open Question Bank* option in the **File** menu to display the Open dialog box. Change the drive and/or folder.

I can't select question banks from multiple disks while using QuickTest.

After selecting question banks from one disk, click the **Locate** button, eject the question bank disk, and insert the next disk. To tell the software that you switched disks, click the **Done** button. The software will now display the question banks on the new disk.

A menu option is dim and can't be selected.

All of the menu options are not active at all times. For example, the *Close* option in the **File** menu is available only when a window is currently open. Often, while you work in a dialog box, many of the menu options will be inactive.

Printing a test produces an error message or a garbled printout.

If you experience problems printing a test, verify that the printer is on-line, the paper is inserted and aligned properly, and the printer cables are not loose. Try to print again. If the printer does not respond this time, the problem is most likely a hardware problem and not a software issue.

If the printout is garbled, check the *Page Setup* option in the **File** menu. Verify that the correct printer is specified.

Can graphics be created from scratch and used with the test generator?

Yes. Any graphic used with the test generator must be created using a paint program that saves graphics in a PICT format. Use the *Get Picture* command in the **Special** menu to retrieve a picture from disk or simply paste it from the paint program.

I received an error message trying to save a file.

Verify that your data disk has been properly formatted and that it is in the appropriate drive. If you receive a disk full message, remove any unneeded files and then try to save the file again. Also, the disk should not be write-protected. Slide the write-protect switch to the closed position.

There is not enough memory to run the program.

If you receive this error message when you start the program, you must free additional memory. Quit any other open application. A minimum of 900K **free** memory is required to run the program.

There is not enough memory for an operation.

If you create very large question banks or tests, you may encounter this message. Question banks or tests larger than 60 pages should probably be split into smaller units. Large tests can be separated by using the beginning question number option in the Print Test dialog box. If your computer has extra memory, choose the *Get Info* option from the Finder and increase the Preferred size for the program.

I am unable to select by criteria.

Not all supplied question banks contain question information (topics, objectives, etc.).

I cannot change the starting question number when printing a test.

The question number cannot be changed if the current test layout option for question numbering is not set to continuous (e.g., MC 1-8 TF 9-25).

Narratives are not printing with the test questions.

If you create your own narrative, you must link the narrative to each of the questions that refer to it. Choose to edit the question information and enter the appropriate narrative number in the field.

A narrative also may not print if you gave it the same name as another narrative already included in the test. Narrative names must be unique.

SOFTWARE SUPPORT CENTER

Glencoe provides toll-free telephone assistance for teachers who experience difficulty while using our software or templates. Before calling for assistance, please check the following:

- Is your computer working properly? Try some other software, which you know is working, on the same computer.
- Are you certain the software is not working properly? Try the software on another computer.
- Can you repeat the problem? Does the software seem to malfunction at the same point each time?

In order for the Support Center to help you as quickly as possible, have the following information at hand before calling for assistance:

- the exact title and ISBN number from the disk label or package
- the brand, model, and configuration of the computer you are using
- the version of the operating system installed on your computer

The Glencoe Support Center toll-free number is **800/437-3715**. The Support Center is available from 8:00 a.m. to 6:00 p.m. Eastern Time. You can also send an E-mail to the following address: epgtech@mcgraw-hill.com.

MACINTOSH USER'S GUIDE

INDEX (MACINTOSH TEST GENERATOR)

MACINTOSH USER'S GUIDE

MACINTOSH USER'S GUIDE

CHAPTER OBJECTIVES

CHAPTER 1

1. Describe three jobs that depend on the use of biology.
2. List five tools of biologists.
3. Compare the features of the light microscope, stereomicroscope, and electron microscope.
4. Explain how SI units are grouped.
5. List the SI units of measure for length, volume, mass, time, and temperature.
6. Measure objects using SI units.
7. Explain the steps of the scientific method.
8. Compare the difference between a hypothesis and a theory.
9. Explain how technology is used to solve everyday problems.

CHAPTER 2

1. Describe eight features common to all living things.
2. List the elements that make up living things.
3. State the major ideas of the cell theory.
4. List the parts of the cell.
5. Describe the functions of the cell parts.
6. Explain the process of diffusion in a cell.
7. Describe the process of osmosis in a cell.
8. Communicate how cells, tissues, organs, and organ systems are organized.

CHAPTER 3

1. Give examples of items in daily life that are grouped.
2. Explain how and why we classify things.
3. Explain Aristotle's classification of living things.
4. Compare Linnaeus' system of classification with Aristotle's.
5. Name the levels of classification that are used today.
6. List traits used in classifying living things.
7. State the function of scientific names.
8. List the five kingdoms scientists recognize today.

CHAPTER 4

1. Identify the traits of viruses.
2. Tell how viruses reproduce.
3. List examples of how viruses affect living things.
4. Identify the traits of bacteria.
5. Explain how bacteria affect other living things.
6. Compare the traits of bacteria and blue-green bacteria.

CHAPTER 5

1. Identify the general characteristics of protists.
2. Compare the traits of animal-like protists, plantlike protists, and funguslike protists.
3. Give an example of each kind of protist.
4. List the traits of fungi and compare the traits of the major kinds of fungi.
5. Tell how fungi can be harmful and helpful.

CHAPTER 6

1. Describe two features common to most plants.
2. Compare vascular and nonvascular plants.
3. Compare mosses and liverworts with other plants.
4. Sequence the steps in the life cycle of a moss.
5. List three ways mosses are important to other living things.
6. Compare the traits of ferns, conifers, and flowering plants.
7. Explain how ferns, conifers, and flowering plants reproduce.
8. Describe how conifers and flowering plants are important to other living things.

CHAPTER 7

1. List four traits of animals.
2. Identify nine major phyla of animals and give an example of each.
3. List the traits of sponges.
4. Describe the traits of stinging-cell animals.
5. List the three main phyla of worms and give an example of each.
6. Identify the main features of flatworms, roundworms, and segmented worms.
7. Identify the major features of soft-bodied animals.
8. Explain how soft-bodied animals are classified.

CHAPTER 8

1. Identify the major traits of jointed-leg animals.
2. Compare insects with other jointed-leg animals.
3. Describe the traits of spiny-skin animals.
4. Compare the traits of jawless fish, cartilage fish, and bony fish.
5. Describe the major traits of amphibians, reptiles, and birds.
6. Identify the characteristics of mammals.

CHAPTER 9

1. List six important nutrients that the body needs.
2. Explain how each of the six important nutrients is used by the body.
3. Define a balanced diet.
4. Describe how a Calorie is used by the body.
5. Compare the number of Calories found in different nutrients.
6. Compare the number of Calories used in different activities.

CHAPTER 10

1. Relate the importance of the digestive system.
2. Compare a physical change and a chemical change in the digestive system.
3. Explain the role of enzymes in a chemical change.
4. Trace the path of food from the mouth to body cells.
5. Compare the human digestive system with those of other animals.
6. Identify the problems of the digestive system.

CHAPTER 11

1. Identify the circulatory system.
2. Compare the circulatory systems of earthworms, insects, and humans.
3. Describe how blood is pumped through the heart.
4. Explain what causes the sounds the heart makes.
5. Trace the pathway of blood through the left and right sides of the heart.
6. Discuss the importance of arteries.
7. List four traits of veins.
8. Give the function of capillaries.
9. Explain how blood pressure is measured.
10. Trace the events before and after a heart attack.
11. Relate ways to help prevent and correct heart problems.

CHAPTER 12

1. Identify the pickup and delivery jobs of the blood.
2. Explain the pickup and delivery system in animals without blood.
3. Describe the living and nonliving parts of blood.
4. Give the functions of the blood cells and cell-like parts.
5. Explain the problems that may occur with blood cells and platelets.
6. Compare the red cells and plasma proteins in the four main blood types.
7. Explain why blood types can't be mixed.
8. Describe how the immune system works.
9. Explain how shots prevent disease.
10. Discuss the AIDS virus.

CHAPTER 13

1. Define the role of the respiratory system.
2. Explain why cells need oxygen and give off carbon dioxide.
3. Compare the respiratory systems of different animals.
4. Give the function of different parts of the respiratory system.
5. Compare the pathways of gases as they enter and leave the body.
6. Sequence the movements of the diaphragm and the rib cage during the breathing process.
7. Relate the effects of carbon monoxide poisoning and how to avoid the gas.
8. Explain the cause of pneumonia.
9. Describe emphysema.
10. Discuss the importance of the excretory system.

11. Sequence the steps for filtering of blood in a kidney.
12. Describe the skin as part of the excretory system.

CHAPTER 14

1. Explain the functions and growth of the skeleton.
2. Define the six tissues of bones.
3. Identify three types of joints.
4. Compare three kinds of muscles.
5. Explain how muscles work to move body parts.
6. Relate how muscles work in pairs.
7. Discuss problems of the skeletal system.
8. Give examples of problems of the muscular system.
9. Explain the purpose of new designs for products.

CHAPTER 15

1. Explain how animals keep in touch with their body parts and their surroundings.
2. Compare the nervous systems of common animals.
3. Explain how nerve cells carry messages through the body.
4. State the functions of the three major organs of the nervous system.
5. Describe a reflex action.
6. Explain the function of the endocrine system.
7. Relate the importance of the pituitary and thyroid glands.
8. Identify problems that damage the brain.
9. Explain the importance of insulin.

CHAPTER 16

1. Relate ways a planarian and an earthworm sense light.
2. Compare the sense organs of a cricket and a snake.
3. State the functions of the parts of the eye.
4. Explain the jobs of the nose, tongue, and skin as sense organs.
5. Describe the parts of the outer, middle, and inner ear.
6. Describe how common vision problems are corrected.
7. Discuss reasons for protecting your ears against loud noises.
8. Explain ways of correcting hearing problems.

CHAPTER 17

1. Explain the difference between a stimulus and a response.
2. Explain innate behavior and give examples.
3. Describe how behavior is learned and give examples of learned behavior.
4. Explain how courting behaviors help an animal species reproduce.
5. Describe how behavior helps an animal find food, shelter, and protection from enemies.
6. Compare reproduction in animals that give parental care with reproduction in animals that give no care.

CHAPTER 18

1. Compare prescription and over-the-counter drugs.
2. Relate the importance of information listed on drug labels.
3. Describe how drugs stop pain.
4. Describe the effects of stimulants and depressants on the body.
5. Discuss how psychedelic drugs and inhalants affect the body.
6. Give the function of antihistamines and cough suppressants.
7. Explain the role of antacids in the body.
8. List reasons for not using other people's drugs.
9. Discuss the problems caused by using caffeine, nicotine, cocaine, and alcohol.

CHAPTER 19

1. Examine and compare the parts of a leaf in different plants.
2. Give the function of the cells in a leaf.
3. Explain the process of transpiration.
4. Describe the process of photosynthesis.
5. Explain the chemical equation for photosynthesis.
6. Compare the importance of sugar in photosynthesis and respiration.
7. Determine why plants are important to other things.
8. List different uses of leaves.
9. Explain why leaves change color.

CHAPTER 20

1. Discuss the traits of herbaceous stems.
2. Describe the five layers of woody stems.
3. Explain how stems grow.
4. Explain how a stem serves as a transport system.
5. Discuss the storage function of stems.
6. Identify how stems are useful to humans.
7. Compare taproots and fibrous roots.
8. Sequence the layers of root cells.
9. Describe how roots grow.
10. Describe root hairs and their function.
11. Relate how roots anchor the plant and store nutrients.
12. Discuss the benefits and problems of roots.

CHAPTER 21

1. Explain how hormones affect plant growth.
2. Compare short-day, long-day, and day-neutral plants.
3. Distinguish among tropisms and other plant movements.
4. Compare annual, biennial, and perennial plants.
5. List the growth requirements of plants.
6. Explain how bacteria and viruses affect plants.

7.   Describe how a fungus can kill a plant.
8.   Relate two ways that insects damage plants.

CHAPTER 22

1.   Relate some benefits of mitosis.
2.   Identify cell parts involved in mitosis.
3.   Trace the steps of mitosis.
4.   Explain the results of meiosis.
5.   Trace the steps of meiosis.
6.   Compare the sex cells of males and females.
7.   Explain some effects of aging.
8.   Describe the causes and effects of cancer.

CHAPTER 23

1.   Explain how plants reproduce asexually from roots.
2.   Describe how plants can reproduce asexually from leaves.
3.   Compare asexual reproduction from runners, tubers, bulbs, cuttings, and grafting.
4.   List the parts of a flower and their functions.
5.   Describe two methods of pollination.
6.   Sequence the steps that lead to fertilization in flowering plants.
7.   Describe how fruits and seeds develop.
8.   Explain how seeds are scattered and grow into new plants.
9.   Compare asexual and sexual reproduction in plants.

CHAPTER 24

1.   Identify the features of asexual reproduction.
2.   Describe types of asexual reproduction.
3.   Describe the features of sexual reproduction.
4.   Compare internal and external fertilization.
5.   Discuss ways animals improve chances of fertilization.
6.   Identify the reproductive parts of humans and the stages of human reproduction.
7.   Compare changes in the menstrual cycle with and without fertilization.
8.   Discuss symptoms and problems with sexually transmitted diseases.

CHAPTER 25

1.   Sequence the changes that take place in a fertilized egg until it attaches to the uterus.
2.   Explain how the needs of an embryo are met as it develops.
3.   Describe the stages of human development from the first month until birth.
4.   Compare development in frogs, birds, and reptiles.
5.   Explain how the needs of a chick embryo are met.
6.   Sequence the stages of frog metamorphosis.
7.   Explain incomplete metamorphosis.
8.   Describe complete metamorphosis.

CHAPTER 26

1. Compare the number of chromosomes in sex cells and body cells.
2. Distinguish between dominant and recessive genes.
3. Describe how different gene combinations result from fertilization and how traits are passed to offspring.
4. Discuss the purpose of a Punnett square.
5. Compare expected results and observed results.
6. Explain the importance of Gregor Mendel's work.

CHAPTER 27

1. Compare the chromosome numbers in body cells and sex cells.
2. Describe methods that doctors use to study chromosomes of a fetus.
3. Compare the chromosomes of males and females.
4. Compare recessive and dominant traits with incomplete dominance.
5. Describe different ways human traits can be inherited.
6. Describe some genetic disorders in humans.
7. Give examples of how genetic counseling can help families.

CHAPTER 28

1. Describe the structure of DNA.
2. Explain how DNA controls genetic traits.
3. Describe how DNA copies itself and works to make proteins.
4. Describe how mutations occur.
5. Describe how cloning and breeding produce offspring with desired traits.
6. Explain how recombinant DNA and gene therapy can help humans.

CHAPTER 29

1. Give examples of how adaptations help organisms survive.
2. Explain how changes in life-forms occur.
3. Describe the classification and evolution of primates and humans.
4. Communicate Darwin's main ideas.
5. Describe evidence that supports evolution.

CHAPTER 30

1. Relate the importance and methods of counting populations.
2. Discuss why populations change in size.
3. Explain how limiting factors affect a population.
4. Describe different parts of a community.
5. Explain the importance of producers, consumers, and decomposers.
6. Trace the path of energy and materials through a community.
7. Explain how food chains are connected.
8. Give examples of mutualism.

9. Describe commensalism.
10. Compare parasitism with predation.

CHAPTER 31

1. Describe the parts of an ecosystem.
2. Describe how the water cycle affects an ecosystem.
3. Explain the nitrogen cycle and the oxygen-carbon dioxide cycle.
4. Describe succession in a land community.
5. Describe succession in a water community.
6. Explain how climate helps determine what living things live in an area.
7. Describe the major land biomes and water ecosystems.

CHAPTER 32

1. Explain how wildlife and plants are affected by humans.
2. Describe how water and soil can be lost to the environment.
3. Explain why fossil fuels are being used up.
4. Discuss the causes of air pollution and acid rain.
5. Discuss problems that come from nonbiodegradable chemicals that pollute water.
6. Explain methods of conserving resources.
7. Discuss ways to keep the environment clean.

CHAPTER 1—THE STUDY OF LIFE

TRUE/FALSE

1. Most people do not use biology in their everyday lives.

   ANS: F   DIF: B   OBJ: 1-1

2. Only scientists use the steps of the scientific method.

   ANS: F   DIF: A   OBJ: 1-7

3. The cubic meter is the commonly used unit of volume in the laboratory.

   ANS: F   DIF: B   OBJ: 1-5

4. The first step in using the scientific method is recognizing the problem.

   ANS: T   DIF: B   OBJ: 1-7

5. An astronaut weighs the same on the moon as on Earth.

   ANS: F   DIF: A   OBJ: 1-6

6. Measurements used in science are from the International System of Units.

   ANS: T   DIF: B   OBJ: 1-4

7. Scientists measure temperature in Fahrenheit degrees.

   ANS: F   DIF: B   OBJ: 1-6

8. Computers are used by biologists to find, process, and store information.

   ANS: T   DIF: A   OBJ: 1-2

9. The artificial heart is the result of technology.

   ANS: T   DIF: A   OBJ: 1-9

MULTIPLE CHOICE

1. A microscope used for viewing things through which light cannot pass is a(n) _____.
   a. stereomicroscope
   b. light microscope
   c. electron microscope

   ANS: A   DIF: B   OBJ: 1-3

2. The recorded measurements taken during an experiment are _____.
   a. conclusions
   b. data
   c. variables
   d. controls

   ANS: B   DIF: B   OBJ: 1-7

3. A microscope that can magnify up to 500 000 times is the _____.
   a. light microscope
   b. electron microscope
   c. stereomicroscope

   ANS: B   DIF: B   OBJ: 1-3

4. A liter is used to measure _____.
   a. length
   b. volume
   c. mass
   d. weight

   ANS: B   DIF: B   OBJ: 1-5

5. The use of discoveries in science to solve everyday problems is _____.
   a. research
   b. experimenting
   c. technology
   d. industry

   ANS: C   DIF: B   OBJ: 1-9

6. On the Celsius scale, the boiling point of water is _____.
   a. 32 degrees
   b. 0 degrees
   c. 100 degrees
   d. 20 degrees

   ANS: C   DIF: B   OBJ: 1-6

7. The SI unit of length is the _____.
   a. meter
   b. liter
   c. gram
   d. newton

   ANS: A   DIF: B   OBJ: 1-5

8. The prefix kilo- means _____.
   a. 10
   b. 100
   c. 1000
   d. 1/1000

   ANS: C   DIF: B   OBJ: 1-4

9. Biologists study _____.
   a. planets
   b. rockets
   c. living and once-living things
   d. minerals

   ANS: C   DIF: B   OBJ: 1-1

10. A statement that can be tested is the _____.
   a. experiment
   b. observation
   c. variable
   d. hypothesis

   ANS: D   DIF: B   OBJ: 1-7

11. Changes that occur during an experiment are compared with a _____.
   a. variable
   b. control
   c. hypothesis
   d. conclusion

   ANS: B   DIF: B   OBJ: 1-7

12. A hypothesis that has been tested again and again, with similar results each time is a(n) _____.
   a. conclusion
   b. problem
   c. theory
   d. experiment

   ANS: B   DIF: B   OBJ: 1-8

13. Testing a hypothesis is _____.
   a. the SI system
   b. a conclusion
   c. an experiment
   d. a theory

   ANS: C   DIF: B   OBJ: 1-7

14. At the end of an experiment, a scientist forms a(n) _____.
   a. problem
   b. hypothesis
   c. observation
   d. conclusion

   ANS: D   DIF: B   OBJ: 1-7

15. Which of the following groups correctly lists SI units from largest to smallest?
   a. centi, kilo, milli
   b. kilo, centi, milli
   c. milli, centi, kilo
   d. kilo, milli, centi

   ANS: B   DIF: A   OBJ: 1-4

16. Which of the following tools might a biologist NOT use?
   a. hand lens
   b. microscope
   c. telescope
   d. ruler

   ANS: C   DIF: B   OBJ: 1-2

17. Which of the following tools would help with magnifying?
   a. hand lens and ruler
   b. microscope and computer
   c. microscope and hand lens
   d. binoculars and compass

   ANS: C   DIF: B   OBJ: 1-2

Figure 1-1

18. The low power objective of the microscope in Figure 1-1 magnifies _____.
   a. 10 times
   b. 40 times
   c. 100 times
   d. 400 times

   ANS: A   DIF: A   OBJ: 1-3

19. The total magnification of the microscope in Figure 1-1 on high power is _____.
    a. 100 times
    b. 400 times
    c. 1000 times
    d. 4000 times

    ANS: B   DIF: A   OBJ: 1-3

20. The eyepiece in the microscope shown in Figure 1-1 magnifies _____.
    a. 10 times
    b. 40 times
    c. 100 times
    d. 400 times

    ANS: A   DIF: A   OBJ: 1-3

21. The total magnification of the microscope in Figure 1-1 on low power is _____.
    a. 10 times
    b. 40 times
    c. 50 times
    d. 100 times

    ANS: D   DIF: A   OBJ: 1-3

22. Which area of technology is most likely being used in making an artificial limb?
    a. farming
    b. industry
    c. medicine

    ANS: C   DIF: A   OBJ: 1-9

23. Which area of technology is most likely being used in using staples to close an incision?
    a. farming
    b. industry
    c. medicine

    ANS: C   DIF: A   OBJ: 1-9

24. Which area of technology is most likely being used in adding a weed killer to the soil?
    a. farming
    b. industry
    c. medicine

    ANS: A   DIF: A   OBJ: 1-9

25. Which area of technology is most likely being used in having a car run on solar power?
    a. farming
    b. industry
    c. medicine

    ANS: B   DIF: A   OBJ: 1-9

26. Which area of technology is most likely being used with a battery-operated saw?
    a. farming
    b. industry
    c. medicine

    ANS: B   DIF: A   OBJ: 1-9

27. Which area of technology is most likely being used in having chickens produce larger eggs?
    a. farming
    b. industry
    c. medicine

    ANS: A   DIF: A   OBJ: 1-9

28. Which tool would you use to make calculations?
    a. binoculars
    b. computer
    c. light microscope
    d. stereomicroscope

    ANS: B   DIF: A   OBJ: 1-2

29. Which tool would you use to look at fingerprints?
    a. binoculars
    b. computer
    c. light microscope
    d. stereomicroscope

    ANS: D   DIF: A   OBJ: 1-2

30. Which tool would you use to identify birds in a forest?
    a. binoculars
    b. computer
    c. light microscope
    d. stereomicroscope

    ANS: A   DIF: A   OBJ: 1-2

31. Which tool would you use to examine pond water for living things?
    a. binoculars
    b. computer
    c. light microscope
    d. stereomicroscope

    ANS: C   DIF: A   OBJ: 1-2

COMPLETION

1. The _____ sends light through the microscope.

    ANS: mirror   DIF: B   OBJ: 1-3

1-7 (continued)

2. On a microscope, the _____ moves the body tube up and down to start focusing.

   ANS: coarse adjustment   DIF: B   OBJ: 1-3

3. On a microscope, the _____ brings objects into fine focus.

   ANS: fine adjustment   DIF: B   OBJ: 1-3

4. On a microscope, the _____ supports the slide.

   ANS: stage   DIF: B   OBJ: 1-3

5. On a microscope, the _____ controls light entering the microscope.

   ANS: diaphragm   DIF: B   OBJ: 1-3

MATCHING

Match each item in Figure 1-2 to the following questions. You may use a letter more than once.

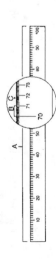

Figure 1-2

1. Which measurement in Figure 1-2 is one centimeter?
2. Which measurement in Figure 1-2 is one millimeter?
3. Which measurement in Figure 1-2 multiplied by 1000 equals one kilometer?
4. Which measurement in Figure 1-2 multiplied by 100 equals one meter?
5. Which measurement in Figure 1-2 equals 0.001 meters?
6. Which measurement in Figure 1-2 divided by 1000 equals one millimeter?

1. ANS: B   DIF: A   OBJ: 1-6
2. ANS: C   DIF: A   OBJ: 1-6
3. ANS: A   DIF: A   OBJ: 1-4
4. ANS: B   DIF: A   OBJ: 1-4
5. ANS: C   DIF: A   OBJ: 1-6
6. ANS: A   DIF: A   OBJ: 1-4

Match each item with the correct statement below.

a. Kelvin
b. mass
c. kilogram
d. variable
e. weight

7. how much matter is in something

1-8

8. SI unit of mass
9. that which changes in an experiment
10. a measure of the force of gravity on an object
11. SI scale for measuring temperature

7. ANS: B   DIF: B   OBJ: 1-5
8. ANS: C   DIF: B   OBJ: 1-5
9. ANS: D   DIF: B   OBJ: 1-7
10. ANS: E   DIF: B   OBJ: 1-5
11. ANS: A   DIF: B   OBJ: 1-5

Match each item with the correct statement below.

a. crime lab technician
b. beekeeper
c. mushroom grower
d. optometrist

12. must choose the best soil for a good crop
13. uses a microscope to study hair, fibers, skin, and blood
14. has studied the eyes and how they work
15. must know where to place beehives to get the most honey

12. ANS: C   DIF: A   OBJ: 1-1
13. ANS: A   DIF: A   OBJ: 1-1
14. ANS: D   DIF: A   OBJ: 1-1
15. ANS: B   DIF: A   OBJ: 1-1

SHORT ANSWER

1. Which units of the SI system would you use to find the mass of a horse?

   ANS: kilograms   DIF: A   OBJ: 1-5

2. Which units of the SI system would you use to find the height of a tree?

   ANS: meters   DIF: A   OBJ: 1-5

3. Which units of the SI system would you use to find the length of a tooth?

   ANS: meters   DIF: A   OBJ: 1-5

4. Which units of the SI system would you use to find the volume of a fish tank?

   ANS: liters   DIF: A   OBJ: 1-5

5. Which units of the SI system would you use to find the capacity of your lungs?

   ANS: liters   DIF: A   OBJ: 1-5

6. The school football team will win today's game. Is this statement a theory or hypothesis?

ANS: hypothesis DIF: A OBJ: 1-8

7. The pull of gravity acts on all objects. Is this statement a theory or hypothesis?

ANS: theory DIF: A OBJ: 1-8

8. A child may be born with birthmarks if the mother is accidentally burned during her pregnancy. Is this statement a theory or hypothesis?

ANS: hypothesis DIF: A OBJ: 1-8

9. What is the length in centimeters of a box that is 12 millimeters long?

ANS: 1.2 DIF: A OBJ: 1-6

10. What is the length in meters of a box that is 12 millimeters long?

ANS: 0.012 DIF: A OBJ: 1-6

11. What is the volume in kiloliters of a beaker that holds 4.2 liters of water?

ANS: 0.0042 DIF: A OBJ: 1-6

12. What is the volume in milliliters of a beaker that holds 4.2 liters of water?

ANS: 4200 DIF: A OBJ: 1-6

13. What is the mass in centigrams of a seed that has a mass of 14 grams?

ANS: 1400 DIF: A OBJ: 1-6

14. What is the mass in milligrams of a seed that has a mass of 14 grams?

ANS: 14 000 DIF: A OBJ: 1-6

15. Explain how a zookeeper might use biology in his or her job.

ANS: A zookeeper must be familiar with traits of the animals; must know what foods to be given to each animal; length of pregnancy for each type; harmful types; life spans. Student answers may vary.

DIF: A OBJ: 1-1

16. Explain how a florist might use biology in his or her job.

ANS: Florists must be able to identify plants by name; how to reduce spoilage of cut flowers; how often to water potted plants; how often to fertilize potted plants. Student answers may vary.

DIF: A OBJ: 1-1

17. You wish to magnify an object 200 times its natural size and see it in color. Why would you NOT use a stereomicroscope?

ANS: Stereomicroscopes cannot magnify 200 times.

DIF: A OBJ: 1-3

18. You wish to magnify an object 200 times its natural size and see it in color. Why would you NOT use an electron microscope?

ANS: Electron microscopes do not show colors.

DIF: A OBJ: 1-3

19. You wish to magnify an object 1000 times and must do it quickly. Why would you NOT use an electron microscope?

ANS: The process for preparing a sample for the electron microscope is time consuming and requires special training.

DIF: A OBJ: 1-3

20. You wish to magnify an object such as a sand grain. Which microscope would you use and why?

ANS: A stereomicroscope should be used. A sand grain is a large object and a three-dimensional view will be seen. Also, a sand grain will not allow light to pass through it.

DIF: A OBJ: 1-3

21. What step in the scientific method is illustrated when you state that a lamp fails to go on when you flip the switch?

ANS: the problem DIF: A OBJ: 1-7

22. What step in the scientific method is illustrated when you believe that a fuse has been blown?

ANS: forming a hypothesis DIF: A OBJ: 1-7

23. What step in the scientific method are you using when you decide to change the fuse when a lamp fails to go on when you flip the switch?

ANS: experimenting DIF: A OBJ: 1-7

CHAPTER 2—FEATURES OF LIFE AND THE CELL

MULTIPLE CHOICE

1. All living things are made of small units called _____.
   a. oxygen
   b. cells
   c. vacuoles
   d. mitochondria

   ANS: B   DIF: B   OBJ: 2-3

2. A biologist would expect any newly discovered organism to be made of cells because of _____.
   a. adaptation
   b. osmosis
   c. water
   d. the cell theory

   ANS: D   DIF: A   OBJ: 2-3

3. Osmosis is the movement of _____ into and out of cells.
   a. chemicals
   b. oxygen
   c. water
   d. cytoplasm

   ANS: C   DIF: B   OBJ: 2-7

4. The body is made up of many _____ working together.
   a. tissues
   b. organs
   c. organ systems
   d. organisms

   ANS: C   DIF: B   OBJ: 2-8

5. A substance made up of only one kind of atom is a(n) _____.
   a. mixture
   b. element
   c. compound
   d. molecule

   ANS: B   DIF: B   OBJ: 2-2

6. Anything that has mass and occupies space is _____.
   a. energy
   b. an atom
   c. a compound
   d. matter

   ANS: D   DIF: B   OBJ: 2-2

7. Most of the cell's chemical reactions take place in the _____.
   a. nucleus
   b. vacuole
   c. cytoplasm
   d. centriole

   ANS: C   DIF: B   OBJ: 2-5

8. A group of similar cells carrying out a job is a(n) _____.
   a. organ
   b. tissue
   c. organ system
   d. organism

   ANS: B   DIF: B   OBJ: 2-8

9. The part of a plant cell that gives it support and shape is the _____.
   a. cell membrane
   b. chloroplast
   c. cytoplasm
   d. cell wall

   ANS: D   DIF: B   OBJ: 2-5

10. Water is a(n) _____.
    a. element
    b. atom
    c. symbol
    d. compound

    ANS: D   DIF: A   OBJ: 2-2

11. The cell part that controls most of the cell's activities is the _____.
    a. nucleus
    b. vacuole
    c. cytoplasm
    d. centriole

    ANS: A   DIF: B   OBJ: 2-5

12. Over 97 percent of the matter in living things is made up of _____.
    a. 4 elements
    b. 6 elements
    c. 10 elements
    d. 20 elements

    ANS: B   DIF: B   OBJ: 2-2

13. The smallest amount of a compound is a(n) _____.
    a. atom
    b. molecule
    c. element
    d. building block

    ANS: B   DIF: B   OBJ: 2-2

14. Living things get energy from food in the process of _____.
    a. osmosis
    b. diffusion
    c. photosynthesis
    d. cellular respiration

    ANS: D   DIF: B   OBJ: 2-1

15. Which of the following cell parts have similar or related jobs?
    a. mitochondria and cell wall
    b. ribosomes and cell membrane
    c. mitochondria and chloroplasts
    d. nucleus and vacuole

    ANS: C   DIF: A   OBJ: 2-5

16. Which of the following cell parts have similar or related jobs?
    a. chromosomes and vacuoles
    b. nucleus and cell wall
    c. centrioles and ribosomes
    d. ribosomes and nucleolus

    ANS: D   DIF: A   OBJ: 2-5

17. Which of the following cell parts have similar or related jobs?
    a. cell wall and centriole
    b. chloroplasts and vacuoles
    c. cell membrane and nuclear membrane
    d. chloroplasts and nucleolus

    ANS: C   DIF: A   OBJ: 2-5

18. Which of the following cell parts are NOT found in the nucleus?
    a. cell wall and vacuole
    b. chromosomes and mitochondria
    c. nucleolus and chromosomes
    d. nucleolus and centriole

    ANS: A   DIF: A   OBJ: 2-5

19. Which of the following shows the correct sequence of organization for living things?
    a. cell-organ-tissue-organ system
    b. organ-tissue-cell-organ system
    c. cell-organ system-organ-tissue
    d. cell-tissue-organ-organ system

    ANS: D   DIF: A   OBJ: 2-8

20. A tadpole becoming a frog is an example of _____.
    a. reproduction
    b. growth
    c. development
    d. food getting

    ANS: C   DIF: A   OBJ: 2-1

21. Cats having kittens is an example of _____.
    a. reproduction
    b. growth
    c. development
    d. need for food

    ANS: A   DIF: A   OBJ: 2-1

22. A baby gaining ten pounds is an example of _____.
    a. reproduction
    b. growth
    c. development

    ANS: B   DIF: A   OBJ: 2-1

23. A plant grows toward the light because it _____.
    a. uses energy
    b. is made of cells
    c. adapts
    d. responds

    ANS: D   DIF: A   OBJ: 2-1

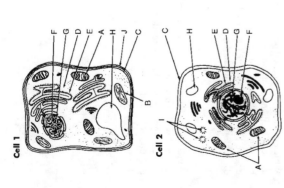

Figure 2-1

24. Cell 1 of Figure 2-1 is probably a plant cell because of the presence of _____.
a. mitochondria
b. chloroplasts
c. a nucleus
d. a vacuole

ANS: B   DIF: A   OBJ: 2-4

25. Cell 2 of Figure 2-1 is probably an animal cell because of the absence of _____.
a. a cell wall
b. mitochondria
c. vacuoles
d. centrioles

ANS: A   DIF: A   OBJ: 2-4

MATCHING

Match each item with the correct statement below.
a. cell theory
b. environment
c. adaptation
d. diffusion
e. osmosis

1. all the living and nonliving things surrounding an organism
2. Cells are the basic units of structure and function in living things.

3. A substance moves from where a large amount is to where a small amount is.
4. All cells come from other cells.
5. the movement of water across a cell membrane
6. a trait that makes a living thing better able to survive
7. A cucumber slice placed in pure water increases in size.
8. All living things are made of one or more cells.

1. ANS: B   DIF: A   OBJ: 2-1
2. ANS: A   DIF: A   OBJ: 2-3
3. ANS: D   DIF: A   OBJ: 2-6
4. ANS: A   DIF: A   OBJ: 2-3
5. ANS: E   DIF: A   OBJ: 2-7
6. ANS: C   DIF: A   OBJ: 2-1
7. ANS: E   DIF: A   OBJ: 2-7
8. ANS: A   DIF: A   OBJ: 2-3

Choose the letter in Figure 2-1 that best matches each statement. A letter may be used more than once.

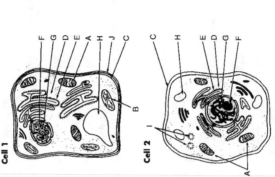

Figure 2-1

9. vacuole
10. centriole
11. cytoplasm
12. ribosome
13. cell membrane
14. nucleolus
15. chromosome

16. mitochondria
17. chloroplast
18. contains chlorophyll
19. controls movement of material into and out of cells
20. where proteins are made
21. release energy
22. carries information that determines traits
23. helps make ribosomes
24. protects and supports plant cells
25. stores food, water, and minerals

9. ANS: H DIF: B OBJ: 2-4
10. ANS: I DIF: B OBJ: 2-4
11. ANS: D DIF: B OBJ: 2-4
12. ANS: E DIF: B OBJ: 2-4
13. ANS: C DIF: B OBJ: 2-4
14. ANS: F DIF: B OBJ: 2-4
15. ANS: G DIF: B OBJ: 2-4
16. ANS: A DIF: B OBJ: 2-4
17. ANS: B DIF: B OBJ: 2-4
18. ANS: B DIF: A OBJ: 2-4
19. ANS: C DIF: A OBJ: 2-5
20. ANS: E DIF: A OBJ: 2-5
21. ANS: A DIF: A OBJ: 2-5
22. ANS: G DIF: A OBJ: 2-5
23. ANS: F DIF: A OBJ: 2-5
24. ANS: J DIF: A OBJ: 2-5
25. ANS: H DIF: A OBJ: 2-5

Figure 2-2 shows a cell and nitrogen gas molecules undergoing diffusion. Nitrogen gas can pass through the pores of the cell. Write the letter of the diagram being described.

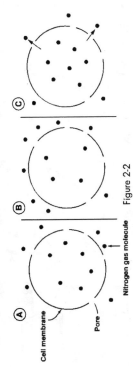

Cell membrane

Pore

Nitrogen gas molecule   Figure 2-2

26. Equal numbers of nitrogen gas molecules are in and out of the cell.
27. Fewer nitrogen gas molecules are inside the cell than outside.
28. More nitrogen gas molecules are outside the cell than inside.
29. Which diagram shows the final result of diffusion?
30. Movement of nitrogen gas molecules from inside to outside the cell is taking place.

---

26. ANS: A DIF: A OBJ: 2-6
27. ANS: B DIF: A OBJ: 2-6
28. ANS: B DIF: A OBJ: 2-6
29. ANS: A DIF: A OBJ: 2-6
30. ANS: C DIF: A OBJ: 2-6

SHORT ANSWER

1. An object is found to contain only the elements Fe (iron), Cl (chlorine), and Si (silicon). Could this object be living or might it once have been alive? Why or why not?

   ANS: No; all living or once-living things must contain the elements oxygen and carbon.

   DIF: A   OBJ: 2-2

2. Why is it impossible to have tissues without cells?

   ANS: Cells are needed to form tissues.   DIF: A   OBJ: 2-8

3. Why is it impossible to have organs without tissues?

   ANS: Tissues are needed to form organs.

   DIF: A   OBJ: 2-8

4. What part of a plant cell will usually appear green?

   ANS: chloroplast   DIF: A   OBJ: 2-4

5. What part of an animal cell has a specific shape?

   ANS: cell membrane   DIF: A   OBJ: 2-4

6. What part of a plant cell has a tough outer cover?

   ANS: cell wall   DIF: A   OBJ: 2-4

7. What cell part is found throughout the cytoplasm or along the canal network?

   ANS: ribosome   DIF: A   OBJ: 2-4

8. A chemical compound has the following formula: NH_3. How many different elements are present?

   ANS: 2   DIF: A   OBJ: 2-2

TRUE/FALSE

1. The scientific names of living things seldom change.

   ANS: T   DIF: B   OBJ: 3-7

2. Food is not grouped in a grocery store.

   ANS: F   DIF: A   OBJ: 3-7

Group 1

Group 2

Figure 3-1

3. Group 1 in Figure 3-1 has traits that differ from those of group 2.

   ANS: T   DIF: A   OBJ: 3-2

4. Group 1 in Figure 3-1 has only straight lines, group 2 does not.

   ANS: T   DIF: A   OBJ: 3-2

5. Group 2 in Figure 3-1 has notches along its sides, group 1 does not.

   ANS: F   DIF: A   OBJ: 3-2

6. The grouping shown in Figure 3-1 is wrong.

   ANS: F   DIF: A   OBJ: 3-2

7. The same six objects in Figure 3-1 could probably be grouped in a different way.

   ANS: T   DIF: A   OBJ: 3-2

8. Group 1 in Figure 3-1 could be called Kingdom Round.

   ANS: F   DIF: A   OBJ: 3-2

9. Group 1 in Figure 3-1 could be divided into Phylum Rectangle and Phylum Diamond.

   ANS: T   DIF: A   OBJ: 3-2

10. Grouping helps to show how living things are alike.

    ANS: T   DIF: A   OBJ: 3-2

---

9. A chemical compound has the following formula: NH_3. How many molecules of this compound are shown?

   ANS: 1   DIF: A   OBJ: 2-2

10. A chemical compound has the following formula: NH_3. How many atoms of N are present?

    ANS: 1   DIF: A   OBJ: 2-2

11. A chemical compound has the following formula: NH_3. How many atoms of H are present?

    ANS: 3   DIF: A   OBJ: 2-2

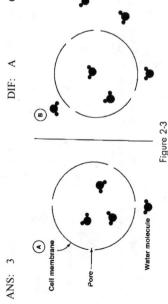

Figure 2-3

12. Are there more water molecules inside or outside cell A of Figure 2-3?

    ANS: inside   DIF: A   OBJ: 2-7

13. Are there more water molecules inside or outside cell B of Figure 2-3?

    ANS: outside   DIF: A   OBJ: 2-7

14. In which direction will water molecules move in cell A of Figure 2-3?

    ANS: out of cell   DIF: A   OBJ: 2-7

15. In which direction will water molecules move in cell B of Figure 2-3?

    ANS: into cell   DIF: A   OBJ: 2-7

16. How many water molecules will be present outside cell A of Figure 2-3 after osmosis occurs?

    ANS: 2   DIF: A   OBJ: 2-7

17. How many water molecules will be present inside cell B of Figure 2-3 after osmosis occurs?

    ANS: 3   DIF: A   OBJ: 2-7

11. Grouping helps to make things easier to find.

ANS: T   DIF: A   OBJ: 3-2

12. A group that is larger than a class is a family.

ANS: F   DIF: A   OBJ: 3-5

MULTIPLE CHOICE

1. Scientific names show the classification groups of _____.
   a. kingdom and phylum
   b. phylum and species
   c. genus and species
   d. family and kingdom

ANS: C   DIF: B   OBJ: 3-7

2. The word classify means to _____.
   a. group
   b. write
   c. count
   d. find things

ANS: A   DIF: A   OBJ: 3-2

3. The first scientist to classify living things into two main groups was _____.
   a. Hooke
   b. Brown
   c. Aristotle
   d. Linnaeus

ANS: C   DIF: B   OBJ: 3-3

4. Different kinds of living things do not have the same _____.
   a. common name
   b. phylum name
   c. scientific name
   d. kingdom name

ANS: C   DIF: A   OBJ: 3-7

5. The largest groups into which living things are classified are _____.
   a. families
   b. species
   c. orders
   d. kingdoms

ANS: D   DIF: B   OBJ: 3-5

6. Scientific names are understood by all scientists because the names are written in _____.
   a. English
   b. Latin
   c. Spanish
   d. Russian

ANS: B   DIF: B   OBJ: 3-7

7. In Aristotle's system _____.
   a. plants were classified on the basis of where they lived
   b. animals were classified on the basis of where they lived
   c. there were three kingdoms
   d. all living things were placed in one kingdom

ANS: B   DIF: A   OBJ: 3-3

8. Linnaeus based his classification system on _____.
   a. specific traits
   b. size
   c. where organisms lived
   d. number of cells

ANS: A   DIF: A   OBJ: 3-4

9. To determine how to classify organisms, modern biologists may use _____.
   a. structure of body parts
   b. body chemistry
   c. common ancestors
   d. a, b, and c are all correct.

ANS: D   DIF: A   OBJ: 3-6

10. Of the following, *Felis leo* is most closely related to _____.
    a. *Rana pipiens*
    b. *Felis domesticus*
    c. *Xenopus laevis*
    d. *Homo sapiens*

ANS: B   DIF: A   OBJ: 3-7

11. Foods in a supermarket are classified to _____.
    a. put them in order
    b. make them easier to find
    c. show how they are alike
    d. a, b, and c are all correct.

ANS: D   DIF: A   OBJ: 3-2

12. Which of the following is NOT a way that books might be grouped in a library?
a. by subject
b. by author
c. by title
d. by cost

ANS: D   DIF: B   OBJ: 3-1

13. A ruler, beaker, and balance are grouped together. This may be because they all are _____.
a. the same size
b. the same color
c. used to measure
d. equal in cost

ANS: C   DIF: A   OBJ: 3-1

14. Aristotle used what trait to separate plants from animals?
a. animals were green while plants were not
b. plants were able to move while animals were not
c. plants were green while animals were not
d. plants are not living while animals are

ANS: C   DIF: B   OBJ: 3-4

15. You see a plant with only one stem. If you were Aristotle, how would you have grouped the plant?
a. tree
b. shrub
c. herb
d. nonliving

ANS: A   DIF: A   OBJ: 3-4

16. Aristotle placed all fish into the same group. This was because they all _____.
a. have scales
b. live in water
c. breathe by lungs
d. have fins

ANS: B   DIF: A   OBJ: 3-4

17. Which is the correct list of classification levels in order from largest to smallest?
a. species-genus-kingdom-class
b. kingdom-phylum-class-order
c. kingdom-class-species-family
d. phylum-family-class-genus

ANS: B   DIF: A   OBJ: 3-5

18. Using the comparison of an address to classification groups, a person living in New York and Erie County would match which levels of classification?
a. kingdom-phylum
b. phylum-kingdom
c. phylum-class
d. genus-species

ANS: C   DIF: A   OBJ: 3-5

19. A new animal is to be classified. It does not look at all like any known animal. Which of the following may help in its classification?
a. matching body chemistry
b. matching similar body parts
c. both a and b
d. neither a nor b

ANS: C   DIF: A   OBJ: 3-6

20. As a way of classifying similar living things, which of the following groups most likely have the same ancestors?
a. dog and wolf
b. dog and cat
c. dog and guinea pig
d. dog and horse

ANS: A   DIF: A   OBJ: 3-6

MATCHING

Match each item with the correct statement below.
a. plant
b. animal
c. protist
d. moneran
e. fungus

1. includes mushrooms and molds
2. made of one cell having a nucleus
3. one cell having no nucleus
4. cannot make its own food, may move about, and is many-celled
5. makes its own food and cannot move about
6. includes bacteria
7. has cell wall and cannot make its own food

1. ANS: E   DIF: B   OBJ: 3-8
2. ANS: C   DIF: B   OBJ: 3-8
3. ANS: D   DIF: B   OBJ: 3-8
4. ANS: B   DIF: B   OBJ: 3-8
5. ANS: A   DIF: B   OBJ: 3-8
6. ANS: D   DIF: B   OBJ: 3-8

TRUE/FALSE

1. Communicable diseases can be caused by bacteria or viruses.

   ANS: T   DIF: B   OBJ: 4-5

2. One way AIDS is spread is by sexual contact with an infected person.

   ANS: T   DIF: B   OBJ: 4-3

3. Pneumonia, strep throat, and tuberculosis are communicable diseases.

   ANS: T   DIF: B   OBJ: 4-5

4. Syphilis and gonorrhea are examples of diseases caused by viruses.

   ANS: F   DIF: B   OBJ: 4-5

MULTIPLE CHOICE

1. Bacteria reproduce by _____.
   a. chains
   b. fission
   c. spores
   d. colonies

   ANS: B   DIF: B   OBJ: 4-4

2. Viruses consist of a protein coat around a _____.
   a. cell
   b. nucleus
   c. chromosome-like part
   d. chloroplast

   ANS: C   DIF: B   OBJ: 4-1

3. Which of the following is NOT a common shape of bacteria?
   a. round
   b. cube
   c. spiral
   d. rod

   ANS: B   DIF: B   OBJ: 4-4

---

7. ANS: E   DIF: B   OBJ: 3-8

Match each item with the correct statement below.
a. genus
b. species
c. genus and species

8. is always written first in a scientific name
9. make up a scientific name
10. In the scientific name *Crotalus atrox*, *atrox* is the
11. *Rana pipiens* and *Rana catesbiana* are in the same
12. the smallest division of living things

8. ANS: A   DIF: B   OBJ: 3-7
9. ANS: C   DIF: B   OBJ: 3-7
10. ANS: B   DIF: A   OBJ: 3-7
11. ANS: A   DIF: A   OBJ: 3-7
12. ANS: B   DIF: B   OBJ: 3-5

SHORT ANSWER

Figure 3-2

1. Which diagrams in Figure 3-2 would Aristotle have classified together?

   ANS: 1 and 6   DIF: A   OBJ: 3-3

2. Which diagram in Figure 3-2 belongs to the moneran kingdom?

   ANS: 4   DIF: A   OBJ: 3-8

3. Which diagram in Figure 3-2 belongs to the protist kingdom?

   ANS: 7   DIF: A   OBJ: 3-8

4. Which diagram in Figure 3-2 belongs to the fungus kingdom?

   ANS: 3   DIF: A   OBJ: 3-8

5. Which of the diagram(s) in Figure 3-2 is (are) in the plant kingdom?

   ANS: 2, 5   DIF: A   OBJ: 3-8

4. When growing conditions are not right, many bacteria form _____.
   a. antibodies
   b. acid
   c. buds
   d. endospores

   ANS: D   DIF: B   OBJ: 4-4

5. Chemicals made by the body that help destroy viruses and harmful bacteria are _____.
   a. antibodies
   b. vaccines
   c. endospores
   d. antibiotics

   ANS: A   DIF: B   OBJ: 4-3

6. The common cold is caused by _____.
   a. bacteria
   b. blue-green bacteria
   c. viruses

   ANS: C   DIF: B   OBJ: 4-3

7. Some viruses cause the host cell to reproduce both itself and the viruses. Groups of these cells become _____.
   a. polio
   b. tumors
   c. mumps
   d. rabies

   ANS: B   DIF: B   OBJ: 4-2

8. The trait that viruses share with living things is the ability to _____.
   a. adapt
   b. use food
   c. respond
   d. reproduce

   ANS: B   DIF: A   OBJ: 4-1

9. Viruses can be observed only with a(n) _____.
   a. compound microscope
   b. electron microscope
   c. stereoscopic microscope

   ANS: B   DIF: A   OBJ: 4-1

10. Chemicals used to kill bacteria on living things are _____.
    a. saprophytes
    b. disinfectants
    c. antiseptics
    d. postulates

    ANS: C   DIF: B   OBJ: 4-5

11. Developing new forms of bacteria that produce useful products is an example of _____.
    a. photosynthesis
    b. reproduction
    c. biotechnology
    d. interferon

    ANS: C   DIF: A   OBJ: 4-5

12. Bacterial cells do not contain a _____.
    a. cell membrane
    b. nucleus
    c. cell wall
    d. chromosome

    ANS: B   DIF: B   OBJ: 4-4

13. High temperatures are used to prepare canned foods because the heat _____.
    a. improves the taste of the food
    b. kills the bacteria in the food
    c. helps bacteria grow
    d. allows bacteria to reproduce

    ANS: B   DIF: A   OBJ: 4-5

14. A vaccine against a specific virus is usually made from _____.
    a. bacteria
    b. chemicals
    c. dead or weakened viruses
    d. plastic

    ANS: C   DIF: B   OBJ: 4-3

15. Vaccines cause the body to make _____.
    a. antibodies
    b. interferon
    c. food
    d. more of a certain virus type

    ANS: A   DIF: B   OBJ: 4-3

16. Your dog receives a shot from the vet for a virus disease called distemper. Most likely the shot is
   a. interferon
   b. a vaccine
   c. harmful
   d. an antibody
   ANS: B   DIF: A   OBJ: 4-3

17. A flagellum on some bacteria allows them to _____.
   a. move
   b. reproduce
   c. make endospores
   d. make food
   ANS: A   DIF: B   OBJ: 4-4

18. In bacteria, the opposite of a parasite would be a _____.
   a. virus
   b. endospore
   c. saprophyte
   d. chromosome
   ANS: C   DIF: B   OBJ: 4-4

MATCHING

Examine Figure 4-1. Choose the letter of the diagram that best matches each statement.

Figure 4-1

1. These have no cell parts.
2. This is in the same kingdom as blue-green bacteria.
3. This organism can produce oxygen.
4. Members of this group have three basic cell shapes.
5. These have a protein coat.
6. This organism may have an outer jellylike layer.
7. These organisms can make their own food.
8. Members of this group can live as parasites, saprophytes, or help their host.
9. Members of this group live only as parasites.
10. These organisms contain chlorophyll and other pigments.
11. This member can reproduce only in living cells.
12. Members of this group can cause many diseases, including polio.
13. Members of this group are important in making cheese and other foods.

14. Crystals of these can be stored for years.
15. These organisms help cows digest food.
16. Members of this group may be classified according to the kind of cell they infect.
17. Overgrowth of this organism produces water pollution.

#	ANS:	DIF:	OBJ:
1.	C	A	4-1
2.	A	A	4-6
3.	B	A	4-6
4.	A	A	4-4
5.	C	A	4-1
6.	B	A	4-6
7.	B	A	4-6
8.	A	A	4-5
9.	C	A	4-1
10.	B	A	4-6
11.	C	A	4-2
12.	C	A	4-3
13.	A	A	4-5
14.	C	A	4-1
15.	A	A	4-5
16.	C	A	4-3
17.	B	A	4-6

Match each item with the correct statement below.
   a. antiseptic
   b. dehydration
   c. freezing
   d. medicines
   e. pasteurization

18. heating milk to kill bacteria
19. removing water from food
20. using iodine, hydrogen peroxide, or alcohol
21. lowering the temperature of food
22. giving a vaccine

#	ANS:	DIF:	OBJ:
18.	E	A	4-5
19.	B	A	4-5
20.	A	A	4-5
21.	C	A	4-5
22.	D	A	4-5

Match each item with the correct statement below.
   a. problem caused by bacteria
   b. problem caused by viruses
   c. helpful bacteria

23. producing antibiotics
24. fire blight

25. vitamins in the intestine
26. rabies in dogs
27. making linen and rope
28. crown gall
29. flavors food
30. insulin production for humans
31. anthrax
32. cold sores, measles, polio, AIDS
33. break down dead matter

	ANS:		DIF:		OBJ:
23.	C		A		4-5
24.	A		A		4-5
25.	C		A		4-5
26.	B		A		4-3
27.	C		A		4-5
28.	A		A		4-5
29.	C		A		4-5
30.	C		A		4-5
31.	A		A		4-5
32.	B		A		4-3
33.	C		A		4-5

SHORT ANSWER

1. The following steps may be used to prove that certain bacteria cause a disease. List the steps in their correct order. a. Bacteria are taken from the first host and grown in the laboratory. b. Laboratory-grown bacteria are injected into a second host and must cause the same disease as in the first host. c. Bacteria are removed from the second host and must be identified as the same found in the first host. d. Bacteria are found in a living host.

ANS: d, a, b, c   DIF: A   OBJ: 4-5

2. Nothing can cure the common cold. Why is this statement true?

ANS: Drugs such as antibiotics do not kill viruses. The common cold is caused by a virus.

DIF: A   OBJ: 4-3

3. You are asked to decide if a virus is or is not living. List two living and two nonliving traits.

ANS: Living traits: made of a chromosome-like part, has a protein coat, reproduces, carries hereditary materials on a chromosome-like part. Nonliving traits: does not grow, does not respond, takes on a crystal form, not made of cells.

DIF: A   OBJ: 4-1

4. Explain how the terms parasite and host are related.

ANS: A parasite lives off another living thing. The other living thing is called a host.

DIF: A   OBJ: 4-1

5. Describe several different ways that viruses are classified.

ANS: grouped as to the type of cell they infect, shape of protein coat, size of virus

DIF: A   OBJ: 4-1

6. Give an example that shows how a virus is very specific to its host.

ANS: Tobacco mosaic virus will infect only tobacco plants and not corn or wheat. A rabies virus will infect only the cells of the nervous system.

DIF: A   OBJ: 4-1

7. Why might it be correct to say that you can never be cured of a cold sore even though you may not always see it as a blister?

ANS: The virus is present in your skin cells but only shows its effect when it begins to reproduce. This results in the appearance of the blister.

DIF: A   OBJ: 4-2

8. Compare the speeds at which a cold sore and a mumps virus reproduce.

ANS: Cold sore viruses may reproduce slowly and remain dormant for long periods of time. The mumps virus reproduces rapidly after entering your body.

DIF: A   OBJ: 4-2

9. Compare the effects of the host cell with a virus causing flu and a virus causing warts.

ANS: Host cells infected by a flu virus are destroyed by the virus. A wart virus causes the infected cell to reproduce itself, forming a tumor.

DIF: A   OBJ: 4-2

10. Compare the ways in which the AIDS virus and a plant virus are spread.

ANS: The AIDS virus is spread through sexual contact, blood products, sharing contaminated needles, and from pregnant mother to her developing baby. A plant virus is spread by wind or when an insect feeds off a plant part.

DIF: A   OBJ: 4-2

CHAPTER 5—PROTISTS AND FUNGI

TRUE/FALSE

1. The slime mold produces spores in the first stage.

   ANS: F   DIF: B   OBJ: 5-2

2. Plantlike protists provide food for other living things, such as fish and snails.

   ANS: T   DIF: B   OBJ: 5-2

3. Cells of fungi often have more than one nucleus.

   ANS: T   DIF: B   OBJ: 5-4

4. Most fungi are made of branching hyphae called false feet.

   ANS: F   DIF: B   OBJ: 5-4

5. Fungi digest food inside their bodies.

   ANS: F   DIF: B   OBJ: 5-4

6. It is not safe to eat any unidentified wild mushroom.

   ANS: T   DIF: B   OBJ: 5-5

7. Rusts and smuts destroy entire crops of corn, wheat, and oats.

   ANS: T   DIF: B   OBJ: 5-5

8. Dutch elm disease is caused by a fungus.

   ANS: T   DIF: B   OBJ: 5-5

9. In a lichen, the organism with chlorophyll provides the food.

   ANS: T   DIF: B   OBJ: 5-4

10. Reindeer moss is a lichen.

    ANS: T   DIF: B   OBJ: 5-4

11. Athlete's foot is a disease caused by a protist.

    ANS: F   DIF: B   OBJ: 5-5

---

11. Give five conditions that most bacteria need to live.

    ANS: moisture, certain temperatures, food, oxygen, and darkness

    DIF: A   OBJ: 4-4

12. A bear will hibernate when food runs out and temperatures drop. What do some bacteria do that is similar to hibernation?

    ANS: They form a structure called an endospore that lets them survive until living conditions return to normal.

    DIF: A   OBJ: 4-4

13. Describe where the capsule is found in bacteria.

    ANS: outside of cell   DIF: A   OBJ: 4-4

14. Describe where the cytoplasm is found in bacteria.

    ANS: within capsule and membrane   DIF: A   OBJ: 4-4

15. Describe where the chromosome is found in bacteria.

    ANS: within the cytoplasm   DIF: A   OBJ: 4-4

MULTIPLE CHOICE

1. A special cell that develops into a new living thing is a _____.
   a. vacuole
   b. chloroplast
   c. virus
   d. spore

   ANS: D   DIF: B   OBJ: 5-2

2. Which of the following is NOT a member of the protist kingdom?
   a. bacteria
   b. slime mold
   c. paramecium
   d. amoeba

   ANS: A   DIF: B   OBJ: 5-3

3. Which cell part is NOT found in an amoeba?
   a. nucleus
   b. cell membrane
   c. cell wall
   d. vacuole

   ANS: C   DIF: B   OBJ: 5-2

4. Which of the following is NOT a trait of a euglena?
   a. can move about
   b. a flagellum
   c. contains chlorophyll
   d. has false feet

   ANS: D   DIF: B   OBJ: 5-2

5. A living thing, usually with one cell that has a nucleus and other cell parts, is a _____.
   a. moneran
   b. virus
   c. protist
   d. fungus

   ANS: C   DIF: B   OBJ: 5-1

6. In one stage of its life cycle, the slime mold flows like a(n) _____.
   a. paramecium
   b. euglena
   c. diatom
   d. amoeba

   ANS: D   DIF: B   OBJ: 5-2

7. The relationship between a fungus and a green organism is an example of _____.
   a. neighbors
   b. mutualism
   c. parasitism
   d. saprophytes

   ANS: B   DIF: B   OBJ: 5-4

8. Malaria is caused by a _____.
   a. sporozoan
   b. diatom
   c. dinoflagellate
   d. fungus

   ANS: A   DIF: B   OBJ: 5-2

9. A mushroom absorbs food through its _____.
   a. cap
   b. spores
   c. stalk
   d. hyphae

   ANS: D   DIF: B   OBJ: 5-4

10. Protists that reproduce by forming spores are _____.
    a. paramecia
    b. amoebas
    c. sporozoans
    d. diatoms

    ANS: C   DIF: B   OBJ: 5-2

11. Fungi reproduce by _____.
    a. pieces of hyphae
    b. spores
    c. fission
    d. both a and b

    ANS: D   DIF: B   OBJ: 5-4

12. A main difference between fungi and plants is that fungi _____.
    a. have no cell walls
    b. produce spores
    c. cannot make food

    ANS: C   DIF: B   OBJ: 5-4

13. The plantlike protist that has some animal traits is the _____.
a. amoeba
b. alga
c. paramecium
d. euglena

ANS: C   DIF: B   OBJ: 5-2

14. Which statement is true for both bacteria and protists?
a. both have cells with a nucleus
b. most or all are usually only one cell in size
c. most can move about

ANS: B   DIF: A   OBJ: 5-1

15. Which statement is true for protists?
a. may be producers or consumers
b. most can be seen without a microscope
c. all cause disease in humans

ANS: A   DIF: A   OBJ: 5-1

MATCHING

Examine Figure 5-1. Choose the letter of the diagram that best matches each statement.

Figure 5-1

1. used to bake bread
2. club fungi
3. grow on bread
4. sporangium fungi
5. make alcohol
6. shelf fungi, rusts, and smuts are in the same group
7. penicillin is made by a member of this group
8. powdery mildews are in this group
9. some may cause death if eaten

1. ANS: C   DIF: A   OBJ: 5-5
2. ANS: A   DIF: A   OBJ: 5-4
3. ANS: B   DIF: A   OBJ: 5-5
4. ANS: B   DIF: A   OBJ: 5-4
5. ANS: C   DIF: A   OBJ: 5-5

6. ANS: A   DIF: A   OBJ: 5-4
7. ANS: C   DIF: A   OBJ: 5-5
8. ANS: C   DIF: A   OBJ: 5-4
9. ANS: A   DIF: A   OBJ: 5-5

Examine Figure 5-2. Choose the letter of the structure that best matches each statement.

Figure 5-2

10. false feet
11. cilia
12. removes excess water
13. directs cell activity
14. food is taken in here
15. food is digested here
16. flagellum
17. chloroplast
18. used to sweep food into the mouth

10. ANS: B   DIF: A   OBJ: 5-2
11. ANS: F   DIF: A   OBJ: 5-2
12. ANS: D   DIF: A   OBJ: 5-2
13. ANS: A   DIF: A   OBJ: 5-1
14. ANS: E   DIF: A   OBJ: 5-2
15. ANS: C   DIF: A   OBJ: 5-2
16. ANS: G   DIF: A   OBJ: 5-2
17. ANS: H   DIF: A   OBJ: 5-2
18. ANS: F   DIF: A   OBJ: 5-2

Match each item with the correct statement below.
a. diatom
b. dinoflagellate
c. euglena

19. has an eyespot
20. cell covering made of two parts
21. has one flagellum
22. cause red tides
23. usually are red or brown and live in oceans
24. have glasslike shells
25. shaped like boats, rods, disks, or triangles
26. used in toothpaste, scouring powders, and filters

19. ANS: C   DIF: B   OBJ: 5-3

20. ANS: A DIF: B OBJ: 5-3
21. ANS: C DIF: B OBJ: 5-3
22. ANS: B DIF: B OBJ: 5-3
23. ANS: B DIF: B OBJ: 5-3
24. ANS: A DIF: B OBJ: 5-3
25. ANS: A DIF: B OBJ: 5-3
26. ANS: A DIF: B OBJ: 5-3

Match each item with the correct statement below.
a. animal-like protist
b. plantlike protist
c. funguslike protist
d. animal-like and funguslike protists

27. algae
28. protozoans
29. use cilia to move about
30. slime molds
31. pass from a slimy mass to spores to amoebalike cells to a slimy mass
32. all can make their own food
33. feed on rotting logs and decaying leaves
34. are consumers

27. ANS: B DIF: A OBJ: 5-2
28. ANS: A DIF: A OBJ: 5-2
29. ANS: A DIF: A OBJ: 5-2
30. ANS: C DIF: A OBJ: 5-2
31. ANS: C DIF: A OBJ: 5-2
32. ANS: B DIF: A OBJ: 5-2
33. ANS: C DIF: A OBJ: 5-2
34. ANS: D DIF: A OBJ: 5-2

Choose the word from the following list that best matches each statement below. The statements describe some actions of different kinds of fungi.
a. helpful
b. harmful

35. break down waste materials
36. cause skin disease
37. attack corn or wheat crops
38. used in baking bread
39. cause elm tree destruction
40. make blue cheese
41. used in making alcohol
42. growing on the roots of plants
43. mildew growing on your leather shoes

35. ANS: A DIF: A OBJ: 5-5
36. ANS: B DIF: A OBJ: 5-5

37. ANS: B DIF: A OBJ: 5-5
38. ANS: A DIF: A OBJ: 5-5
39. ANS: B DIF: A OBJ: 5-5
40. ANS: A DIF: A OBJ: 5-5
41. ANS: A DIF: A OBJ: 5-5
42. ANS: A DIF: A OBJ: 5-5
43. ANS: B DIF: A OBJ: 5-5

PROBLEM

1.

Table 5-1

Fungus Group	Reproduce by	Example
a.	spores in saclike parts	b.
Sporangium fungus	c.	bread mold
d.	spores on club-shaped parts	e.

Complete Table 5-1 by filling in the missing information.

ANS:

Table 5-1

Fungus Group	Reproduce by	Example
a. sacfungus	spores in saclike parts	b. yeast, penicillium
Sporangium fungus	c. spores on sporangia	bread mold
d. clubfungus	spores on club-shaped parts	e. mushrooms

DIF: A   OBJ: 5-4

CHAPTER 6—PLANTS

MULTIPLE CHOICE

1. The process that best separates plants from animals is _____.
   a. respiration
   b. reproduction
   c. photosynthesis
   d. osmosis

   ANS: C   DIF: B   OBJ: 6-1

2. Structures that anchor vascular plants and take in water and minerals are _____.
   a. roots
   b. stems
   c. leaves
   d. flowers

   ANS: A   DIF: B   OBJ: 6-2

3. A female reproductive cell is a(n) _____.
   a. sperm
   b. egg
   c. spore
   d. seed

   ANS: B   DIF: B   OBJ: 6-4

4. Reproduction of a living thing from two reproductive cells is _____.
   a. sexual reproduction
   b. asexual reproduction
   c. budding
   d. fission

   ANS: A   DIF: B   OBJ: 6-4

5. Nonvascular plants that are flat, leaflike, and grow very close to the soil are _____.
   a. algae
   b. grasses
   c. liverworts
   d. conifers

   ANS: C   DIF: B   OBJ: 6-3

6. Some mosses live on rocks and break the rocks down into _____.
   a. sphagnum
   b. pigments
   c. fertilizers
   d. soil

   ANS: D   DIF: B   OBJ: 6-5

7. Liverworts, mosses, and ferns do NOT produce _____.
   a. multicellular plants
   b. chlorophyll
   c. seeds
   d. spores

   ANS: C   DIF: B   OBJ: 6-4

8. The leaves of a fern grow from an underground _____.
   a. stem
   b. flower
   c. spore
   d. root

   ANS: A   DIF: B   OBJ: 6-6

9. Mosses and liverworts absorb water from the soil by the process of _____.
   a. fission
   b. respiration
   c. osmosis
   d. spore formation

   ANS: C   DIF: B   OBJ: 6-2

10. Seed plants are divided into two groups called _____.
    a. conifers and flowering plants
    b. mosses and liverworts
    c. conifers and ferns
    d. ferns and mosses

    ANS: A   DIF: B   OBJ: 6-6

11. Fir and pine trees are classified as _____.
    a. conifers
    b. flowering plants
    c. shrubs
    d. mosses

    ANS: A   DIF: B   OBJ: 6-6

12. Grasses and rose bushes are classified as _____.
    a. flowering plants
    b. liverworts
    c. conifers
    d. evergreens

    ANS: A   DIF: B   OBJ: 6-6

13. A small new plant is found inside a _____.
a. leaf
b. seed
c. spore
d. root
ANS: B   DIF: B   OBJ: 6-7

COMPLETION

1. In the life cycle of a moss, male plants form _____.
ANS: sperm   DIF: A   OBJ: 6-4

2. In the life cycle of a moss, female plants form _____.
ANS: eggs   DIF: A   OBJ: 6-4

3. In the life cycle of a moss, sperm swim to egg and results in _____.
ANS: fertilization   DIF: A   OBJ: 6-4

4. In the life cycle of a moss, a stalk grows after fertilization and forms _____.
ANS: spores in a capsule   DIF: A   OBJ: 6-4

5. In the life cycle of a moss, spores form _____.
ANS: new leafy plants   DIF: A   OBJ: 6-4

MATCHING

Match each item with the correct statement below.
a. vascular
b. nonvascular
c. both vascular and nonvascular

1. are usually green
2. some form new plants by seeds
3. mosses and liverworts
4. conifers and ferns
5. roots, stems, and leaves do NOT have tubelike cells
6. have tubelike cells
7. usually are tall plants
8. carry on photosynthesis
9. flowering plants
10. some form new plants by spores

1. ANS: C   DIF: A   OBJ: 6-1
2. ANS: A   DIF: A   OBJ: 6-7
3. ANS: B   DIF: A   OBJ: 6-3
4. ANS: A   DIF: A   OBJ: 6-6
5. ANS: B   DIF: A   OBJ: 6-2
6. ANS: A   DIF: A   OBJ: 6-2
7. ANS: A   DIF: A   OBJ: 6-6
8. ANS: C   DIF: A   OBJ: 6-1
9. ANS: A   DIF: A   OBJ: 6-6
10. ANS: C   DIF: A   OBJ: 6-4

Match each item with the correct statement below.
a. plants
b. animals
c. both plants and animals

11. can make their own food
12. are living things
13. use energy from the sun to make food
14. do not have cell walls
15. usually can move about
16. have chlorophyll
17. carry on photosynthesis
18. contain green chloroplasts

11. ANS: A   DIF: A   OBJ: 6-1
12. ANS: C   DIF: A   OBJ: 6-1
13. ANS: A   DIF: A   OBJ: 6-1
14. ANS: B   DIF: A   OBJ: 6-1
15. ANS: B   DIF: A   OBJ: 6-1
16. ANS: A   DIF: A   OBJ: 6-1
17. ANS: A   DIF: A   OBJ: 6-1
18. ANS: A   DIF: A   OBJ: 6-1

Match each item with the correct statement below.
a. mosses and liverworts
b. plants other than mosses and liverworts
c. mosses, liverworts, and all other plants

19. are green in color
20. belong to the plant kingdom
21. are nonvascular
22. are vascular
23. do have roots
24. do NOT have roots
25. contain tubelike cells

19. ANS: C   DIF: A   OBJ: 6-3

20.	ANS: C	DIF: A	OBJ: 6-3
21.	ANS: A	DIF: A	OBJ: 6-3
22.	ANS: B	DIF: A	OBJ: 6-3
23.	ANS: B	DIF: A	OBJ: 6-3
24.	ANS: A	DIF: A	OBJ: 6-3
25.	ANS: B	DIF: A	OBJ: 6-3

Match each item with the correct statement below.

a. conifers
b. flowering plants
c. both conifers and flowering plants

26. supply humans with most of our food
27. supply humans with most of our paper
28. add oxygen to the air
29. supply us with turpentine and disinfectants
30. supply us with most of our wood
31. use carbon dioxide for photosynthesis
32. are grown as lawn grass
33. provide homes, shelter, and food to forest animals

26.	ANS: B	DIF: A	OBJ: 6-8
27.	ANS: A	DIF: A	OBJ: 6-8
28.	ANS: C	DIF: A	OBJ: 6-8
29.	ANS: A	DIF: A	OBJ: 6-8
30.	ANS: A	DIF: A	OBJ: 6-8
31.	ANS: C	DIF: A	OBJ: 6-8
32.	ANS: B	DIF: A	OBJ: 6-8
33.	ANS: C	DIF: A	OBJ: 6-8

Match each item with the correct statement below.

a. ferns
b. conifers
c. flowering plants
d. conifers and flowering plants
e. ferns, conifers, and flowering plants
f. neither ferns, conifers, nor flowering plants

34. are nonvascular plants
35. are vascular plants
36. contain xylem and phloem cells
37. must obtain their food from the soil
38. uses cones or flowers during reproduction
39. tubelike cells carry food and water throughout the plant
40. tomato plants, grass, and pine trees are examples
41. Many of these plants formed our coal beds.
42. carry on photosynthesis
43. supply us with paper, cardboard, and food
44. Sperm must travel in water for fertilization to occur.

45. Sperm do NOT have to travel in water for fertilization to occur.
46. uses spores during reproduction
47. uses seeds during reproduction
48. Pollen cells are produced during reproduction.
49. Cones are used in reproduction.
50. Flowers are used in reproduction.
51. Sperm and egg cells are formed during reproduction.

34.	ANS: F	DIF: A	OBJ: 6-6
35.	ANS: E	DIF: A	OBJ: 6-6
36.	ANS: E	DIF: A	OBJ: 6-6
37.	ANS: F	DIF: A	OBJ: 6-6
38.	ANS: D	DIF: A	OBJ: 6-6
39.	ANS: E	DIF: A	OBJ: 6-6
40.	ANS: D	DIF: A	OBJ: 6-6
41.	ANS: A	DIF: A	OBJ: 6-6
42.	ANS: E	DIF: A	OBJ: 6-6
43.	ANS: D	DIF: A	OBJ: 6-6
44.	ANS: A	DIF: A	OBJ: 6-7
45.	ANS: D	DIF: A	OBJ: 6-7
46.	ANS: A	DIF: A	OBJ: 6-7
47.	ANS: D	DIF: A	OBJ: 6-7
48.	ANS: D	DIF: A	OBJ: 6-7
49.	ANS: B	DIF: A	OBJ: 6-7
50.	ANS: C	DIF: A	OBJ: 6-7
51.	ANS: E	DIF: A	OBJ: 6-7

Examine Figure 6-1. Choose the letter of the plant part that best matches each function. A part may have more than one function.

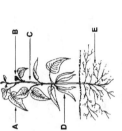

Figure 6-1

52. carries water to all parts of the plant
53. anchors the plant
54. supports the plant
55. takes in water and minerals from the soil
56. produces the egg cells and sperm cells
57. holds the leaves up to the sunlight
58. contains a small new plant

70. ANS: B DIF: A OBJ: 6-3
71. ANS: A DIF: A OBJ: 6-7
72. ANS: B DIF: A OBJ: 6-4
73. ANS: A DIF: A OBJ: 6-6
74. ANS: C DIF: A OBJ: 6-7
75. ANS: B DIF: A OBJ: 6-3
76. ANS: A DIF: A OBJ: 6-6

Match each item with the correct statement below.
a. describes how mosses are important to other living things
b. describes how mosses are NOT important to other living things

77. can be used as a fuel
78. form a slippery mat near moist surfaces
79. hold soil in place
80. may be food for other small animals
81. do NOT have any tubelike cells
82. increases amount of water that soil can hold

77. ANS: A DIF: A OBJ: 6-5
78. ANS: B DIF: A OBJ: 6-5
79. ANS: A DIF: A OBJ: 6-5
80. ANS: A DIF: A OBJ: 6-5
81. ANS: B DIF: A OBJ: 6-5
82. ANS: A DIF: A OBJ: 6-5

---

59. makes food

52. ANS: C DIF: A OBJ: 6-2
53. ANS: E DIF: A OBJ: 6-2
54. ANS: C DIF: A OBJ: 6-2
55. ANS: E DIF: A OBJ: 6-2
56. ANS: B DIF: A OBJ: 6-7
57. ANS: C DIF: A OBJ: 6-2
58. ANS: D DIF: A OBJ: 6-7
59. ANS: A DIF: A OBJ: 6-2

Examine Figure 6-2. Choose the letter of the diagram that best matches each statement.

Figure 6-2

60. provides cereals, fruits, and vegetables
61. provides food for animals such as worms and snails
62. forms bark, buds, and seeds eaten by animals
63. lacks tubelike cells
64. provides three-fourths of the world's lumber
65. forms peat from decayed sphagnum
66. provides most of the world's paper and cardboard
67. breaks down rocks into soil
68. provides turpentine and fuel
69. may use the help of insects or wind in reproduction
70. never grows tall
71. produces seeds in cones
72. produces spores in capsules
73. has tough, needlelike leaves
74. produces seeds in a flower
75. has no xylem
76. sometimes called evergreens

60. ANS: C DIF: A OBJ: 6-8
61. ANS: B DIF: A OBJ: 6-3
62. ANS: A DIF: A OBJ: 6-8
63. ANS: B DIF: A OBJ: 6-3
64. ANS: A DIF: A OBJ: 6-8
65. ANS: B DIF: A OBJ: 6-5
66. ANS: A DIF: A OBJ: 6-8
67. ANS: B DIF: A OBJ: 6-5
68. ANS: A DIF: A OBJ: 6-8
69. ANS: C DIF: A OBJ: 6-7

CHAPTER 7—SIMPLE ANIMALS

TRUE/FALSE

1. Planaria have segmented bodies.

   ANS: F   DIF: B   OBJ: 7-6

2. A free-living worm is NOT parasitic.

   ANS: T   DIF: B   OBJ: 7-6

3. A sponge has radial symmetry.

   ANS: T   DIF: B   OBJ: 7-3

4. Segmented worms are the simplest worms.

   ANS: F   DIF: B   OBJ: 7-6

5. A tapeworm uses food another animal eats.

   ANS: T   DIF: B   OBJ: 7-6

6. A planarian is a parasite.

   ANS: F   DIF: B   OBJ: 7-5

7. All animals must take in food.

   ANS: T   DIF: A   OBJ: 7-1

8. All animals are all one cell in size.

   ANS: F   DIF: A   OBJ: 7-1

9. All animals are consumers.

   ANS: T   DIF: A   OBJ: 7-1

10. Many animals have a number of systems.

    ANS: T   DIF: A   OBJ: 7-1

11. Animals may be vertebrates but never invertebrates.

    ANS: F   DIF: A   OBJ: 7-1

12. Animals usually are multicellular.

    ANS: T   DIF: A   OBJ: 7-1

13. Most animals show no type of symmetry.

    ANS: F   DIF: A   OBJ: 7-1

14. All animals are unable to move about.

    ANS: F   DIF: A   OBJ: 7-1

15. All animals digest and store food in their bodies.

    ANS: T   DIF: A   OBJ: 7-1

16. Animals may be invertebrates but never vertebrates.

    ANS: F   DIF: A   OBJ: 7-1

MULTIPLE CHOICE

1. All of the following are features of animals except _____.
   a. move about
   b. have tissues and organs
   c. have many cells
   d. make their own food

   ANS: D   DIF: A   OBJ: 7-1

2. The most complex animals are the _____.
   a. worms
   b. chordates
   c. sponges
   d. invertebrates

   ANS: B   DIF: B   OBJ: 7-1

3. All _____ have backbones.
   a. invertebrates
   b. animals
   c. vertebrates
   d. roundworms

   ANS: C   DIF: B   OBJ: 7-1

4. Soft-bodied animals with two shells include scallops, oysters, and _____.
a. squid
b. snails
c. slugs
d. clams

ANS: D   DIF: B   OBJ: 7-8

5. Which of the following is NOT a stinging-cell animal?
a. hydra
b. jellyfish
c. sponge
d. coral

ANS: C   DIF: B   OBJ: 7-2

6. The largest phylum of animals is made up of _____.
a. sponges
b. jointed-leg animals
c. stinging-cell animals
d. chordates

ANS: B   DIF: B   OBJ: 7-2

7. Eight of the nine phyla in the animal kingdom are made up of _____.
a. vertebrates
b. chordates
c. invertebrates
d. jointed-leg animals

ANS: C   DIF: B   OBJ: 7-2

8. Jellyfish are classified as stinging-cell animals because they have a _____.
a. hollow body
b. segmented body
c. shell
d. round body

ANS: A   DIF: A   OBJ: 7-4

9. Hookworms are parasitic _____.
a. snails
b. flatworms
c. roundworms
d. leeches

ANS: C   DIF: B   OBJ: 7-5

10. The body of a sponge is made up of _____ layers of cells.
a. 2
b. 4
c. 6
d. 8

ANS: A   DIF: B   OBJ: 7-3

11. Hydra can reproduce asexually by _____.
a. fission
b. buds
c. fertilization
d. egg and sperm

ANS: B   DIF: B   OBJ: 7-4

12. The armlike parts that surround the mouth of a jellyfish are _____.
a. stinging cells
b. discs
c. tentacles
d. mantles

ANS: C   DIF: B   OBJ: 7-4

13. Tapeworms form _____ in the muscles of their hosts.
a. eggs
b. body sections
c. cysts
d. discs

ANS: C   DIF: B   OBJ: 7-6

14. How do snails and slugs differ?
a. snails are living, slugs are not
b. snails live on land, slugs do not
c. snails have a shell, slugs do not
d. snails have a mantle, slugs do not

ANS: C   DIF: B   OBJ: 7-8

15. What is found on the tip end of a large snail's tentacles?
a. a trail of slime
b. a tongue
c. eyes
d. the shell

ANS: C   DIF: B   OBJ: 7-8

16. The foot in different classes of soft-bodied animals _____.
a. looks exactly the same
b. gives off a slime trail
c. is used to capture food
d. looks different and has a different job

ANS: D   DIF: B   OBJ: 7-8

17. Which trait is true for all soft-bodied animals?
a. all are invertebrates
b. all have tentacles and arms
c. all have segmented bodies
d. all have a shell

ANS: A   DIF: B   OBJ: 7-8

MATCHING

Choose the word or phrase from the following list that best matches each statement below.
a. soft-bodied animals
b. sponges
c. stinging-cell animals

1. Water enters and leaves the body by pores and canals.
2. These use muscle and nerve cells to move tentacles.
3. The body is covered by a mantle.
4. These make up the smallest animal phylum.
5. The body is usually protected by a hard shell.
6. Many catch food with tentacles.
7. These usually have a muscular foot for moving.
8. Most have no definite shape.
9. Many attach to the ocean bottom with a disc.
10. These do NOT have tissues and organs.
11. Food-getting cells trap food from water flowing in.
12. Many provide food for humans and other animals.
13. Their skeletons make them useful to humans for cleaning and washin'
14. Some live on land.
15. These are the simplest of all animals.

1. ANS: B   DIF: A   OBJ: 7-3
2. ANS: C   DIF: A   OBJ: 7-4
3. ANS: A   DIF: A   OBJ: 7-7
4. ANS: B   DIF: A   OBJ: 7-2
5. ANS: A   DIF: A   OBJ: 7-7
6. ANS: C   DIF: A   OBJ: 7-4
7. ANS: A   DIF: A   OBJ: 7-7
8. ANS: B   DIF: A   OBJ: 7-3
9. ANS: C   DIF: A   OBJ: 7-4

10. ANS: B   DIF: A   OBJ: 7-3
11. ANS: B   DIF: A   OBJ: 7-3
12. ANS: A   DIF: A   OBJ: 7-7
13. ANS: B   DIF: A   OBJ: 7-3
14. ANS: A   DIF: A   OBJ: 7-7
15. ANS: B   DIF: A   OBJ: 7-2

Choose the word or phrase from the following list that best matches each statement below.
a. radial symmetry
b. bilateral symmetry
c. no symmetry

16. body can be divided lengthwise into two equal parts
17. having a variety of different body shapes with no pattern
18. a sponge has this type of body plan
19. body parts are arranged in a circle around a center point
20. a sea anemone has this type of body plan
21. a bee has this type of body plan
22. humans have this type of symmetry
23. the type of symmetry shown by a bicycle wheel

16. ANS: B   DIF: A   OBJ: 7-1
17. ANS: C   DIF: A   OBJ: 7-1
18. ANS: C   DIF: A   OBJ: 7-1
19. ANS: A   DIF: A   OBJ: 7-1
20. ANS: A   DIF: A   OBJ: 7-1
21. ANS: B   DIF: A   OBJ: 7-1
22. ANS: B   DIF: A   OBJ: 7-1
23. ANS: A   DIF: A   OBJ: 7-1

Choose the word or phrase from the following list that best matches each living thing below.
a. flatworms
b. roundworms
c. segmented worms

24. earthworm
25. pork tapeworm
26. leech
27. hookworm
28. tapeworm

24. ANS: C   DIF: B   OBJ: 7-5
25. ANS: A   DIF: B   OBJ: 7-5
26. ANS: C   DIF: B   OBJ: 7-5
27. ANS: B   DIF: B   OBJ: 7-5
28. ANS: A   DIF: B   OBJ: 7-5

Choose the word from the following list that best matches each statement below.
a. snail
b. clam
c. octopus

29. has no skeleton
30. has one shell
31. has two shells
32. uses its foot to bury itself in sand
33. its foot is divided into 8 arms or tentacles
34. uses its foot to glide along
35. may live on land or in water
36. moves by shooting a jet of water

29. ANS: C   DIF: A   OBJ: 7-8
30. ANS: A   DIF: A   OBJ: 7-8
31. ANS: B   DIF: A   OBJ: 7-8
32. ANS: B   DIF: A   OBJ: 7-8
33. ANS: C   DIF: A   OBJ: 7-8
34. ANS: A   DIF: A   OBJ: 7-8
35. ANS: A   DIF: A   OBJ: 7-8
36. ANS: C   DIF: A   OBJ: 7-8

Examine Figure 7-1. Choose the letter that best matches each structure or function.

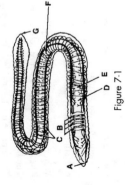

Figure 7-1

37. anus
38. blood vessels
39. mouth
40. grinds food
41. hearts
42. holds food
43. digests food

37. ANS: G   DIF: A   OBJ: 7-6
38. ANS: C   DIF: A   OBJ: 7-6
39. ANS: A   DIF: A   OBJ: 7-6
40. ANS: E   DIF: A   OBJ: 7-6
41. ANS: B   DIF: A   OBJ: 7-6

42. ANS: D   DIF: A   OBJ: 7-6
43. ANS: F   DIF: A   OBJ: 7-6

Choose the word from the following list that best matches each statement below.
a. earthworm
b. planarian
c. hookworm

44. has bristles that grip soil
45. in the same phylum as leeches
46. in the same phylum as the tapeworm
47. free-living flatworm
48. has organs to get rid of wastes
49. uses matter from the soil for food
50. whips about when it moves

44. ANS: A   DIF: B   OBJ: 7-6
45. ANS: A   DIF: B   OBJ: 7-6
46. ANS: B   DIF: B   OBJ: 7-6
47. ANS: B   DIF: B   OBJ: 7-6
48. ANS: A   DIF: B   OBJ: 7-6
49. ANS: A   DIF: B   OBJ: 7-6
50. ANS: C   DIF: B   OBJ: 7-6

SHORT ANSWER

1. How does a sponge get food if it cannot move about to capture it?

ANS: Food is present in ocean water. Water, along with food, is carried into the animal's body through pores.

DIF: A   OBJ: 7-3

2. How is water pulled into the inside of a sponge?

ANS: Cells with flagella line the inside of a sponge's body. These flagella beat and draw the water inside.

DIF: A   OBJ: 7-3

3. How does a sponge reproduce asexually?

ANS: Small pieces of the sponge may break off or the sponge may form buds. Buds and sponge pieces develop into new animals.

DIF: A   OBJ: 7-3

4. What evidence allows you to conclude that stinging-cell animals have muscles?

ANS: They can move their tentacles and bodies.

DIF: A   OBJ: 7-4

5. What evidence allows you to conclude that food enters and undigested food exits from a stinging cell animal through the same opening?

ANS: They have only one opening to their bodies.

DIF: A   OBJ: 7-4

6. What evidence allows you to conclude that stinging-cell animals have nerve cells that allow them to coordinate their feeding movements?

ANS: Once they trap food with their tentacles, the tentacles will move toward the mouth, pushing the trapped food into the animal's body.

DIF: A   OBJ: 7-4

7. What evidence allows you to conclude that the stinging cells on tentacles still work even after the death of the animal?

ANS: Stepping on these animals after they have washed up on a beach will release the stinging cells into the bottom of your feet.

DIF: A   OBJ: 7-4

8. Describe the general body shape and appearance of a flatworm.

ANS: flat body, three cell layers, may have suckers on front end

DIF: A   OBJ: 7-5

9. Describe the general body shape and appearance of a roundworm.

ANS: round body, three cell layers, long shape, small in size

DIF: A   OBJ: 7-5

10. Describe the general body shape and appearance of a segmented worm.

ANS: body divided into segments, three cell layers

DIF: A   OBJ: 7-5

11. Describe the method that soft-bodied animals such as snails use to gather food.

ANS: They have a tongue-like structure that is covered with teeth. The tongue-like part scrapes food from surfaces upon which the animals crawl.

DIF: A   OBJ: 7-7

12. What is the function of the mantle?

ANS: It covers the body and forms the animal's shell.

DIF: A   OBJ: 7-7

13. Where do soft-bodied animals live?

ANS: They live on land, in fresh water (streams and ponds), and in the ocean on rocks, in the water, or buried in sand.

DIF: A   OBJ: 7-7

Figure 7-2

14. Which part of Figure 7-2 is sensitive to light?

ANS: B   DIF: A   OBJ: 7-6

15. Which part of Figure 7-2 takes in food?

ANS: C   DIF: A   OBJ: 7-6

16. Which part of Figure 7-2 helps in digesting food?

ANS: D   DIF: A   OBJ: 7-6

17. Which part of Figure 7-2 are eyespots?

ANS: B   DIF: A   OBJ: 7-6

18. Which part(s) of Figure 7-2 allows response to the environment?

ANS: A, B   DIF: A   OBJ: 7-6

CHAPTER 8—COMPLEX ANIMALS

TRUE/FALSE

1. Your genus name is sapiens.

   ANS: F   DIF: A   OBJ: 8-6

2. Perch, trout, bass, and flounder are cartilage fish.

   ANS: F   DIF: A   OBJ: 8-4

3. Over 80 percent of known animal types are in the jointed-leg animal phylum.

   ANS: T   DIF: A   OBJ: 8-1

4. Besides jointed-leg animals, chordates are the only other group of animals to have members that fly.

   ANS: T   DIF: A   OBJ: 8-5

5. Pouched animals are NOT fully developed at birth.

   ANS: T   DIF: A   OBJ: 8-6

6. Spiny-skin animals have bilateral symmetry.

   ANS: F   DIF: A   OBJ: 8-3

7. Lampreys live as parasites.

   ANS: T   DIF: A   OBJ: 8-4

8. The lateral line fills with gases and helps a fish float.

   ANS: F   DIF: A   OBJ: 8-5

9. Only a few spiders have poison that causes serious sickness in humans.

   ANS: T   DIF: A   OBJ: 8-2

10. A bird that cannot fly is the ostrich.

    ANS: T   DIF: A   OBJ: 8-5

11. Cartilage fish do NOT have paired fins.

    ANS: F   DIF: A   OBJ: 8-4

12. Spiny-skinned animals are invertebrates.

    ANS: T   DIF: B   OBJ: 8-3

13. A starfish usually has an eight part body design.

    ANS: F   DIF: B   OBJ: 8-3

14. Sand dollars and sea urchins belong to the jointed-leg animal phylum.

    ANS: F   DIF: B   OBJ: 8-3

15. Spiny-skin animals are found only in ocean waters.

    ANS: T   DIF: B   OBJ: 8-3

MULTIPLE CHOICE

1. An animal that has eight legs, two body sections, and no antennae is a(n) _____.
   a. insect
   b. spider
   c. centipede
   d. lobster

   ANS: B   DIF: A   OBJ: 8-2

2. There are more kinds of _____ than all other animals combined.
   a. insects
   b. millipedes
   c. spiders
   d. scorpions

   ANS: A   DIF: B   OBJ: 8-2

3. An exoskeleton is a skeleton _____.
   a. made of a hard, waterproof substance
   b. on the outside of the body
   c. that provides a place for muscles to attach
   d. all of the above

   ANS: D   DIF: B   OBJ: 8-1

4. Insects have _____ pairs of legs.
   a. one
   b. four
   c. two
   d. three

   ANS: D   DIF: B   OBJ: 8-2

5. The body of most jointed-leg animals is divided into the head, thorax, and _____.
   a. stomach
   b. jointed legs
   c. abdomen
   d. wings

   ANS: C   DIF: B   OBJ: 8-1

6. The process of shedding an exoskeleton is _____.
   a. hibernation
   b. growth
   c. mating
   d. molting

   ANS: D   DIF: B   OBJ: 8-1

7. Insect antennae are _____ organs.
   a. sense
   b. digestive
   c. reproductive
   d. respiratory

   ANS: A   DIF: B   OBJ: 8-2

8. A structure used by fish to breathe is the _____.
   a. lung
   b. skin
   c. gill
   d. lateral line

   ANS: C   DIF: B   OBJ: 8-4

9. Reptiles and other animals with backbones are classified in the _____ phylum.
   a. amphibian
   b. chordate
   c. jointed-leg animals

   ANS: B   DIF: B   OBJ: 8-5

10. Animals that must live part of their lives in water and part on land are _____.
    a. amphibians
    b. reptiles
    c. warm-blooded
    d. mammals

    ANS: A   DIF: B   OBJ: 8-5

11. Because birds keep a constant body temperature in any environment, birds are _____.
    a. warm-blooded
    b. cold-blooded
    c. amphibians
    d. mammals

    ANS: A   DIF: B   OBJ: 8-5

12. Which of the following is NOT a reptile?
    a. turtle
    b. alligator
    c. toad
    d. snake

    ANS: C   DIF: A   OBJ: 8-5

13. All animals that have hair and feed milk to their young are _____.
    a. birds
    b. mammals
    c. bears
    d. cold-blooded

    ANS: B   DIF: B   OBJ: 8-6

14. Which of the following is NOT a trait of mammals?
    a. body hair
    b. cold-blooded
    c. care for young
    d. young are born alive

    ANS: B   DIF: B   OBJ: 8-6

15. Mammary glands of females supply young with _____.
    a. warmth
    b. care
    c. milk
    d. a constant body temperature

    ANS: C   DIF: B   OBJ: 8-6

16. Which of the following is NOT a category of classification for a human?
    a. kingdom animal
    b. phylum chordate
    c. genus homo
    d. class reptile

    ANS: D   DIF: B   OBJ: 8-6

COMPLETION

1. An animal that has dry, scaly skin and can live on land is a(n) _____

   ANS: reptile   DIF: B   OBJ: 8-5

2. Legs and wings are _____ found on jointed-leg animals.

   ANS: appendages   DIF: B   OBJ: 8-1

3. A skeleton on the inside of the body of a fish is an _____.

   ANS: endoskeleton   DIF: B   OBJ: 8-4

4. A fish body part that detects water movement is the _____.

   ANS: lateral line   DIF: B   OBJ: 8-4

5. The state of being inactive during cold weather is called _____.

   ANS: hibernation   DIF: B   OBJ: 8-5

6. The suction cup-like parts that help a starfish move are _____.

   ANS: tube feet   DIF: B   OBJ: 8-3

7. Reptiles breathe with their _____.

   ANS: lungs   DIF: B   OBJ: 8-5

8. Most _____ develop inside the mother's body and are born alive.

   ANS: mammals   DIF: B   OBJ: 8-6

9. Birds have _____ bones.

   ANS: hollow   DIF: B   OBJ: 8-5

MATCHING

Examine Figure 8-1. Choose the letter of the diagram that best match each statement.

A   B   C   D   E

Figure 8-1

1. is in the same class as scorpions, ticks, and mites
2. some animals in the same class destroy food crops
3. has a clawlike pair of legs that grabs and holds food
4. appendages on its first segment are poison claws
5. is in the same class as shrimp, lobsters, and crabs
6. slow-moving animal with many legs
7. many have two pairs of wings
8. has compound eyes only
9. has two pairs of antennae
10. each segment has one pair of walking legs

1. ANS: C   DIF: A   OBJ: 8-2
2. ANS: D   DIF: A   OBJ: 8-2
3. ANS: B   DIF: A   OBJ: 8-2
4. ANS: A   DIF: A   OBJ: 8-2
5. ANS: B   DIF: A   OBJ: 8-2
6. ANS: E   DIF: A   OBJ: 8-2
7. ANS: D   DIF: A   OBJ: 8-2
8. ANS: B   DIF: A   OBJ: 8-2
9. ANS: B   DIF: A   OBJ: 8-2
10. ANS: A   DIF: A   OBJ: 8-2

Choose the phrase from the following list that best matches each statement.

a. jawless fish
b. cartilage fish
c. bony fish

11. have toothlike scales
12. tubelike bodies with slime
13. do NOT have paired fins
14. have smooth scales
15. have a swim bladder
16. sharks and rays are examples
17. do NOT have scales
18. have gill covers

19. the lamprey is an example
20. perch and bass are examples

11. ANS: B DIF: B OBJ: 8-.
12. ANS: A DIF: B OBJ: 8-4
13. ANS: A DIF: B OBJ: 8-4
14. ANS: C DIF: B OBJ: 8-4
15. ANS: C DIF: B OBJ: 8-4
16. ANS: B DIF: A OBJ: 8-4
17. ANS: A DIF: B OBJ: 8-4
18. ANS: C DIF: B OBJ: 8-4
19. ANS: A DIF: A OBJ: 8-4
20. ANS: C DIF: A OBJ: 8-4

Choose the phrase from the following list that best matches each statement.
a. only amphibians
b. only reptiles
c. only birds
d. reptiles and birds
e. amphibians, reptiles, and birds

21. these animals are vertebrates
22. these animals have well-developed body systems
23. these animals are able to fly
24. these animals have scales on all or part of their bodies
25. these animals must lay their eggs in water
26. these animals spend part of their life in water and part on land
27. these animals are warm-blooded
28. these animals have clawed toes (if they have legs)
29. these animals are cold-blooded and lay eggs on land
30. these animals lay eggs with shells
31. these animals are chordates

21. ANS: E DIF: A OBJ: 8-5
22. ANS: E DIF: A OBJ: 8-5
23. ANS: C DIF: A OBJ: 8-5
24. ANS: D DIF: A OBJ: 8-5
25. ANS: A DIF: A OBJ: 8-5
26. ANS: A DIF: A OBJ: 8-5
27. ANS: C DIF: A OBJ: 8-5
28. ANS: D DIF: A OBJ: 8-5
29. ANS: B DIF: A OBJ: 8-5
30. ANS: D DIF: A OBJ: 8-5
31. ANS: E DIF: A OBJ: 8-5

SHORT ANSWER

1. Insects such as cockroaches go "crunch" when you step on them. Explain what makes this sound.

ANS: The crunch is caused by the breaking of the tough exoskeleton.

DIF: A OBJ: 8-1

2. Why must jointed-leg animals undergo molting?

ANS: Growth is difficult with an exoskeleton. Once the skeleton is shed, body growth can occur.

DIF: A OBJ: 8-1

3. What traits of the duck-billed platypus are mammal-like and what traits are reptile-like?

ANS: Mammal-like: has hair, nurses young with milk from mammary glands Reptile-like: lays eggs, eggs have a shell

DIF: B OBJ: 8-6

4. Give three ways that birds and mammals are alike.

ANS: warm-blooded, vertebrates, endoskeleton, four limbs, well-developed lungs

DIF: B OBJ: 8-6

5. Give three ways that birds and mammals differ.

ANS: Birds have feathers, are capable of flight, have hollow bones, no teeth, have a beak, scales on skin of legs.

DIF: B OBJ: 8-6

Compare the traits of jointed-leg animals with those of segmented worms. If a trait is the same for both phyla, mark the statement "same." If they are NOT alike, mark the statement "different."

6. body is segmented

ANS: same DIF: A OBJ: 8-1

7. an exoskeleton is present

ANS: different DIF: A OBJ: 8-1

8. appendages are present

ANS: different DIF: A OBJ: 8-1

9. an invertebrate phylum

ANS: same   DIF: A   OBJ: 8-1

10. undergoes molting

ANS: different   DIF: A   OBJ: 8-1

11. is a consumer organism

ANS: same   DIF: A   OBJ: 8-1

12. number of species in each phylum

ANS: different   DIF: A   OBJ: 8-1

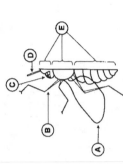

Figure 8-2

13. Is Animal A of Figure 8-2 in the spiny-skinned animal phylum? Give two traits that helped you decide.

ANS: Yes; it has five part body design, spines on skin, and radial symmetry.

DIF: A   OBJ: 8-3

14. Is Animal B of Figure 8-2 in the spiny-skinned animal phylum? Give two traits that helped you decide.

ANS: No; body design does not show five part organization, body is segmented, and has bilateral symmetry.

DIF: A   OBJ: 8-3

15. Is Animal C of Figure 8-2 in the spiny-skinned animal phylum? Give two traits that helped you decide.

ANS: Yes; it has five part body design, spines on skin, and radial symmetry.

DIF: A   OBJ: 8-3

PROBLEM

Figure 8-3

1. Figure 8-3 shows certain body parts of an insect. Compare these body parts with those of a crayfish and a spider by completing Table 8-1.

Table 8-1

Insect part	Information asked for	Crayfish	Spider
A	present or absent		
B	number of pairs		
C	present or absent		
C	type (simple or compound)		
D	present or absent		
E	number present		

ANS:

Table 8-1

Insect part	Information asked for	Crayfish	Spider
A	present or absent	absent	absent
B	number of pairs	5	4
C	present or absent	present	present
C	type (simple or compound)	compound	simple
D	present or absent	present	absent
E	number present	2	2

DIF: A   OBJ: 8-2

CHAPTER 9—NUTRITION

TRUE/FALSE

1. Calcium is used to form strong bones.

   ANS: T   DIF: B   OBJ: 9-2

2. A balanced diet is one that has the right amount of each nutrient.

   ANS: T   DIF: B   OBJ: 9-3

3. The six food groups include the fat group and the protein group.

   ANS: F   DIF: B   OBJ: 9-3

4. A Calorie is a unit that measures energy.

   ANS: T   DIF: B   OBJ: 9-4

5. In general, as an activity becomes more difficult, fewer Calories are used.

   ANS: F   DIF: B   OBJ: 9-6

6. A large person needs more Calories than a small person when performing the same activity.

   ANS: T   DIF: B   OBJ: 9-6

7. Sleeping requires no Calories.

   ANS: F   DIF: B   OBJ: 9-6

8. Standing in one place for 15 minutes uses fewer Calories than walking for the same amount of time.

   ANS: T   DIF: B   OBJ: 9-6

9. Calories not used by the body are stored as fat.

   ANS: T   DIF: B   OBJ: 9-6

10. A person will gain weight if he or she uses more Calories than taken in.

    ANS: F   DIF: B   OBJ: 9-6

Jim takes in 1 gram of calcium a day. Anita takes in 0.5 grams of calcium a day. The RDA for calcium is 1 gram. Giselle takes in 400 milligrams of magnesium a day. The RDA for magnesium is 325 milligrams.

11. Anita has met her RDA for calcium.

    ANS: F   DIF: A   OBJ: 9-2

12. Giselle has met her RDA for magnesium.

    ANS: T   DIF: A   OBJ: 9-2

13. Anita has taken in only half of her RDA for calcium.

    ANS: T   DIF: A   OBJ: 9-2

14. Jim has NOT met his RDA for calcium.

    ANS: F   DIF: A   OBJ: 9-2

15. Jim has taken 100 percent of his RDA for calcium.

    ANS: T   DIF: A   OBJ: 9-2

16. Giselle must take 75 more milligrams to meet her RDA for magnesium.

    ANS: F   DIF: A   OBJ: 9-2

17. Anita needs to take 0.5 grams more calcium to meet her RDA.

    ANS: T   DIF: A   OBJ: 9-2

MULTIPLE CHOICE

1. Examples of minerals are calcium and ____.
   a. fats
   b. enzymes
   c. water
   d. iron

   ANS: D   DIF: B   OBJ: 9-1

2. Fuel for your body is in the form of ____.
   a. enzymes
   b. vitamins
   c. minerals
   d. food

   ANS: D   DIF: B   OBJ: 9-1

3. When comparing equal masses, the nutrient that has the most Calories is _____.
   a. protein
   b. fat
   c. water
   d. carbohydrate

   ANS: B   DIF: B   OBJ: 9-5

4. The food that is often stored and used later as an energy source is _____.
   a. fat
   b. protein
   c. water
   d. vitamins

   ANS: A   DIF: B   OBJ: 9-2

5. A person who takes in more Calories that he or she uses will _____.
   a. gain weight
   b. get sick
   c. lose weight
   d. not change

   ANS: A   DIF: B   OBJ: 9-4

6. The nutrient stored under the skin and around body organs is _____.
   a. protein
   b. fat
   c. water
   d. carbohydrate

   ANS: B   DIF: B   OBJ: 9-2

7. A Calorie is the amount of energy that will raise 1000 grams of water by _____.
   a. 1 degree C
   b. 1000 degrees C
   c. 50 degrees C
   d. 0 degrees C

   ANS: A   DIF: B   OBJ: 9-4

8. 50 percent to 60 percent of the body is made up of _____.
   a. vitamins
   b. fat
   c. protein
   d. water

   ANS: D   DIF: B   OBJ: 9-2

9. RDA means _____.
   a. ready daily amount
   b. recommended daily allowance
   c. recommended dairy allotment
   d. recommended diet amount

   ANS: B   DIF: B   OBJ: 9-2

10. All the chemicals that food is made up of are _____.
    a. vitamins
    b. Calories
    c. nutrients
    d. RDA

    ANS: C   DIF: B   OBJ: 9-1

11. Which of the following is NOT a nutrient?
    a. oxygen
    b. protein
    c. fat
    d. water

    ANS: A   DIF: B   OBJ: 9-1

12. Which of the following are nutrients needed by your body?
    a. fat, protein, and carbohydrate
    b. water, vitamins, and minerals
    c. both a and b
    d. neither a nor b

    ANS: C   DIF: B   OBJ: 9-1

13. Which of the following is NOT a food group?
    a. meat group
    b. milk group
    c. grain group
    d. mineral group

    ANS: D   DIF: B   OBJ: 9-3

14. Which of the following are NOT examples of the food groups?
    a. meat, eggs, and beans
    b. fruit
    c. water and fat
    d. bread and cereal

    ANS: C   DIF: B   OBJ: 9-3

Use this information to answer the following questions. A person eats a sandwich made of: 2 slices of bread, 60 Calories in each slice; 3 slices of ham, 50 Calories in each slice; 1 slice of tomato, 5 Calories in each slice; 2 spoonfuls of mayonnaise, 70 Calories in each spoonful.

15. The entire sandwich contains how many Calories?
a. 185
b. 400
c. 415
d. 345
ANS: C   DIF: A   OBJ: 9-5

16. The food that supplies the most Calories would be _____.
a. bread
b. ham
c. tomato
d. mayonnaise
ANS: B   DIF: A   OBJ: 9-5

17. The food that supplies the least Calories would be _____.
a. bread
b. ham
c. tomato
d. mayonnaise
ANS: C   DIF: A   OBJ: 9-5

18. How many Calories would be supplied if only the ham were eaten?
a. 120
b. 140
c. 150
d. 400
ANS: C   DIF: A   OBJ: 9-5

19. If the sandwich were made with only one slice of bread, how many Calories would have been eaten?
a. 225
b. 285
c. 355
d. 265
ANS: C   DIF: A   OBJ: 9-5

MATCHING

Choose the word or phrase from the following list that best matches each statement.
a. vitamins
b. minerals
c. both vitamins and minerals
d. neither vitamins nor minerals

1. Riboflavin and niacin are examples.
2. This nutrient is needed in amounts equal to that needed for water.
3. needed by the body in very small amounts
4. generally supplied to the body in a balanced diet
5. allows cells to use carbohydrates and proteins
6. may cause anemia or muscle twitching if missing
7. Amount needed each day is given as a percent of RDA.
8. needed for growth and tissue repair
9. needed as an energy source
10. needed to help form certain cell parts

1. ANS: A   DIF: A   OBJ: 9-2
2. ANS: D   DIF: A   OBJ: 9-2
3. ANS: C   DIF: A   OBJ: 9-2
4. ANS: C   DIF: A   OBJ: 9-2
5. ANS: A   DIF: A   OBJ: 9-2
6. ANS: B   DIF: A   OBJ: 9-2
7. ANS: C   DIF: A   OBJ: 9-2
8. ANS: A   DIF: A   OBJ: 9-2
9. ANS: D   DIF: A   OBJ: 9-2
10. ANS: C   DIF: A   OBJ: 9-2

Choose the word or phrase from the following list that best matches each statement.
a. fat
b. protein
c. carbohydrate
d. both fat and carbohydrate

11. found in foods such as starch and sugar
12. used to form muscle, bone, and skin
13. provides energy
14. not stored in large amounts
15. needed in greatest amount each day
16. butter and oil

11. ANS: C   DIF: A   OBJ: 9-2
12. ANS: B   DIF: A   OBJ: 9-2
13. ANS: D   DIF: A   OBJ: 9-2
14. ANS: C   DIF: A   OBJ: 9-2
15. ANS: C   DIF: A   OBJ: 9-2

16. ANS: A   DIF: A   OBJ: 9-2

Choose the phrase from the following list that best matches each statement.
a. milk group
b. meat group
c. vegetable group
d. grain group

17. ice cream
18. peas and carrots
19. bread and cereal
20. fish and eggs
21. pork and beef
22. cottage and cream cheese
23. potatoes and broccoli
24. pasta and waffles

17. ANS: A   DIF: A   OBJ: 9-3
18. ANS: C   DIF: A   OBJ: 9-3
19. ANS: D   DIF: A   OBJ: 9-3
20. ANS: B   DIF: A   OBJ: 9-3
21. ANS: B   DIF: A   OBJ: 9-3
22. ANS: A   DIF: A   OBJ: 9-3
23. ANS: C   DIF: A   OBJ: 9-3
24. ANS: D   DIF: A   OBJ: 9-3

SHORT ANSWER

1. A mass of 1000 grams of water has a starting temperature of 14 degrees C. After heating, its temperature rises to 18 degrees C. How many Calories were added to the water?

ANS: 4 Calories   DIF: A   OBJ: 9-4

2. A mass of 1000 grams of water has a starting temperature of 30 degrees C. Five Calories of heat are added. What will the final temperature of the water be after heating?

ANS: 35 degrees   DIF: A   OBJ: 9-4

3. List three reasons why your body cells require nutrients.

ANS: for cell growth, cell repair, energy for cells

DIF: A   OBJ: 9-1

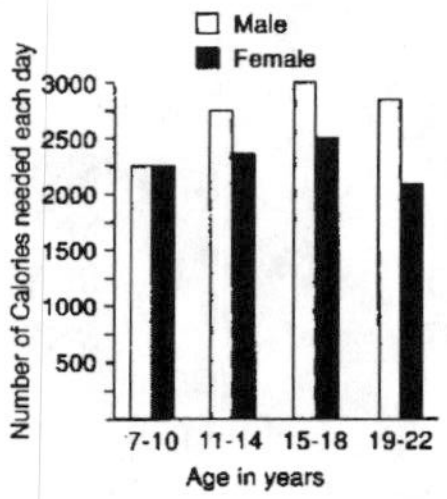

Figure 9-1

4. Compare the number of Calories that are needed each day by a 15-year-old male and a 15-year-old female. Refer to Figure 9-1.

ANS: A male needs 3000 while a female needs 2500.   DIF: A   OBJ: 9-6

5. Compare the number of Calories that are needed each day by a 7-year-old male and a 7-year-old female. Refer to Figure 9-1.

ANS: Both need about 2250.   DIF: A   OBJ: 9-6

6. Compare the number of Calories that are needed each day by a 10-year-old female and a 20-year-old female. Refer to Figure 9-1.

ANS: A 10-year-old female needs 2250 while a 20-year-old needs 2000.   DIF: A   OBJ: 9-6

7. Compare the number of Calories that are needed each day by a 20-year-old male and a 20-year-old female. Refer to Figure 9-1.

ANS: A male needs 2875 while a female needs 2000.   DIF: A   OBJ: 9-6

8. Using Figure 9-1, explain how the need for Calories changes as a male goes from age 7 to 18.

ANS: number of Calories needed each day increases   DIF: A   OBJ: 9-6

9. Using Figure 9-1, explain how the need for Calories changes as a female goes from age 7 to 18.

ANS: number of Calories needed each day increases   DIF: A   OBJ: 9-6

10. Using Figure 9-1, explain how the need for Calories changes as a female goes from age 18 to 22.

ANS: number of Calories needed each day decreases

DIF: A   OBJ: 9-6

CHAPTER 10—DIGESTION

TRUE/FALSE

1. The mouth helps in the chemical changing of fats.

ANS: F   DIF: A   OBJ: 10-4

2. A chemical that speeds up the chemical change of food is called an enzyme.

ANS: T   DIF: B   OBJ: 10-3

3. Bile helps in the digestion of protein.

ANS: F   DIF: A   OBJ: 10-4

4. The breakdown of food into usable molecules is a chemical change.

ANS: T   DIF: B   OBJ: 10-2

5. Digestion is the changing of food into a usable form.

ANS: T   DIF: B   OBJ: 10-1

6. Glucose molecules result from protein digestion.

ANS: F   DIF: B   OBJ: 10-2

7. Changes brought about by bile result in a physical change.

ANS: T   DIF: A   OBJ: 10-2

8. Changes brought about by the teeth result in a chemical change.

ANS: F   DIF: A   OBJ: 10-2

9. Changes brought about by enzymes result in a chemical change.

ANS: T   DIF: A   OBJ: 10-2

10. Changes brought about when starch is digested to glucose result in a physical change.

ANS: F   DIF: A   OBJ: 10-2

MULTIPLE CHOICE

1. Most digested food is absorbed in the _____.
   a. stomach
   b. esophagus
   c. large intestine
   d. small intestine

   ANS: D   DIF: B   OBJ: 10-4

2. During digestion, foods do NOT pass through the _____.
   a. liver
   b. stomach
   c. esophagus
   d. large intestine

   ANS: A   DIF: A   OBJ: 10-4

3. Mayonnaise is an example of a _____.
   a. protein
   b. vitamin
   c. fat
   d. carbohydrate

   ANS: C   DIF: B   OBJ: 10-4

4. The _____ has no digestive system.
   a. cow
   b. tapeworm
   c. chicken
   d. rabbit

   ANS: B   DIF: B   OBJ: 10-5

5. Enzymes and _____ may work together to form an ulcer.
   a. proteins
   b. acids
   c. bile
   d. fat

   ANS: B   DIF: B   OBJ: 10-6

6. The inside surface area of the small intestine is increased by the presence of the _____.
   a. pancreas
   b. villi
   c. gallbladder
   d. anus

   ANS: B   DIF: B   OBJ: 10-4

7. Digestion is the breaking down of food into small, usable _____.
   a. molecules
   b. enzymes
   c. vitamins
   d. energy

   ANS: A   DIF: B   OBJ: 10-1

8. The length of the human digestive system is about _____.
   a. 150 centimeters
   b. 275 centimeters
   c. 700 centimeters
   d. 900 centimeters

   ANS: D   DIF: B   OBJ: 10-4

9. A long digestive system is usually found in animals that eat only _____.
   a. meat
   b. fish
   c. plants
   d. other animals

   ANS: C   DIF: B   OBJ: 10-5

10. Chewing food to break it into smaller pieces is a(n) _____ change.
    a. chemical
    b. physical
    c. enzyme
    d. molecule

    ANS: B   DIF: B   OBJ: 10-2

11. The system used to change food into a usable form is your _____ system.
    a. muscular
    b. skeletal
    c. digestive
    d. excretory

    ANS: C   DIF: B   OBJ: 10-1

12. The general shape of the digestive system is tube-like. If it were solid rather than hollow, food would NOT be able to _____.
    a. pass through
    b. be changed
    c. both a and b
    d. neither a nor b

    ANS: C   DIF: B   OBJ: 10-1

13. Which statement is true for food as it passes through your body?
    a. it remains unchanged
    b. it is changed
    c. it is broken down into water
    d. it forms new food

    ANS: B   DIF: B   OBJ: 10-1

14. Where in your body are enzymes made that change food into usable form?
    a. muscular system
    b. skeletal system
    c. lungs
    d. digestive system

    ANS: D   DIF: B   OBJ: 10-3

15. Enzymes always bring about _____ changes.
    a. physical
    b. chemical
    c. slow
    d. harmful

    ANS: B   DIF: B   OBJ: 10-3

16. Starch is a food that can be changed by an enzyme into a sugar called _____.
    a. glucose
    b. protein
    c. digestion
    d. bread

    ANS: A   DIF: B   OBJ: 10-3

17. The pancreas empties its enzymes into the _____.
    a. large intestine
    b. small intestine
    c. both choices a and b
    d. neither choice a nor b

    ANS: B   DIF: B   OBJ: 10-4

18. The salivary glands empty their enzymes into the _____.
    a. small intestine
    b. large intestine
    c. pancreas
    d. mouth

    ANS: D   DIF: B   OBJ: 10-4

19. The gallbladder empties its chemicals into the _____.
    a. stomach
    b. pancreas
    c. both a and b are correct
    d. neither a nor b is correct

    ANS: D   DIF: B   OBJ: 10-4

20. Food spends most of its time in the _____.
    a. large intestine
    b. liver
    c. small intestine
    d. stomach

    ANS: C   DIF: A   OBJ: 10-4

21. Food spends the least amount of time in the _____.
    a. large intestine
    b. stomach
    c. esophagus
    d. small intestine

    ANS: C   DIF: A   OBJ: 10-4

22. The small intestine, when compared with the large intestine, is _____.
    a. the shorter of the two
    b. the narrower of the two
    c. the longer of the two
    d. both b and c are correct

    ANS: D   DIF: A   OBJ: 10-4

23. Heartburn is caused by acid moving from the stomach into the _____.
    a. pancreas
    b. heart
    c. esophagus
    d. small intestine

    ANS: C   DIF: B   OBJ: 10-6

24. A covering of _____ usually protects the linings of the stomach and intestine against the action of acids and enzymes.
    a. saliva
    b. mucus
    c. bile
    d. villi

    ANS: B   DIF: B   OBJ: 10-6

MATCHING

Match each phrase in the list below with the appropriate term.

a. makes chemicals that digest only carbohydrates
b. makes chemicals that digest only fat
c. makes chemicals that digest protein and carbohydrates
d. makes no chemical that digests food
e. makes chemicals that digest fat, protein, and carbohydrates
f. makes chemicals that digest only protein

1. salivary glands
2. pancreas
3. liver
4. stomach
5. small intestine
6. large intestine

1. ANS: A DIF: A OBJ: 10-4
2. ANS: E DIF: A OBJ: 10-4
3. ANS: D DIF: A OBJ: 10-4
4. ANS: F DIF: A OBJ: 10-4
5. ANS: C DIF: A OBJ: 10-4
6. ANS: D DIF: A OBJ: 10-4

Examine Figure 10-1. Choose the letter that best matches each statement.

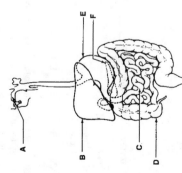

Figure 10-1

7. where most digestion occurs
8. pancreas
9. makes bile
10. removes water from undigested food
11. large intestine
12. makes an acid

13. makes three enzymes
14. stomach
15. where carbohydrates are first chemically changed
16. where villi are located

7. ANS: C DIF: A OBJ: 10-4
8. ANS: F DIF: B OBJ: 10-4
9. ANS: B DIF: B OBJ: 10-4
10. ANS: D DIF: A OBJ: 10-4
11. ANS: D DIF: B OBJ: 10-4
12. ANS: E DIF: A OBJ: 10-4
13. ANS: F DIF: B OBJ: 10-4
14. ANS: E DIF: B OBJ: 10-4
15. ANS: A DIF: A OBJ: 10-4
16. ANS: C DIF: B OBJ: 10-4

Choose the word from the following list that best matches each statement below.

a. hydra
b. earthworm
c. tapeworm

17. This animal has specialized organs for digestion.
18. This animal has no digestive system.
19. This animal has a single opening that serves as both mouth and anus.
20. This animal has two openings to the digestive system.

17. ANS: B DIF: B OBJ: 10-5
18. ANS: C DIF: B OBJ: 10-5
19. ANS: A DIF: A OBJ: 10-5
20. ANS: B DIF: B OBJ: 10-5

SHORT ANSWER

1. Explain why a long digestive system is needed by animals that eat plants.

ANS: Plant material is difficult to digest. A long tube allows for more time in the digestive system and, therefore, more time for digestion.

DIF: A OBJ: 10-5

2. Explain why an earthworm rather than a hydra has a digestive system more like humans.

ANS: It has two openings and has specialized areas or organs for specific jobs, like the human system.

DIF: A OBJ: 10-5

3. Why doesn't a tapeworm need a digestive system?

ANS: It is a parasite and lives in the digestive system of its host. All food that it receives is already digested.

DIF: A   OBJ: 10-5

4. What evidence supports the idea that the esophagus does not have a mucus covering?

ANS: When acids back up from within the stomach, a burning sensation is detected. If a mucus covering were present, the burning sensation would not be detected.

DIF: A   OBJ: 10-6

5. What problem of the stomach supports the idea that the stomach itself is made of protein? Explain why.

ANS: An ulcer; the combination of acid and enzymes in the stomach normally digest protein. An ulcer results from the stomach protein being digested.

DIF: A   OBJ: 10-6

6. An antacid may be used to treat both ulcers and heartburn. Explain why. (HINT - an antacid is a chemical that turns stomach acid into water and a gas)

ANS: Both problems are the result of acid attacking the lining of these organs. By getting rid of the acid, both problems can be controlled.

DIF: A   OBJ: 10-6

7. Explain what corresponds in the digestive system to new products leaving a factory.

ANS: food changed into usable form for cell use

DIF: A   OBJ: 10-1

8. Explain what corresponds in the digestive system to raw materials entering a factory.

ANS: food entering the digestive system

DIF: A   OBJ: 10-1

9. Explain what corresponds in the digestive system to usable materials made in a factory.

ANS: food that is being digested   DIF: A   OBJ: 10-1

10. Explain what corresponds in the digestive system to the factory itself.

ANS: the organs of the digestive system

DIF: A   OBJ: 10-1

11. Tomatoes are added to a blender and mixed. Is this a physical or chemical change? Explain why.

ANS: Physical change; tomatoes have been broken down into smaller pieces but the tomatoes still taste like tomatoes.

DIF: A   OBJ: 10-2

12. A slice of bread is placed in a toaster and accidentally burned to a crisp. Is this a physical or chemical change? Explain why.

ANS: Chemical change; bread no longer looks like, tastes like, or even smells like bread. Its form has been totally changed.

DIF: A   OBJ: 10-2

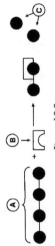

Figure 10-2

13. Explain how the glucose molecules marked A in Figure 10-2 differ in appearance from the glucose marked C.

ANS: Glucose molecules A are strung together in a chain and are connected to one another.

DIF: A   OBJ: 10-3

14. Explain the role of the enzyme marked B in Figure 10-2.

ANS: Enzyme B will help speed up the freeing or pulling apart of glucose molecules from the chain.

DIF: A   OBJ: 10-3

15. Explain why the body cannot use glucose molecules A but can use glucose molecules C. Refer to Figure 10-2.

ANS: Glucose molecules A are too large to be used by the body. Molecule C is in a smaller form and can be used.

DIF: A   OBJ: 10-3

CHAPTER 11—CIRCULATION

TRUE/FALSE

1. The aorta is the body's largest vein.

   ANS: F   DIF: B   OBJ: 11-5

2. All veins carry blood away from the heart.

   ANS: F   DIF: A   OBJ: 11-7

3. Clogged coronary vessels can lead to a heart attack.

   ANS: T   DIF: B   OBJ: 11-10

4. Capillaries are the smallest blood vessels.

   ANS: T   DIF: B   OBJ: 11-8

5. The heart is a muscle that pumps blood.

   ANS: T   DIF: B   OBJ: 11-1

6. Arteries carry blood to the heart.

   ANS: F   DIF: B   OBJ: 11-6

7. Capillaries in the heart keep blood flowing in one direction.

   ANS: F   DIF: B   OBJ: 11-4

8. A disease in which blood pressure remains high is called a heart attack.

   ANS: F   DIF: B   OBJ: 11-9

9. Blood pressure is measured only when the ventricles are contracting.

   ANS: F   DIF: A   OBJ: 11-9

10. Animals with a circulatory system have no blood.

   ANS: F   DIF: B   OBJ: 11-2

11. The coronary blood vessels supply blood to your brain.

   ANS: F   DIF: B   OBJ: 11-10

12. Nutrients such as oxygen and food are NOT needed by heart muscle.
ANS: F   DIF: B   OBJ: 11-10

13. A blood clot may clog coronary vessels.
ANS: T   DIF: B   OBJ: 11-10

14. Death of heart muscle is what we call a heart attack.
ANS: T   DIF: B   OBJ: 11-10

Write T for true if a statement is connected with blood pressure. Write F for false if the statement is NOT connected with blood pressure.

15. Blood is squeezed by heart pumping.
ANS: T   DIF: A   OBJ: 11-6

16. The heart has less room for blood when it squeezes.
ANS: T   DIF: A   OBJ: 11-6

17. Blood is forced into arteries when the heart pumps.
ANS: T   DIF: A   OBJ: 11-6

18. A circulatory system is NOT found in hydra.
ANS: F   DIF: A   OBJ: 11-6

19. A pulse results from blood pressure.
ANS: T   DIF: A   OBJ: 11-6

MULTIPLE CHOICE

1. Hypertension is a disease caused by ____.
a. low blood pressure
b. high blood pressure
c. leaky valves.
d. blockage of coronary vessels
ANS: B   DIF: B   OBJ: 11-9

2. Your heart, blood, and blood vessels make up your ____.
a. body
b. main body weight
c. circulatory system
d. only body system
ANS: C   DIF: B   OBJ: 11-1

3. An open circulatory system has ____.
a. five hearts
b. vessels but no heart
c. a heart but no vessels
d. no blood
ANS: C   DIF: B   OBJ: 11-2

4. A closed circulatory system has ____.
a. three hearts
b. no blood
c. vessels but no heart
d. vessels and a heart
ANS: D   DIF: B   OBJ: 11-2

5. Preventing heart problems can be helped by ____.
a. proper diet
b. not smoking
c. exercise
d. a, b, and c
ANS: D   DIF: A   OBJ: 11-11

6. The main role of the circulatory system is to deliver needed materials such as ____.
a. oxygen
b. food
c. water
d. choices a, b, and c
ANS: D   DIF: B   OBJ: 11-1

7. Needed materials are delivered by the circulatory system to ____.
a. all cells
b. pickup points
c. nutrients
d. blood
ANS: A   DIF: B   OBJ: 11-1

8. Waste materials such as _____ are carried by the circulatory system.
   a. oxygen
   b. food
   c. carbon dioxide
   d. blood

   ANS: C   DIF: B   OBJ: 11-1

9. A resting heart will pump about _____ times in one minute.
   a. 150 - 180
   b. 100
   c. 10 - 20
   d. 60 - 80

   ANS: D   DIF: B   OBJ: 11-3

10. In order for blood to be pumped, muscle of the heart must _____.
   a. stop
   b. rest
   c. squeeze together
   d. relax

   ANS: C   DIF: B   OBJ: 11-3

11. While atria are pumping, ventricles are _____.
   a. also pumping
   b. relaxed
   c. squeezing together
   d. blocked

   ANS: B   DIF: B   OBJ: 11-3

12. While ventricles are pumping, atria are _____.
   a. relaxed
   b. also pumping
   c. working
   d. closing

   ANS: A   DIF: B   OBJ: 11-3

13. A valve located between right atrium and right ventricle is the _____.
   a. semilunar
   b. bicuspid
   c. tricuspid
   d. aorta

   ANS: C   DIF: B   OBJ: 11-4

14. A valve located between left ventricle and aorta is the _____.
   a. semilunar
   b. vena cava
   c. bicuspid
   d. tricuspid

   ANS: A   DIF: B   OBJ: 11-4

15. Semilunar valves are described as doors. However, they can only open in a(n) _____ direction the ventricles.
   a. downward, away from
   b. upward, away from
   c. downward, toward
   d. upward, toward

   ANS: B   DIF: B   OBJ: 11-4

16. The first heart sound is caused when _____.
   a. semilunar valves open
   b. bicuspid and tricuspid valves open
   c. bicuspid and tricuspid valves close
   d. semilunar valves close

   ANS: C   DIF: B   OBJ: 11-4

17. The second heart sound is caused when _____.
   a. semilunar valves open
   b. bicuspid and tricuspid valves open
   c. bicuspid and tricuspid valves close
   d. semilunar valves close

   ANS: D   DIF: B   OBJ: 11-4

18. The top number of a blood pressure reading matches which event in your body?
   a. atria pumping
   b. ventricles relaxed
   c. ventricles pumping
   d. aorta is emptying

   ANS: C   DIF: B   OBJ: 11-9

19. The bottom number of a blood pressure reading matches which event in your body?
   a. ventricles pumping
   b. ventricles relaxed
   c. atria relaxed
   d. vena cava is emptying

   ANS: B   DIF: B   OBJ: 11-9

20. Arteries that are too narrow for easy movement of blood may result in ____.
   a. low blood pressure
   b. poor circulation
   c. high blood pressure
   d. veins taking over their job

   ANS: C   DIF: B   OBJ: 11-9

21. Which answer will help to reduce the risk of high blood pressure?
   a. lower the amount of water and vitamins in the diet
   b. raise the amount of cholesterol and protein in the diet
   c. lower the amount of cholesterol and salt in the diet
   d. raise the amount of salt and minerals in the diet

   ANS: C   DIF: B   OBJ: 11-9

22. An overweight person's heart must work harder because ____.
   a. he or she has less cholesterol
   b. the heart is surrounded by extra fat
   c. the heart muscle is weaker
   d. the heart is too small

   ANS: B   DIF: B   OBJ: 11-11

23. Nicotine found in tobacco smoke causes heart problems. Nicotine results in the ____.
   a. narrowing of blood vessels
   b. loss of capillaries
   c. widening of blood vessels
   d. increase in capillaries

   ANS: A   DIF: B   OBJ: 11-11

24. A person with a blocked coronary blood vessel may be helped by all the following EXCEPT
   a. drugs that dissolve the clot
   b. replacing the vessel with one from another part of the body
   c. increasing the amount of cholesterol in the diet
   d. receiving a heart transplant

   ANS: C   DIF: B   OBJ: 11-11

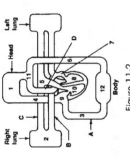

Figure 11-2

25. The correct pathway of blood starting with number 3 in Figure 11-2 is ____.
   a. 3, 9, 4, 1, 11
   b. 3, 9, 10, 8, 7
   c. 3, 9, 10, 5, 2

   ANS: C   DIF: A   OBJ: 11-5

26. The correct pathway of blood starting with number 7 in Figure 11-2 is ____.
   a. 7, 8, 11, 1, 4
   b. 7, 6, 2, 5, 10
   c. 7, 8, 5, 2, 6

   ANS: A   DIF: A   OBJ: 11-5

MATCHING

Examine the diagram of the heart in Figure 11-1. Choose the letter that best matches each statement. Some letters may be used more than once.

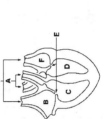

Figure 11-1

1. chamber that pumps blood to the lungs
2. vessels that carry blood away from heart
3. the right ventricle
4. chamber that receives blood from the body
5. the left atrium
6. vessels that carry blood to heart
7. chamber that pumps blood to the body
8. the left ventricle

9. parts that cause heart sounds
10. receives blood from lungs

1. ANS: C   DIF: A   OBJ: 11-5
2. ANS: A   DIF: A   OBJ: 11-5
3. ANS: C   DIF: A   OBJ: 11-5
4. ANS: B   DIF: A   OBJ: 11-5
5. ANS: F   DIF: A   OBJ: 11-5
6. ANS: G   DIF: A   OBJ: 11-5
7. ANS: D   DIF: A   OBJ: 11-5
8. ANS: D   DIF: A   OBJ: 11-5
9. ANS: E   DIF: A   OBJ: 11-4
10. ANS: F   DIF: A   OBJ: 11-5

Examine the diagram of the circulatory system in Figure 11-2. Choose the letter that best matches each statement below.

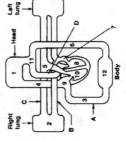

Figure 11-2

11. pulmonary artery
12. aorta
13. pulmonary vein
14. vena cava

a. artery
b. vein
c. capillary
d. artery, vein, and capillary

11. ANS: C   DIF: A   OBJ: 11-5
12. ANS: D   DIF: A   OBJ: 11-5
13. ANS: B   DIF: A   OBJ: 11-5
14. ANS: A   DIF: A   OBJ: 11-5

Choose the word or phrase from the following list that best matches each statement below.

15. blood vessel leading into right atrium
16. blood vessel carrying blood away from the heart
17. makes up part of the circulatory system
18. carries blood
19. carries blood to the heart

20. only one cell thick
21. place where blood delivers oxygen and food to cells
22. blood vessel leading into left atrium
23. blood vessel leaving right ventricle
24. blood vessel with highest pressure
25. most common blood vessel in body
26. thickest of all vessels
27. contains many one-way valves

15. ANS: B   DIF: A   OBJ: 11-5
16. ANS: A   DIF: A   OBJ: 11-6
17. ANS: D   DIF: A   OBJ: 11-6
18. ANS: D   DIF: A   OBJ: 11-6
19. ANS: B   DIF: A   OBJ: 11-7
20. ANS: C   DIF: B   OBJ: 11-8
21. ANS: C   DIF: A   OBJ: 11-8
22. ANS: B   DIF: A   OBJ: 11-5
23. ANS: A   DIF: A   OBJ: 11-5
24. ANS: A   DIF: A   OBJ: 11-6
25. ANS: C   DIF: B   OBJ: 11-8
26. ANS: A   DIF: B   OBJ: 11-6
27. ANS: B   DIF: B   OBJ: 11-7

Choose the phrase from the following list that best matches each statement below.
a. no system present
b. open system
c. closed system

28. humans
29. grasshopper
30. hydra
31. sponge
32. earthworm
33. sea anemone
34. fly

28. ANS: C   DIF: B   OBJ: 11-2
29. ANS: B   DIF: B   OBJ: 11-2
30. ANS: A   DIF: B   OBJ: 11-2
31. ANS: A   DIF: B   OBJ: 11-2
32. ANS: C   DIF: B   OBJ: 11-2
33. ANS: A   DIF: B   OBJ: 11-2
34. ANS: B   DIF: B   OBJ: 11-2

Choose the blood pressure reading from the following list that best matches each statement below.

a. 200/100
b. 130/70
c. 80/40

35. a young adult with low blood pressure
36. a young adult with normal blood pressure
37. a young adult with high blood pressure
38. a young adult whose arteries are too narrow for normal blood flow

35. ANS: C   DIF: A   OBJ: 11-9
36. ANS: B   DIF: A   OBJ: 11-9
37. ANS: A   DIF: A   OBJ: 11-9
38. ANS: A   DIF: A   OBJ: 11-9

Choose the phrase from the following list that best matches each statement below.

a. blood with much oxygen and little carbon dioxide
b. blood with much carbon dioxide and little oxygen

39. blood present in left atrium
40. blood present in right ventricle
41. blood present in right atrium
42. blood present in left ventricle
43. blood present in pulmonary artery
44. blood present in pulmonary vein
45. blood present in aorta

39. ANS: A   DIF: B   OBJ: 11-5
40. ANS: B   DIF: B   OBJ: 11-5
41. ANS: B   DIF: B   OBJ: 11-5
42. ANS: A   DIF: B   OBJ: 11-5
43. ANS: B   DIF: B   OBJ: 11-5
44. ANS: A   DIF: B   OBJ: 11-5
45. ANS: A   DIF: B   OBJ: 11-5

Examine Figure 11-3. Choose either diagram A or B that best matches each statement.

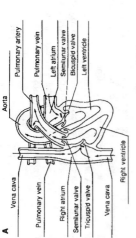

A
Pulmonary vein
Aorta
Pulmonary artery
Pulmonary vein
Right atrium
Left atrium
Semilunar valve
Semilunar valve
Bicuspid valve
Tricuspid valve
Left ventricle
Vena cava
Right ventricle

B

Figure 11-3

46. The atria are pumping.
47. Semilunar valves are closed.
48. Bicuspid and tricuspid valves are closed.
49. Atria are relaxed.
50. Ventricles are pumping.
51. Ventricles are relaxed.

46. ANS: B   DIF: A   OBJ: 11-3
47. ANS: B   DIF: A   OBJ: 11-4
48. ANS: A   DIF: A   OBJ: 11-4
49. ANS: A   DIF: A   OBJ: 11-3
50. ANS: A   DIF: A   OBJ: 11-3
51. ANS: B   DIF: A   OBJ: 11-3

SHORT ANSWER

1. What process studied in an earlier chapter may explain how water in blood vessels is delivered to body cells?

   ANS: osmosis   DIF: A   OBJ: 11-1

2. What process studied in an earlier chapter may explain how food in blood vessels is delivered to body cells?

   ANS: diffusion   DIF: A   OBJ: 11-1

3. What process studied in an earlier chapter may explain how waste chemicals are picked up from body cells by blood vessels?

   ANS: diffusion   DIF: A   OBJ: 11-1

4. Many people suffer from a condition called varicose veins. Their leg veins tend to widen as they fill with blood. Veins in these people lack functioning valves. Explain why their leg veins widen as they fill with blood.

ANS: It is difficult for the blood in the leg veins to move against the pull of gravity toward the heart. Functioning valves are not present to help with this movement. Therefore, blood tends to pool or collect in the veins, causing them to swell.

DIF: A   OBJ: 11-7

5. Not all arteries carry blood with much oxygen. Not all veins carry blood with much carbon dioxide. Give an example for each blood vessel to support these statements.

ANS: The pulmonary artery carries blood with much carbon dioxide to the lungs. The pulmonary vein carries blood with much oxygen from the lungs.

DIF: A   OBJ: 11-7

6. List several problems that would result if the human body did not have capillaries. (HINT - think in terms of pick up and delivery)

ANS: Student answers may vary. All cells would not receive their needed chemicals such as food and oxygen. All cells would not be able to get rid of their waste chemicals.

DIF: A   OBJ: 11-8

7. Explain why heart sounds are heard when valves close but not when they open.

ANS: Valves are like doors. The sound is heard as the valves close much like the sound heard as a door slams closed. No sound is heard as a valve or door opens.

DIF: A   OBJ: 11-4

8. Why is the first heart sound louder than the second?

ANS: The bi- and tricuspid valves are larger and close harder than the semilunars.

DIF: A   OBJ: 11-4

9. What is a heart murmur?

ANS: A sound heard as blood leaks past valves that do not close properly.

DIF: A   OBJ: 11-4

10. Describe how the pumping action of a heart would be affected if it had no valves. Blood would, therefore, not

ANS: It would not be able to move blood in any specific direction. Blood would, therefore, not circulate throughout the body.

DIF: A   OBJ: 11-4

11. Explain why a closed circulatory system is needed by complex animals.

ANS: The more complex an animal, the more cells and tissues it has. A closed system ensures that all cells and tissues come in close contact with blood.

DIF: A   OBJ: 11-2

12. Describe any evidence that you have to support the fact that your circulatory system is closed rather than open.

ANS: Answers may vary. One can see blood vessels under the skin, one can feel a pulse suggesting blood moving through vessels, a cut does not result in total blood loss.

DIF: A   OBJ: 11-2

13. A person wishes to reduce the amount of cholesterol in his or her diet. List two foods that should be reduced in the diet and two foods that could be used in the diet.

ANS: Reduce amounts of chicken liver and egg yolk; use skim milk, fish, chicken, fruit, and pasta.

DIF: A   OBJ: 11-11

14. A person will notice a rise in his or her pulse rate while smoking a cigarette. Explain why.

ANS: Nicotine causes blood vessels to contract. This raises blood pressure and results in the heart having to pump faster and harder to move the blood through the body.

DIF: A   OBJ: 11-11

PROBLEM

1. The following steps illustrate the events that take place before, during, and after a heart attack. Arrange the steps in correct order from 1 to 6 by numbering each statement.

   a. _____ Heart muscle is cut off from its supply of oxygen.
   b. _____ A blood clot forms within the blood vessels of the body.
   c. _____ Coronary vessels deliver blood and oxygen to heart muscle cells.
   d. _____ The blood clot travels to the coronary vessels.
   e. _____ Coronary vessel becomes blocked with the blood clot.
   f. _____ Heart muscle begins to die.

   ANS: 5, 2, 1, 3, 4, 6

   DIF: A   OBJ: 11-10

CHAPTER 12—BLOOD

TRUE/FALSE

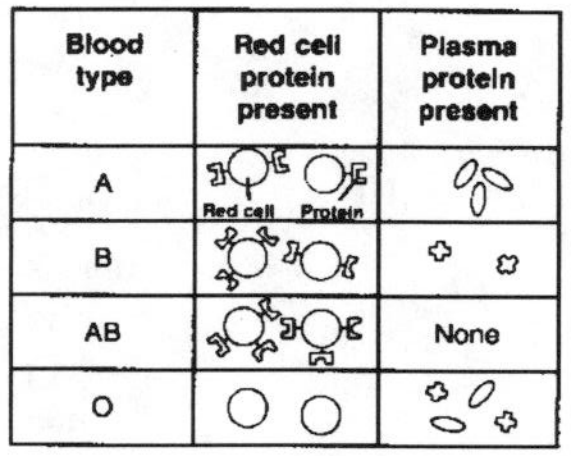

Blood type	Red cell protein present	Plasma protein present
A		
B		
AB		None
O		

Figure 12-4

1. All red blood cells have red cell protein. (Refer to Figure 12-4.)

   ANS: F   DIF: A   OBJ: 12-6

2. Type O blood has red cell proteins like types A and B. (Refer to Figure 12-4.)

   ANS: F   DIF: A   OBJ: 12-6

3. Type B plasma proteins do NOT fit type B red cell proteins. (Refer to Figure 12-4.)

   ANS: T   DIF: A   OBJ: 12-6

4. Type AB blood will clump when mixed with type O blood. (Refer to Figure 12-4.)

   ANS: T   DIF: A   OBJ: 12-7

5. It is not safe for type A blood to receive type B blood. (Refer to Figure 12-4.)

   ANS: T   DIF: A   OBJ: 12-7

6. Type A blood has red cell proteins like no other blood type. (Refer to Figure 12-4.)

   ANS: F   DIF: B   OBJ: 12-6

7. Type B blood has red cell proteins like type AB. (Refer to Figure 12-4.)

   ANS: T   DIF: B   OBJ: 12-6

8. Type AB blood has no plasma proteins. (Refer to Figure 12-4.)

   ANS: T   DIF: B   OBJ: 12-6

9. Type A blood has plasma proteins that fit both type B and AB red blood cell proteins. (Refer to Figure 12-4.)

   ANS: T   DIF: A   OBJ: 12-6

10. Type B blood has plasma proteins that fit both type A and AB red blood cell proteins. (Refer to Figure 12-4.)

    ANS: T   DIF: A   OBJ: 12-6

11. Type AB blood has red blood cell proteins that fit both type A and B plasma proteins. (Refer to Figure 12-4.)

    ANS: T   DIF: A   OBJ: 12-6

12. Type AB blood has red blood cell proteins that fit type O plasma proteins. (Refer to Figure 12-4.)

    ANS: T   DIF: A   OBJ: 12-6

13. Type A blood will clump when mixed with type A blood. (Refer to Figure 12-4.)

    ANS: F   DIF: B   OBJ: 12-7

14. Type O blood will clump when mixed with type B. (Refer to Figure 12-4.)

    ANS: T   DIF: B   OBJ: 12-7

15. Type O blood will clump when mixed with type A. (Refer to Figure 12-4.)

    ANS: T   DIF: B   OBJ: 12-7

16. Type AB blood will clump when mixed with type A. (Refer to Figure 12-4.)

    ANS: T   DIF: B   OBJ: 12-7

MULTIPLE CHOICE

1. Blood carries chemical wastes to the _____.
   a. lungs
   b. kidneys
   c. skin
   d. stomach

   ANS: B   DIF: B   OBJ: 12-1

2. White blood cells can destroy _____.
   a. bacteria
   b. dead cells
   c. viruses
   d. a, b, and c

   ANS: D   DIF: B   OBJ: 12-4

3. Immunity is the body's way of protecting against _____.
   a. disease
   b. blood clots
   c. hemophilia
   d. anemia

   ANS: A   DIF: B   OBJ: 12-8

4. Mixing different blood types together may cause _____.
   a. leukemia
   b. anemia
   c. clumping
   d. a color change

   ANS: C   DIF: B   OBJ: 12-7

5. A healthy person has about _____ red cells in a drop of blood.
   a. 8000
   b. 20 000
   c. 250 000
   d. 5 000 000

   ANS: D   DIF: B   OBJ: 12-4

6. A balanced diet will provide the needed amount of _____.
   a. iron
   b. oxygen
   c. carbon dioxide
   d. platelets

   ANS: A   DIF: B   OBJ: 12-4

7. Blood is a kind of _____.
   a. cell
   b. tissue
   c. organ
   d. system

   ANS: B   DIF: B   OBJ: 12-1

8. Blood types are different because they have different _____.
   a. cells
   b. platelets
   c. hemoglobin
   d. proteins

   ANS: D   DIF: B   OBJ: 12-6

9. A person with _____ may have more than 100 000 white cells in a drop of blood.
   a. anemia
   b. leukemia
   c. type A blood
   d. type B blood

   ANS: B   DIF: B   OBJ: 12-5

10. When you have an infection, _____ cells help destroy bacteria.
    a. white blood
    b. platelet
    c. hemoglobin
    d. red blood

    ANS: A   DIF: B   OBJ: 12-4

11. Blood will deliver which of the following to all your body cells?
    a. carbon dioxide
    b. waste
    c. oxygen
    d. body heat

    ANS: C   DIF: B   OBJ: 12-1

12. Blood will pick up which of the following from all your body cells?
    a. oxygen
    b. waste
    c. food
    d. platelets

    ANS: B   DIF: B   OBJ: 12-1

13. Animals that have no blood usually _____.
    a. die
    b. live on land
    c. live in water

    ANS: C   DIF: A   OBJ: 12-2

14. AIDS is caused by a(n) _____ that invades one kind of white blood cell.
   a. bacterium
   b. virus
   c. amoeba
   d. fungus

   ANS: B   DIF: B   OBJ: 12-10

15. Which of the following are NOT part of your immune system?
   a. skin
   b. teardrops
   c. kidneys
   d. mucus

   ANS: C   DIF: B   OBJ: 12-8

16. White blood cells are either made or stored in which of the following?
   a. spleen and bone marrow
   b. teardrops and mucus
   c. skin and mucus
   d. stomach and kidneys

   ANS: A   DIF: B   OBJ: 12-8

17. It has the job of blocking organisms from entering your body. What organ is being described as part of your immune system?
   a. lymph vessels
   b. thymus gland
   c. spleen
   d. skin

   ANS: D   DIF: B   OBJ: 12-8

18. An antigen may be described as a _____.
   a. blood cell
   b. lymph gland
   c. foreign invader
   d. needed chemical

   ANS: C   DIF: B   OBJ: 12-8

19. A bacterium with an antibody and antigen stuck together on its outside will usually _____.
   a. live
   b. break open
   c. reproduce faster
   d. form a spore

   ANS: B   DIF: B   OBJ: 12-8

20. Receiving a shot against a disease is like receiving a(n) _____ for the disease.
   a. antigen
   b. antibody
   c. lymph gland
   d. antibiotic

   ANS: A   DIF: B   OBJ: 12-9

21. A shot actually helps to refresh your immune system's _____.
   a. blood supply
   b. thymus gland
   c. memory
   d. pathway

   ANS: C   DIF: B   OBJ: 12-9

22. The ability of a person who once had a disease to be protected from getting the same disease again is _____.
   a. immunity
   b. impunity
   c. luck
   d. an antigen

   ANS: A   DIF: B   OBJ: 12-9

23. Examples of diseases for which you may receive shots include _____.
   a. cold sores and flu
   b. cancer and leukemia
   c. diphtheria and tetanus
   d. high and low blood pressure

   ANS: C   DIF: B   OBJ: 12-9

24. A white blood cell invaded by the AIDS virus will _____.
   a. reproduce
   b. move faster
   c. prevent other diseases
   d. die

   ANS: D   DIF: B   OBJ: 12-10

25. A person with AIDS will usually die from _____ that invade the body.
   a. other diseases
   b. poisons
   c. friendly antigens
   d. antibodies

   ANS: A   DIF: B   OBJ: 12-10

26. Sexual contact may result in the AIDS virus being passed to another person. The virus is present in _____ and is passed through broken _____.
   a. red cells, glands
   b. proteins, food molecules
   c. body fluids, tissues
   d. platelets, blood vessels

   ANS: C   DIF: B   OBJ: 12-10

27. A pregnant female can pass the AIDS virus to her _____.
   a. sisters
   b. relatives
   c. unborn child
   d. doctor

   ANS: C   DIF: B   OBJ: 12-10

28. Animals such as sponges have no blood. They obtain their oxygen from _____.
   a. food
   b. the water
   c. their cells
   d. humans

   ANS: B   DIF: B   OBJ: 12-2

29. Which of the following animals does NOT have blood?
   a. jellyfish
   b. flatworms
   c. both a and b
   d. neither a nor b

   ANS: C   DIF: B   OBJ: 12-2

30. A lack of _____ in the diet may result in anemia.
   a. water
   b. vitamins
   c. calcium
   d. iron

   ANS: D   DIF: B   OBJ: 12-5

31. Too few red blood cells may result in _____.
   a. leukemia
   b. anemia
   c. hemophilia
   d. frequent nose bleeds

   ANS: B   DIF: B   OBJ: 12-5

32. A disease called _____ results from having _____ that lack a clotting chemical.
   a. anemia, platelets
   b. leukemia, white cells
   c. hemophilia, platelets

   ANS: C   DIF: B   OBJ: 12-5

33. A chemical in red blood cells that joins with oxygen is _____.
   a. hemophilia
   b. hemoglobin
   c. plasma
   d. platelets

   ANS: B   DIF: B   OBJ: 12-4

34. A shot against a disease causes the immune system to make _____.
   a. antigens
   b. blood
   c. antibodies
   d. marrow

   ANS: C   DIF: B   OBJ: 12-9

35. Which of the following is NOT a way of getting AIDS?
   a. from mother's blood to unborn baby
   b. sharing needles for drug use
   c. transfusion of infected blood
   d. through the air

   ANS: D   DIF: B   OBJ: 12-10

MATCHING

Figure 12-1 shows a tube of blood that has been sitting for an hour. Choose the letter that best matches each statement.

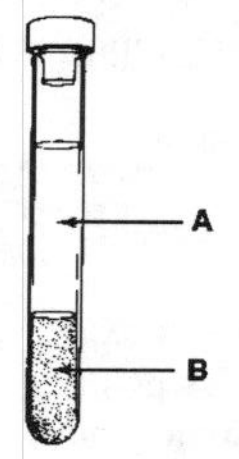

Figure 12-1

1. blood plasma
2. red in color
3. blood cells
4. living part of blood

Figure 12-2 shows how blood might look through a high-power microscope. Choose the letter that best matches each statement.

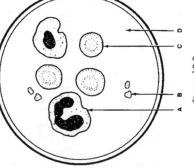

Figure 12-2

14. white blood cell
15. red blood cell
16. platelet
17. increases in an infection
18. increases during leukemia
19. yellow liquid
20. destroys bacteria
21. lacks nucleus when mature
22. carries oxygen
23. important in clotting
24. contains plasma proteins
25. lives for about 120 days
26. cell type that is related to anemia

14. ANS: A   DIF: A   OBJ: 12-4
15. ANS: C   DIF: A   OBJ: 12-4
16. ANS: B   DIF: A   OBJ: 12-4
17. ANS: A   DIF: A   OBJ: 12-4
18. ANS: A   DIF: A   OBJ: 12-5
19. ANS: D   DIF: A   OBJ: 12-3
20. ANS: A   DIF: A   OBJ: 12-4
21. ANS: C   DIF: A   OBJ: 12-4
22. ANS: C   DIF: A   OBJ: 12-4
23. ANS: B   DIF: A   OBJ: 12-4
24. ANS: D   DIF: A   OBJ: 12-3
25. ANS: C   DIF: A   OBJ: 12-4
26. ANS: C   DIF: A   OBJ: 12-5

5. made of water, salts, food, and wastes
6. nonliving part of blood
7. liquid part of blood

1. ANS: A   DIF: A   OBJ: 12-3
2. ANS: B   DIF: A   OBJ: 12-3
3. ANS: B   DIF: A   OBJ: 12-3
4. ANS: B   DIF: A   OBJ: 12-3
5. ANS: A   DIF: A   OBJ: 12-3
6. ANS: A   DIF: A   OBJ: 12-3
7. ANS: A   DIF: A   OBJ: 12-3

Choose the phrase from the following list that best matches each statement below.
a. "pickup" job of blood
b. "delivery" job of blood

8. Chemical wastes are carried by blood.
9. Excess heat is carried to the skin.
10. Digested fat and protein are carried by the blood.
11. Oxygen is carried by blood.
12. Carbon dioxide is carried by blood.
13. Water and vitamins are carried by blood.

8. ANS: A   DIF: A   OBJ: 12-1
9. ANS: A   DIF: A   OBJ: 12-1
10. ANS: B   DIF: A   OBJ: 12-1
11. ANS: B   DIF: A   OBJ: 12-1
12. ANS: A   DIF: A   OBJ: 12-1
13. ANS: B   DIF: A   OBJ: 12-1

Choose the word or phrase from the following list that best matches each statement below.

a. antigens
b. antibodies
c. both antigens and antibodies

27. made by white blood cells
28. destroy bacteria
29. cause disease
30. fit together like pieces of a puzzle
31. a bacterium or virus
32. may be released into blood plasma during a disease

27.	ANS: B	DIF: A	OBJ: 12-8
28.	ANS: B	DIF: A	OBJ: 12-8
29.	ANS: A	DIF: A	OBJ: 12-8
30.	ANS: C	DIF: A	OBJ: 12-8
31.	ANS: A	DIF: A	OBJ: 12-8
32.	ANS: B	DIF: A	OBJ: 12-8

Figure 12-3 shows a cut-away view of a sponge. Sponges live in water and have no blood. Match the letter in the diagram with the statements.

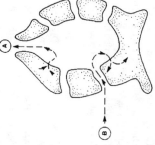

Figure 12-3

33. shows the path of oxygen
34. shows the path of carbon dioxide
35. shows the path of food
36. shows the path of waste chemicals

33.	ANS: B	DIF: A	OBJ: 12-2
34.	ANS: A	DIF: A	OBJ: 12-2
35.	ANS: B	DIF: A	OBJ: 12-2
36.	ANS: A	DIF: A	OBJ: 12-2

SHORT ANSWER

1. Explain how it might be possible for a pregnant woman with AIDS to pass the virus to her unborn child if blood does not mix between mother and child.

 ANS: The virus is small enough to pass from blood of the woman through the placenta and into the blood of the unborn child. This is comparable to the passage of such molecules as food and oxygen.

 DIF: A   OBJ: 12-10

2. Explain how sharing of a needle during drug use can result in the AIDS virus being spread.

 ANS: If the needle is contaminated with blood from a person having the AIDS virus, then the virus may be passed to another person using the dirty needle.

 DIF: A   OBJ: 12-10

3. How is an increase in iron in the diet related to a cure for anemia?

 ANS: Hemoglobin is the chemical present in red blood cells that transports oxygen. Hemoglobin contains iron. Without iron, hemoglobin is incapable of carrying out its job.

 DIF: A   OBJ: 12-5

4. Why does a person with anemia always feel tired?

 ANS: One job of red blood cells is to carry oxygen to body cells to enable food to release energy. With too few red blood cells in anemia, not enough oxygen reaches body cells and too little energy is released, resulting in a person being tired.

 DIF: A   OBJ: 12-5

5. Explain why white blood cells formed in leukemia are not helpful in destroying bacteria.

 ANS: The white blood cells formed during leukemia are abnormal and are incapable of destroying bacteria.

 DIF: A   OBJ: 12-5

6. Why is it unsafe to mix blood types A and B?

 ANS: Blood cells of type A have proteins on their surface that match plasma proteins of type B. When a match occurs, blood cells will clump together and block the normal flow of blood to body organs.

 DIF: A   OBJ: 12-7

7. Why is it safe to mix blood type A and A?

ANS: Blood cells of type A have proteins on their surface that do not match plasma proteins of type A. Therefore, no clumping of blood cells will occur.

DIF: A   OBJ: 12-7

8. It is possible to remove the plasma proteins from type O blood. When this is done, the red cells of type O can be safely given to any blood type. Explain why.

ANS: Red blood cells of type O have no proteins on their surface. Therefore, they can be given to any blood type with no chance of clumping occurring.

DIF: A   OBJ: 12-7

PROBLEM

1. The following steps illustrate the events that take place in your immune system after receiving a shot for the mumps virus and then becoming infected by a living virus. Arrange the steps in correct order from 1 to 6 by numbering each statement.

a. _____ A shot of dead mumps virus is given to a person.
b. _____ The immune system starts to make antibodies against the dead mumps virus.
c. _____ Living mumps virus is destroyed by the already present mumps antibodies.
d. _____ The person never becomes ill from the living mumps virus invasion.
e. _____ Living mumps viruses enter the body of the person having received the shot.
f. _____ The immune system detects the dead mumps virus as an antigen.

ANS: 1, 3, 5, 6, 4, 2   DIF: A   OBJ: 12-9

CHAPTER 13—RESPIRATION AND EXCRETION

TRUE/FALSE

1. Fish use gills for gas exchange.

ANS: T   DIF: B   OBJ: 13-3

2. Frogs may use both their skin and lungs for gas exchange.

ANS: T   DIF: B   OBJ: 13-3

3. Insects use gills and lungs for gas exchange.

ANS: F   DIF: B   OBJ: 13-3

4. The entire body of an earthworm can act as a respiratory organ.

ANS: T   DIF: B   OBJ: 13-3

MULTIPLE CHOICE

1. The kidneys remove _____ from the blood.
   a. oxygen
   b. urea
   c. cells
   d. carbon dioxide

ANS: B   DIF: B   OBJ: 13-11

2. Earthworms breathe through their ____.
   a. skin
   b. stomachs
   c. lungs
   d. gills

ANS: A   DIF: B   OBJ: 13-3

3. Urea is ____.
   a. a nutrient used by cells
   b. a tube from the kidney
   c. a waste formed by cells

ANS: C   DIF: B   OBJ: 13-10

11. The respiratory system helps the body remove _____.
    a. oxygen
    b. carbon dioxide
    c. urea
    d. sweat

    ANS: B   DIF: B   OBJ: 13-1

12. Which have no kidneys?
    a. mice
    b. fish
    c. jellyfish
    d. frogs

    ANS: C   DIF: B   OBJ: 13-3

13. Your skin helps to excrete _____.
    a. water and salt
    b. water and carbon dioxide
    c. urea

    ANS: A   DIF: B   OBJ: 13-12

14. Exchange of gases takes place through the _____ system.
    a. circulatory
    b. digestive
    c. respiratory
    d. muscular

    ANS: C   DIF: B   OBJ: 13-1

15. The needed gas that is brought in by our respiratory system is _____.
    a. carbon dioxide
    b. oxygen
    c. nitrogen
    d. carbon

    ANS: B   DIF: B   OBJ: 13-1

16. Cellular respiration releases _____ from sugar.
    a. energy
    b. food
    c. glucose
    d. oxygen

    ANS: A   DIF: B   OBJ: 13-2

4. The skin is an organ of _____.
   a. respiration
   b. digestion
   c. excretion
   d. circulation

   ANS: C   DIF: B   OBJ: 13-12

5. Carbon monoxide is dangerous because it _____.
   a. blocks the kidneys
   b. keeps oxygen out of the blood
   c. prevents excretion

   ANS: B   DIF: B   OBJ: 13-7

6. The carbon dioxide that we breathe out has come originally from our _____.
   a. cells
   b. skin
   c. diaphragm
   d. urinary bladder

   ANS: A   DIF: B   OBJ: 13-2

7. Oxygen is used in our bodies to _____.
   a. help us sleep
   b. release energy from food
   c. remove carbon dioxide

   ANS: B   DIF: B   OBJ: 13-2

8. The correct pathway for air entering the human respiratory system is _____.
   a. nose, trachea, alveoli, bronchi
   b. nose, bronchi, trachea, alveoli
   c. alveoli, trachea, epiglottis, nose
   d. nose, trachea, bronchi, alveoli

   ANS: D   DIF: A   OBJ: 13-5

9. Pneumonia is a disease that is said to be _____.
   a. deadly
   b. communicable
   c. noncommunicable

   ANS: B   DIF: A   OBJ: 13-8

10. A lung disease that is noncommunicable is _____.
    a. not catching
    b. emphysema
    c. the common cold
    d. both a and b

    ANS: D   DIF: B   OBJ: 13-9

17. Cellular respiration occurs in ___.
   a. only animals
   b. only plants
   c. only protists
   d. all living things

   ANS: D   DIF: B   OBJ: 13-2

18. The process of ___ allows carbon dioxide to pass from ___ into blood.
   a. diffusion, alveoli
   b. osmosis, cells
   c. diffusion, body cells

   ANS: C   DIF: B   OBJ: 13-5

19. The process of ___ allows carbon dioxide to pass from blood into ___.
   a. diffusion, alveoli
   b. osmosis, cells
   c. diffusion, body cells

   ANS: A   DIF: B   OBJ: 13-5

20. The process of ___ allows oxygen to pass from blood into ___.
   a. circulation, body cells
   b. diffusion, body cells
   c. osmosis, alveoli

   ANS: B   DIF: B   OBJ: 13-5

21. The process of ___ allows oxygen to pass from alveoli into ___.
   a. diffusion, blood
   b. diffusion, body cells
   c. osmosis, blood

   ANS: A   DIF: B   OBJ: 13-5

22. Carbon monoxide is difficult to detect because it has no ___.
   a. color
   b. mass
   c. elements present
   d. chemical properties

   ANS: A   DIF: B   OBJ: 13-7

23. Two sources of carbon monoxide are ___.
   a. cigarette smoke and oxygen
   b. car exhaust and cigarette smoke
   c. oxygen and car exhaust
   d. the air and rain water

   ANS: B   DIF: B   OBJ: 13-7

24. Carbon monoxide is formed during the process of ___.
   a. cellular respiration
   b. burning
   c. photosynthesis
   d. osmosis

   ANS: B   DIF: B   OBJ: 13-7

25. Carbon monoxide is described as a(n) ___ gas.
   a. sweet smelling
   b. choking
   c. strong
   d. odorless

   ANS: D   DIF: B   OBJ: 13-7

26. The body rids itself of liquid waste through the ___ system.
   a. digestive
   b. circulatory
   c. excretory
   d. skeletal

   ANS: C   DIF: B   OBJ: 13-10

27. Which organ(s) aid in getting rid of urea?
   a. lungs
   b. kidneys
   c. large and small intestines
   d. lymph glands

   ANS: B   DIF: B   OBJ: 13-10

28. Urea results directly from the breakdown of ___.
   a. water
   b. fats
   c. oxygen
   d. protein

   ANS: D   DIF: B   OBJ: 13-10

29. The actual cause of pneumonia is ___.
   a. a virus
   b. bacteria
   c. neither a nor b
   d. both a and b

   ANS: D   DIF: B   OBJ: 13-8

30. A communicable disease is one that _____.
   a. can be passed to another person
   b. will never give any symptoms
   c. cannot be passed to another person
   d. lies dormant within the host

   ANS: A   DIF: A   OBJ: 13-8

31. Pneumonia actually affects the _____ of lungs.
   a. bronchi
   b. alveoli
   c. epiglottis
   d. trachea

   ANS: B   DIF: B   OBJ: 13-8

32. A person with pneumonia cannot get enough _____ into their blood.
   a. carbon dioxide
   b. food
   c. oxygen
   d. mucus

   ANS: C   DIF: B   OBJ: 13-8

33. Emphysema results from the _____ in the lungs.
   a. collecting of mucus
   b. breakdown of alveoli
   c. breakdown of bronchi

   ANS: B   DIF: B   OBJ: 13-9

34. A person with emphysema is unable to get enough _____ into the blood.
   a. water
   b. carbon dioxide
   c. carbon monoxide
   d. oxygen

   ANS: D   DIF: B   OBJ: 13-9

35. Which of the following is true of a person with emphysema?
   a. they always breathe normally
   b. their skin color is pale
   c. they appear to be out of breath
   d. they always have a fever

   ANS: C   DIF: B   OBJ: 13-9

36. Skin helps with getting rid of waste chemicals and also _____.
   a. protects against infection
   b. causes communicable diseases
   c. removes urea
   d. makes blood cells

   ANS: A   DIF: B   OBJ: 13-12

37. Kidneys differ from skin because kidneys _____
   a. cannot control water loss
   b. cannot control salt loss
   c. can control water loss
   d. cannot repair themselves

   ANS: C   DIF: B   OBJ: 13-12

38. Sweat glands number between _____ in your body.
   a. 2 to 5 hundred
   b. 2 to 5 million
   c. 10 to 20 thousand
   d. 10 to 50

   ANS: B   DIF: B   OBJ: 13-12

39. Humans get rid of urea by _____.
   a. kidneys
   b. diffusion directly into water
   c. tubes connecting to outside

   ANS: A   DIF: A   OBJ: 13-10

40. Mice get rid of urea by _____.
   a. kidneys
   b. diffusion directly into water
   c. tubes connecting to outside

   ANS: A   DIF: A   OBJ: 13-10

41. Earthworms get rid of urea by _____.
   a. kidneys
   b. diffusion directly into water
   c. tubes connecting to outside

   ANS: C   DIF: A   OBJ: 13-10

42. Sponges get rid of urea by _____.
   a. kidneys
   b. diffusion directly into water
   c. tubes connecting to outside

   ANS: B   DIF: A   OBJ: 13-10

43. Jellyfish get rid of urea by _____ .
   a. kidneys
   b. diffusion directly into water
   c. tubes connecting to outside

   ANS: B   DIF: A   OBJ: 13-10

44. Leeches get rid of urea by _____ .
   a. kidneys
   b. diffusion directly into water
   c. tubes connecting to outside

   ANS: C   DIF: A   OBJ: 13-10

45. Hydra get rid of urea by _____ .
   a. kidneys
   b. diffusion directly into water
   c. tubes connecting to outside

   ANS: B   DIF: A   OBJ: 13-10

46. Frogs get rid of urea by _____ .
   a. kidneys
   b. diffusion directly into water
   c. tubes connecting to outside

   ANS: A   DIF: A   OBJ: 13-10

COMPLETION

1. The gas that goes from blood into alveoli is _____ .

   ANS: carbon dioxide   DIF: A   OBJ: 13-5

2. The gas that goes from body cells into blood is _____ .

   ANS: carbon dioxide   DIF: A   OBJ: 13-5

3. The gas that goes from alveoli into blood is _____ .

   ANS: oxygen   DIF: A   OBJ: 13-5

4. The gas that goes from blood into body cells is _____ .

   ANS: oxygen   DIF: A   OBJ: 13-5

MATCHING

Examine Figure 13-1. Choose the letter of the structure that best matches each statement.

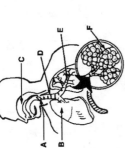

Figure 13-1

1. exchanges gases in blood
2. alveoli
3. epiglottis
4. warms air as it enters the body
5. trachea
6. bronchus
7. closes when you swallow
8. lung
9. nasal chamber

1. ANS: F   DIF: A   OBJ: 13-4
2. ANS: F   DIF: A   OBJ: 13-4
3. ANS: A   DIF: A   OBJ: 13-4
4. ANS: C   DIF: A   OBJ: 13-4
5. ANS: D   DIF: A   OBJ: 13-4
6. ANS: E   DIF: A   OBJ: 13-4
7. ANS: A   DIF: A   OBJ: 13-4
8. ANS: B   DIF: A   OBJ: 13-4
9. ANS: C   DIF: A   OBJ: 13-4

Examine Figure 13-3. Choose the letter of the structure that best matches each statement.

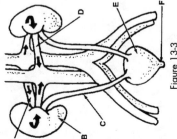

Figure 13-3

10. main organ of excretory system
11. a vein
12. storage area for urine
13. made up of nephrons
14. brings blood to the kidney
15. carries wastes away from kidney
16. carries wastes out of the body
17. removes wastes from blood
18. urinary bladder
19. urethra
20. ureter

10. ANS: B   DIF: A   OBJ: 13-11
11. ANS: D   DIF: A   OBJ: 13-11
12. ANS: E   DIF: A   OBJ: 13-11
13. ANS: B   DIF: A   OBJ: 13-11
14. ANS: A   DIF: A   OBJ: 13-11
15. ANS: C   DIF: A   OBJ: 13-11
16. ANS: F   DIF: A   OBJ: 13-11
17. ANS: B   DIF: A   OBJ: 13-11
18. ANS: E   DIF: A   OBJ: 13-11
19. ANS: F   DIF: A   OBJ: 13-11
20. ANS: C   DIF: A   OBJ: 13-11

Choose the phrase from the following list that best matches each statement below.
a. enters kidney, is not forced out of blood, and returns to body
b. enters kidney, is forced out of blood, enters long tube, and returns to blood
c. enters kidney, is forced out of blood, enters long tube, then leaves body

21. pathway that urea takes through kidney
22. pathway that needed water takes through kidney

23. pathway that excess water takes through kidney
24. pathway that blood cells take through kidney
25. pathway that sugar takes through kidney

21. ANS: C   DIF: A   OBJ: 13-11
22. ANS: B   DIF: A   OBJ: 13-11
23. ANS: C   DIF: A   OBJ: 13-11
24. ANS: A   DIF: A   OBJ: 13-11
25. ANS: B   DIF: A   OBJ: 13-11

Choose the phrase from the following list that best matches each statement below.
a. takes place during breathing in
b. takes place during breathing out

26. Rib cage moves down and in.
27. Diaphragm is relaxed.
28. Diaphragm is domelike in shape.
29. Space within chest gets smaller.
30. Space within chest gets larger.
31. Rib cage moves up and out.

26. ANS: B   DIF: A   OBJ: 13-6
27. ANS: B   DIF: A   OBJ: 13-6
28. ANS: B   DIF: A   OBJ: 13-6
29. ANS: B   DIF: A   OBJ: 13-6
30. ANS: A   DIF: A   OBJ: 13-6
31. ANS: A   DIF: A   OBJ: 13-6

Choose the word or phrase from the following list that best matches each statement below.
a. two short tubes connecting to trachea
b. large space over roof of mouth
c. tiny air sacs
d. prevents food from going into lungs
e. windpipe

32. epiglottis
33. trachea
34. bronchi
35. alveoli
36. nasal chamber

32. ANS: D   DIF: B   OBJ: 13-4
33. ANS: E   DIF: B   OBJ: 13-4
34. ANS: A   DIF: B   OBJ: 13-4
35. ANS: C   DIF: B   OBJ: 13-4
36. ANS: B   DIF: B   OBJ: 13-4

Choose the diagram in Figure 13-4 that shows an example of each statement below.

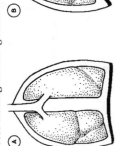

Figure 13-4

37. a person breathing in
38. a person breathing out
39. the space surrounding the lungs being squeezed
40. the space surrounding the lungs being increased
41. the diaphragm contracted
42. the diaphragm flat in shape

37. ANS: A   DIF: A   OBJ: 13-6
38. ANS: B   DIF: A   OBJ: 13-6
39. ANS: B   DIF: A   OBJ: 13-6
40. ANS: A   DIF: A   OBJ: 13-6
41. ANS: A   DIF: A   OBJ: 13-6
42. ANS: A   DIF: A   OBJ: 13-6

SHORT ANSWER

1. Identify the following formulas: CO_2, CO, O_2.

ANS: carbon dioxide, carbon monoxide, oxygen

DIF: A   OBJ: 13-7

2. Explain how sweating helps to cool the body.

ANS: Water on the skin will evaporate. This process of evaporation cools the body.

DIF: A   OBJ: 13-12

3. Describe how the lungs, skin, and kidneys differ by what they excrete and if they can control what they excrete.

ANS:
Lungs excrete carbon dioxide and water --cannot control loss
Skin excretes water and salt--cannot control loss
Kidneys excrete water, salt, and urea--can control loss

DIF: A   OBJ: 13-12

4. Why might wearing a mask over the mouth and nose prevent a person from catching pneumonia, if he or she is in the same room as a person with the disease?

ANS: Pneumonia is a communicable disease and can be spread from one person to another. A mask will prevent you from breathing in the viruses or bacteria if they are present and being expelled into the air by the person with the disease.

DIF: A   OBJ: 13-8

5. Explain how the AIDS virus may increase a person's chance of getting and dying from pneumonia.

ANS: AIDS destroys the immune system and makes a person very susceptible to any other communicable disease.

DIF: A   OBJ: 13-8

6. Explain why carbon monoxide is not a serious problem when released out into the air, but is a serious problem when released into a closed area.

ANS: The gas is not a problem when it mixes with large amounts of air. In a closed area, the gas does not mix with the surrounding air and levels can become too high for safe breathing.

DIF: A   OBJ: 13-7

7. The body's red blood cells normally carry oxygen to all cells. What occurs in these blood cells when carbon monoxide is present? Can human body cells use carbon monoxide?

ANS: Carbon monoxide is carried by red blood cells to body cells. Body cells cannot use the carbon monoxide.

DIF: A   OBJ: 13-7

8. Explain how the respiratory system and circulatory system depend on one another or work together.

ANS: Oxygen is brought into the respiratory system. Once in the lungs, it moves into the blood to be delivered to all body cells. The opposite occurs with carbon dioxide.

DIF: A   OBJ: 13-1

9. Explain why a large surface area is needed in any respiratory organ.

ANS: A large surface is needed to allow for diffusion of gases in or out of the organism.

DIF: A   OBJ: 13-3

10. Scientists believe that an earthworm totally covered by water for a long period of time will die due to lack of oxygen. Explain why this might happen.

ANS: An earthworm breathes through its skin. Enough oxygen may not be available in water to provide the earthworm with its oxygen needs.

DIF: A   OBJ: 13-3

11. You cannot drown an insect by sticking its head in water but you can drown it by sticking its abdomen in water. Why might this be?

ANS: The opening to an insect's respiratory system is located along its abdomen.

DIF: A   OBJ: 13-3

Figure 13-2 shows the process of respiration in its chemical form. Use the figure to answer the following questions.

$$O_2 + C_6H_{12}O_6 \longrightarrow CO_2 + H_2O$$

Figure 13-2

12. The symbol O_2 stands for what gas?

ANS: oxygen   DIF: A   OBJ: 13-2

13. The symbol $C_6H_{12}O_6$ stands for what nutrient?

ANS: food (glucose)   DIF: A   OBJ: 13-2

14. The symbol CO_2 stands for what gas?

ANS: carbon dioxide   DIF: A   OBJ: 13-2

15. The symbol H_2O stands for what nutrient?

ANS: water   DIF: A   OBJ: 13-2

16. What might be released at the letter A?

ANS: energy   DIF: A   OBJ: 13-2

17. Which of the symbols stands for a waste gas?

ANS: CO_2 DIF: A   OBJ: 13-2

18. Which of the symbols stands for a needed gas?

ANS: O_2 DIF: A   OBJ: 13-2

Table 13-1

Gas	Percent Entering Lungs	Percent Leaving Lungs
Nitrogen	80	80
Oxygen	20	16
Carbon Dioxide	0	4

19. What evidence do you have that nitrogen gas is not used by the human body? Refer to Table 13-1.

ANS: The same amount of nitrogen is taken into the lungs and given off by the lungs.

DIF: A   OBJ: 13-4

20. Using Table 13-1, explain the fact that less oxygen is given off than taken in.

ANS: Some of the oxygen taken in is used by body cells during cellular respiration.

DIF: A   OBJ: 13-4

21. What evidence do you have that the body does not use all the oxygen available to its cells? See Table 13-1.

ANS: If all oxygen taken in were used by cells, then the amount being given off would be 0 percent.

DIF: A   OBJ: 13-4

22. Referring to Table 13-1, explain the fact that more carbon dioxide is given off than taken in.

ANS: Body cells form and give off carbon dioxide as a waste chemical of cellular respiration.

DIF: A   OBJ: 13-4

CHAPTER 14—SUPPORT AND MOVEMENT

TRUE/FALSE

1. The tibia, femur, and humerus are all examples of bones.

   ANS: T   DIF: A   OBJ: 14-1

2. Two different muscles are always needed to move the same bone in two different directions because muscles can only shorten.

   ANS: T   DIF: A   OBJ: 14-6

3. When a muscle contracts, it pulls on a ligament which then moves a joint.

   ANS: F   DIF: A   OBJ: 14-5

4. Proof that bone is alive is shown by the fact that an infant's hand has fewer and smaller bones than an adult's.

   ANS: T   DIF: A   OBJ: 14-1

5. Muscular dystrophy is a disease of smooth muscle only.

   ANS: F   DIF: A   OBJ: 14-8

MULTIPLE CHOICE

1. The joints in the skull are _____.
   a. hinge
   b. ball-and-socket
   c. not movable
   d. shoulder-like

   ANS: C   DIF: B   OBJ: 14-3

2. The human body has _____ bones.
   a. 22
   b. 206
   c. 412
   d. 106

   ANS: B   DIF: B   OBJ: 14-1

3. Two muscles are needed to move bones back and forth because _____.
   a. one is not strong enough
   b. joints are hard to move
   c. muscles only pull

   ANS: C   DIF: A   OBJ: 14-6

4. Blood cells are made in the _____.
   a. solid bone
   b. cartilage
   c. spongy bone
   d. marrow

   ANS: D   DIF: B   OBJ: 14-2

5. Muscles move in response to messages from _____.
   a. nerves
   b. bones
   c. glands
   d. blood cells

   ANS: A   DIF: B   OBJ: 14-8

6. Bone is made of _____.
   a. dead cells
   b. living cells
   c. cartilage
   d. material without cells

   ANS: B   DIF: B   OBJ: 14-1

7. The skeleton can store _____.
   a. water
   b. food
   c. oxygen
   d. calcium

   ANS: D   DIF: B   OBJ: 14-1

8. An ankle sprain is the result of injured _____ at the ankle.
   a. tendons
   b. muscles
   c. bones
   d. ligaments

   ANS: D   DIF: B   OBJ: 14-7

9. The soft cushion-like material at the tip of your nose is _____.
   a. bone
   b. cartilage
   c. tendons
   d. ligaments

   ANS: B   DIF: B   OBJ: 14-2

10. Tough tissue that holds muscle to bone is called a _____.
    a. cartilage
    b. ligament
    c. tendon
    d. joint

    ANS: C   DIF: B   OBJ: 14-5

11. The soft center in bone is the _____.
    a. cartilage
    b. tendon
    c. spongy part
    d. marrow

    ANS: D   DIF: B   OBJ: 14-2

12. Muscles that you control are said to be _____.
    a. voluntary
    b. fixed
    c. involuntary
    d. paired

    ANS: A   DIF: B   OBJ: 14-4

13. The hardest, most compact part of bone is _____.
    a. spongy bone
    b. stony bone
    c. solid bone
    d. a tendon

    ANS: C   DIF: B   OBJ: 14-2

14. A well-designed chair can prevent backaches if it _____.
    a. has a flat seat
    b. has short legs
    c. lacks armrests
    d. fits the body

    ANS: D   DIF: A   OBJ: 14-9

15. Involuntary means _____.
    a. paired
    b. you control it
    c. you cannot control it
    d. fixed

    ANS: C   DIF: B   OBJ: 14-4

16. Muscles not connected to bone include _____.
    a. skeletal
    b. cardiac
    c. smooth
    d. both b and c

    ANS: D   DIF: B   OBJ: 14-4

17. A disease of bone joints is _____.
    a. muscular dystrophy
    b. a sprain
    c. arthritis
    d. tendinitis

    ANS: C   DIF: B   OBJ: 14-7

18. As a person ages, his or her bones tend to become brittle. This happens as _____ is lost from bone.
    a. protein
    b. marrow
    c. iron
    d. calcium

    ANS: D   DIF: B   OBJ: 14-7

19. A type of arthritis may affect a person's bone _____, which may prevent movement.
    a. marrow
    b. cartilage
    c. ligaments
    d. strength

    ANS: B   DIF: B   OBJ: 14-7

20. Tearing of fibers results in a muscle _____.
    a. cramp
    b. strain
    c. break
    d. recovery

    ANS: B   DIF: B   OBJ: 14-8

21. Muscle cramping is due to a lack of _____.
    a. carbon dioxide
    b. food
    c. oxygen
    d. water

    ANS: C   DIF: B   OBJ: 14-8

22. Muscle cramps result when a muscle _____ and then cannot _____.
   a. relaxes, contract
   b. contracts, relax
   c. breaks, heal
   d. tears, heal

   ANS: B   DIF: B   OBJ: 14-8

23. A lumbar support helps to reduce _____.
   a. backaches
   b. toothaches
   c. joint problems
   d. bone fractures

   ANS: A   DIF: B   OBJ: 14-9

MATCHING

Examine Figure 14-1. Choose the letter that best matches each part below.

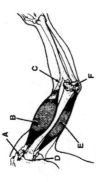

Figure 14-1

1. ligament
2. tendon
3. hinge joint
4. ball-and-socket joint
5. contracted muscle
6. relaxed muscle

1. ANS: A	DIF: A	OBJ: 14-3
2. ANS: C	DIF: A	OBJ: 14-5
3. ANS: F	DIF: A	OBJ: 14-3
4. ANS: D	DIF: A	OBJ: 14-3
5. ANS: B	DIF: A	OBJ: 14-5
6. ANS: E	DIF: A	OBJ: 14-5

Examine Figure 14-2. Choose the letter that best matches each statement below.

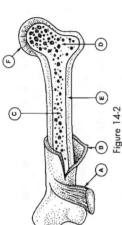

Figure 14-2

7. outer membrane
8. spongy bone
9. solid bone
10. site where blood cells are made
11. is lightweight but still very strong
12. ligament
13. connects bone to bone
14. cartilage
15. contains many nerves and blood vessels

7. ANS: B	DIF: A	OBJ: 14-2
8. ANS: D	DIF: A	OBJ: 14-2
9. ANS: E	DIF: A	OBJ: 14-2
10. ANS: C	DIF: A	OBJ: 14-2
11. ANS: D	DIF: A	OBJ: 14-2
12. ANS: A	DIF: A	OBJ: 14-2
13. ANS: A	DIF: A	OBJ: 14-2
14. ANS: F	DIF: A	OBJ: 14-2
15. ANS: B	DIF: A	OBJ: 14-2

Choose the phrase from the following list that best matches each statement below.

   a. smooth muscle
   b. cardiac muscle
   c. skeletal muscle
   d. cardiac and smooth muscles

16. found in heart
17. has no dark and light stripes
18. is involuntary
19. cells form a tight weave with one another
20. found in intestine and blood vessels
21. makes up the meat that we eat
22. moves bones

16. ANS: B	DIF: A	OBJ: 14-4
17. ANS: A	DIF: A	OBJ: 14-4

18. ANS: D DIF: A OBJ: 14-4
19. ANS: B DIF: A OBJ: 14-4
20. ANS: A DIF: A OBJ: 14-4
21. ANS: C DIF: A OBJ: 14-4
22. ANS: C DIF: A OBJ: 14-4

Choose the word from the following list that best matches each statement below.
a. skeleton
b. muscle

23. moves bones by pulling on them
24. has joints
25. may get arthritis
26. may get a cramp
27. stores calcium
28. protects the brain and heart
29. forms blood cells
30. makes up the heart
31. moves food in digestive system
32. may get a sprain

23. ANS: B DIF: A OBJ: 14-5
24. ANS: A DIF: A OBJ: 14-3
25. ANS: A DIF: A OBJ: 14-7
26. ANS: B DIF: A OBJ: 14-8
27. ANS: A DIF: A OBJ: 14-1
28. ANS: A DIF: A OBJ: 14-1
29. ANS: A DIF: A OBJ: 14-1
30. ANS: B DIF: A OBJ: 14-4
31. ANS: B DIF: A OBJ: 14-4
32. ANS: A DIF: A OBJ: 14-7

Choose the phrase from the following list that best matches each statement below.
a. fixed joint
b. ball-and-socket joint
c. hinge joint

33. found at knee or elbow
34. allows movement in a full circle
35. allows movement back and forth
36. allows no movement
37. found in the skull
38. where pelvis and thigh meet

33. ANS: C DIF: B OBJ: 14-3
34. ANS: B DIF: B OBJ: 14-3
35. ANS: C DIF: B OBJ: 14-3
36. ANS: A DIF: B OBJ: 14-3
37. ANS: A DIF: B OBJ: 14-3

38. ANS: B DIF: B OBJ: 14-3

Examine Figure 14-3. Choose the phrase from the following list that best matches each statement below.

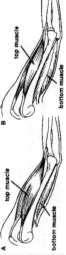

Figure 14-3

a. drawing A
b. drawing B
c. neither A nor B

39. This drawing shows the top arm muscle contracted.
40. This drawing will result in the arm being raised up.
41. This drawing shows the top and bottom arm muscles contracted.
42. This drawing will result in the arm being pulled down.
43. This drawing shows the top arm muscle relaxed.
44. This drawing shows bottom arm muscle contracted.

39. ANS: A DIF: A OBJ: 14-6
40. ANS: A DIF: A OBJ: 14-6
41. ANS: C DIF: A OBJ: 14-6
42. ANS: B DIF: A OBJ: 14-6
43. ANS: B DIF: A OBJ: 14-6
44. ANS: B DIF: A OBJ: 14-6

SHORT ANSWER

1. Compare the cause and prevention of muscle cramps with a muscle strain.

ANS:
Muscle cramps-contraction is too strong; supply muscle with enough oxygen
Muscle strain-lack of exercise; regular exercise will reduce chance of strains occurring

DIF: A OBJ: 14-8

2. Explain how modern technology has helped to solve the problem of diseased joints.

ANS: Artificial joints of plastic or metal are used to replace diseased hip and knee joints.

DIF: A OBJ: 14-7

3. List three problems of the skeletal system.

ANS: arthritis, loss of calcium, sprains DIF: A OBJ: 14-7

TRUE/FALSE

1. Hormones are produced by the nervous system.

   ANS: F   DIF: B   OBJ: 15-6

2. Your nervous system includes your brain, sense organs, and nerves.

   ANS: T   DIF: B   OBJ: 15-4

3. Messages move between neurons only where they touch.

   ANS: F   DIF: B   OBJ: 15-3

4. Diabetes mellitus is caused by too little thyroxine getting into cells.

   ANS: F   DIF: B   OBJ: 15-9

5. Messages can travel in two directions along a neuron pathway.

   ANS: F   DIF: B   OBJ: 15-3

6. Nerves enter and leave the brain through the spinal cord.

   ANS: T   DIF: B   OBJ: 15-4

7. Reflexes help prevent injuries.

   ANS: T   DIF: B   OBJ: 15-5

8. The blood carries messages of the endocrine system.

   ANS: T   DIF: B   OBJ: 15-6

9. Neurons have a smooth, round shape.

   ANS: F   DIF: B   OBJ: 15-3

10. The axon end of a neuron gives off a chemical messenger.

    ANS: T   DIF: B   OBJ: 15-3

11. The dendrite end of a neuron receives a chemical messenger.

    ANS: T   DIF: B   OBJ: 15-3

---

4. Describe some of the problems that have been corrected with new toothbrush design.

   ANS: easier to hold and less likely to drop, bristles will reach all gum and teeth surfaces better

   DIF: A   OBJ: 14-9

5. Why is appearance of a new product no longer as important as its general design to fit body use?

   ANS: New products today are being designed for proper body fit and use rather than how the product actually looks.

   DIF: A   OBJ: 14-9

12. Your nervous system allows you to detect changes around you.

ANS: T   DIF: B   OBJ: 15-1

13. People cannot respond to changes around them.

ANS: F   DIF: B   OBJ: 15-1

14. The most complex nervous system is found in hydras.

ANS: F   DIF: B   OBJ: 15-2

MULTIPLE CHOICE

1. The body's left side is controlled by the cerebrum's _____.
   a. left side
   b. right side
   c. both left and right sides
   d. front half

ANS: B   DIF: B   OBJ: 15-4

2. If a tiger rushes toward you, what are the correct events in your nervous system?
   a. Your brain responds first and then your muscles cause you to move away.
   b. You move away first and then the spinal cord responds.
   c. Your muscles respond first and then your brain reacts.
   d. You detect the change and then your sense organs respond.

ANS: A   DIF: B   OBJ: 15-1

3. Which animal's nervous system has four pairs of eyes, a brain, and many body nerves?
   a. spider
   b. hydra
   c. sponge
   d. flatworm

ANS: A   DIF: B   OBJ: 15-2

4. An involuntary action that uses the spinal cord but NOT the brain is a _____.
   a. gland
   b. reflex
   c. nerve
   d. hormone

ANS: B   DIF: B   OBJ: 15-5

5. Which hormone controls the amount of sugar that can enter a cell?
   a. thyroxine
   b. parathyroid
   c. insulin
   d. pituitary

ANS: C   DIF: B   OBJ: 15-9

6. A gland that forms many different hormones is the _____.
   a. thyroid
   b. adrenal
   c. parathyroid
   d. pituitary

ANS: D   DIF: B   OBJ: 15-7

7. The endocrine system is made up of _____.
   a. many neurons
   b. the brain
   c. several small glands
   d. reflexes

ANS: C   DIF: B   OBJ: 15-6

8. The part of the brain that permits smooth control of muscle movement is the _____.
   a. medulla
   b. cerebrum
   c. cerebellum
   d. spinal cord

ANS: C   DIF: B   OBJ: 15-4

9. A stroke occurs when blood vessels break within _____.
   a. a synapse
   b. a tumor
   c. the brain
   d. body nerves

ANS: C   DIF: B   OBJ: 15-8

10. Glucose in the urine is a sign of _____.
    a. insulin
    b. stroke
    c. pancreas
    d. diabetes mellitus

ANS: D   DIF: B   OBJ: 15-9

11. Reflexes are protective because they _____.
   a. happen quickly
   b. do need the brain
   c. use the endocrine system
   d. are voluntary

   ANS: A   DIF: B   OBJ: 15-5

12. Too little thyroxine in the body will result in a person's _____.
   a. losing weight
   b. producing too much urine
   c. gaining weight
   d. having too much energy

   ANS: C   DIF: B   OBJ: 15-7

13. Being able to detect change and then respond is a job of your _____ system.
   a. skeletal
   b. nervous
   c. circulatory
   d. excretory

   ANS: B   DIF: B   OBJ: 15-1

14. Two nerve cords, eyespots, and a brainlike part best describes the nervous system of a _____.
   a. hydra
   b. planarian
   c. spider
   d. human

   ANS: B   DIF: B   OBJ: 15-2

15. A net-like pattern of nerve cells throughout the body describes the nervous system of a _____.
   a. hydra
   b. planarian
   c. spider
   d. human

   ANS: A   DIF: B   OBJ: 15-2

16. Blood vessels supply the brain with _____.
   a. messages
   b. new cells
   c. food and oxygen
   d. neurons

   ANS: C   DIF: B   OBJ: 15-8

17. A stroke may result in death of _____.
   a. brain cells
   b. hormones
   c. liver cells
   d. the endocrine system

   ANS: A   DIF: A   OBJ: 15-8

MATCHING

Choose the word or phrase from the following list that best matches each statement below.

   a. medulla
   b. cerebrum
   c. spinal cord
   d. cerebellum
   e. medulla and cerebellum

1. controls thought and reason
2. involved in reflexes
3. located at the bottom of the brain
4. controls breathing and heartbeat
5. stores memory
6. the largest part of the brain
7. carries messages to the brain
8. controls blood pressure
9. protected by the vertebrae
10. controls involuntary actions
11. controls muscle movement and balance

1. ANS: B   DIF: A   OBJ: 15-4
2. ANS: C   DIF: A   OBJ: 15-5
3. ANS: A   DIF: A   OBJ: 15-4
4. ANS: A   DIF: A   OBJ: 15-4
5. ANS: B   DIF: A   OBJ: 15-4
6. ANS: B   DIF: A   OBJ: 15-4
7. ANS: C   DIF: A   OBJ: 15-4
8. ANS: A   DIF: A   OBJ: 15-4
9. ANS: C   DIF: A   OBJ: 15-4
10. ANS: E   DIF: A   OBJ: 15-4
11. ANS: D   DIF: A   OBJ: 15-4

Examine Figure 15-1. Choose the letter of the structure that best matches each statement below.

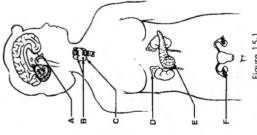

Figure 15-1

12. parathyroids
13. pancreas
14. ovary
15. adrenal
16. thyroid
17. pituitary
18. control calcium balance
19. produces growth hormone
20. controls how fast cells release energy from food
21. brings about female development
22. forms insulin
23. helps body during emergency
24. forms thyroxine

12. ANS: B   DIF: A   OBJ: 15-6
13. ANS: E   DIF: A   OBJ: 15-6
14. ANS: F   DIF: A   OBJ: 15-6
15. ANS: D   DIF: A   OBJ: 15-6
16. ANS: C   DIF: A   OBJ: 15-6
17. ANS: A   DIF: A   OBJ: 15-6
18. ANS: B   DIF: A   OBJ: 15-6
19. ANS: A   DIF: A   OBJ: 15-7
20. ANS: C   DIF: A   OBJ: 15-7
21. ANS: F   DIF: A   OBJ: 15-6

22. ANS: E   DIF: A   OBJ: 15-9
23. ANS: D   DIF: A   OBJ: 15-6
24. ANS: C   DIF: A   OBJ: 15-7

Examine Figure 15-2. Choose the letter of the structure that best matches each statement below.

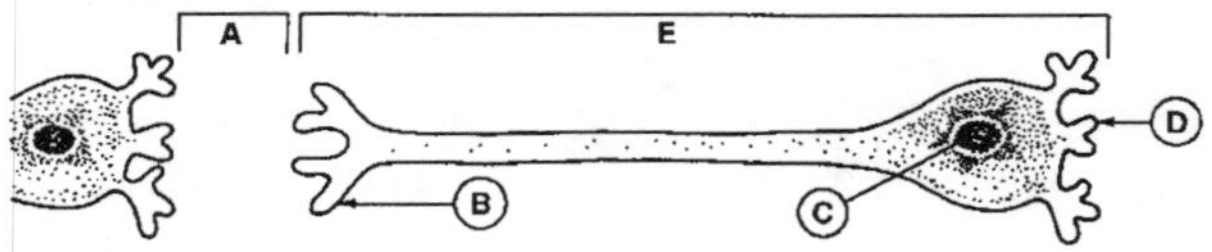

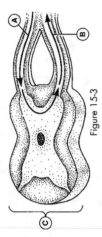

Figure 15-2

25. neuron
26. axon end
27. synapse
28. nucleus
29. end that gives off chemical messenger
30. end that receives chemical messenger
31. dendrite end

25. ANS: E   DIF: A   OBJ: 15-3
26. ANS: B   DIF: A   OBJ: 15-3
27. ANS: A   DIF: A   OBJ: 15-3
28. ANS: C   DIF: A   OBJ: 15-3
29. ANS: B   DIF: A   OBJ: 15-3
30. ANS: D   DIF: A   OBJ: 15-3
31. ANS: D   DIF: A   OBJ: 15-3

Examine Figure 15-3. Choose the letter of the structure that best matches each statement below.

Figure 15-3

32. shows the spinal cord
33. a message enters the spinal cord
34. a message leaves the spinal cord
35. pathway of a message telling your arm muscles to contract
36. pathway of a message detecting a hot stove

32. ANS: C   DIF: A   OBJ: 15-5
33. ANS: A   DIF: A   OBJ: 15-5
34. ANS: B   DIF: A   OBJ: 15-5

35. ANS: B   DIF: A   OBJ: 15-5
36. ANS: A   DIF: A   OBJ: 15-5

Examine Figure 15-4. Choose the letter of the structure that best matches each statement below.

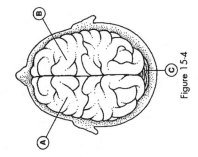

Figure 15-4

37. controls muscles of your right leg
38. receives messages from your left arm
39. left side of cerebrum
40. right side of cerebrum
41. receives messages from your right leg
42. controls muscles of your left hand
43. the cerebellum

37. ANS: A   DIF: A   OBJ: 15-4
38. ANS: B   DIF: A   OBJ: 15-4
39. ANS: A   DIF: A   OBJ: 15-4
40. ANS: B   DIF: A   OBJ: 15-4
41. ANS: A   DIF: A   OBJ: 15-4
42. ANS: B   DIF: A   OBJ: 15-4
43. ANS: C   DIF: A   OBJ: 15-4

SHORT ANSWER

1. Describe the functions that may no longer be possible by the brain if a stroke occurs at the very back of the cerebrum, at the cerebellum, and at the medulla.

ANS: back of the cerebrum-vision; the cerebellum-muscle movements will no longer be smooth and graceful; medulla-breathing and heartbeat may stop, blood pressure will no longer be regulated

DIF: A   OBJ: 15-8

2. Give several problems that may result to the body if a person has diabetes.

ANS: weight loss, blindness, heart disease, possible death

DIF: A   OBJ: 15-9

3. A person with diabetes does not have a shortage of glucose in his or her body. It is actually a shortage of glucose being in the proper place. Explain these two sentences.

ANS: The glucose is present in the blood but is unable to get into the body cells where it is used.

DIF: A   OBJ: 15-9

4. Describe the general makeup of a nervous system.

ANS: It is made up of nerve cells, sense organs, and usually a brain.

DIF: A   OBJ: 15-1

5. List the following animals in order starting with simplest and going to most complex nervous system: human, spider, hydra, planarian.

ANS: hydra, planarian, spider, human   DIF: A   OBJ: 15-2

6. Explain why a planarian can respond more quickly to changes than a hydra.

ANS: A planarian has eyespots that detect changes in light, has a brainlike part to interpret messages, and nerve cords to carry messages to and from body parts.

DIF: A   OBJ: 15-2

7. Name three different functions of the pituitary gland.

ANS: makes hormones that control body growth, causes a person to reach sexual maturity, controls the amount of urine that is formed

DIF: A   OBJ: 15-7

8. Describe a method that scientists might use to determine that the pituitary gland does control body growth.

ANS: Student answers may vary. Remove pituitary gland from a group of young rats. Remove pituitary glands from a second group of rats and inject them with pituitary hormone. Compare body growth of both groups over a period of time with rats not having their pituitary glands removed.

DIF: A   OBJ: 15-7

9. Explain why a person may gain weight if too little thyroxine is made, and why a person may lose weight if too much thyroxine is made.

ANS: Cells not receiving enough thyroxine cannot release energy from food. Food remains unused in cells and the person gains weight. Cells receiving too much thyroxine release too much energy from food. Food is never stored in cells.

DIF: A   OBJ: 15-7

CHAPTER 16—SENSES

TRUE/FALSE

1. Hearing loss may occur if the middle ear bones do not move.

   ANS: T   DIF: A   OBJ: 16-8

2. Each of the three types of cones detects a different color.

   ANS: T   DIF: A   OBJ: 16-3

3. The two parts of the eye that bend light are the cornea and the lens.

   ANS: T   DIF: A   OBJ: 16-3

4. The senses of taste and sight work together.

   ANS: F   DIF: A   OBJ: 16-4

5. Three small bones are in the inner ear.

   ANS: F   DIF: A   OBJ: 16-5

6. Sound waves will set hairlike cells present in the eardrum into motion.

   ANS: F   DIF: B   OBJ: 16-7

7. Hearing damage from loud noises results when hairlike cells become flattened.

   ANS: T   DIF: B   OBJ: 16-7

8. Loud sounds will have decibel values.

   ANS: T   DIF: B   OBJ: 16-7

9. A decibel value of over 25 can damage hearing.

   ANS: F   DIF: B   OBJ: 16-7

10. A shotgun or rock concert can have decibel values over 85.

    ANS: T   DIF: B   OBJ: 16-7

MULTIPLE CHOICE

1. The ear flap helps direct sound waves into the _____.
   a. eardrum
   b. ear canal
   c. cochlea
   d. oval window

   ANS: B   DIF: B   OBJ: 16-5

2. Loud noises can damage hairlike cells in the _____.
   a. eardrum
   b. ear canal
   c. cochlea
   d. stirrup

   ANS: C   DIF: B   OBJ: 16-7

3. Eyespots on the back of a planarian detect _____.
   a. light
   b. food
   c. heat
   d. sound

   ANS: A   DIF: B   OBJ: 16-1

4. Which of the following is NOT one of the four tastes we detect on our tongues?
   a. sweet
   b. hot
   c. salty
   d. bitter

   ANS: B   DIF: A   OBJ: 16-4

5. All messages received by the eyes are interpreted by the _____.
   a. optic nerve
   b. retina
   c. brain
   d. lens

   ANS: C   DIF: B   OBJ: 16-3

6. The human eye is protected and moistened by the _____.
   a. sclera
   b. iris
   c. eyelid
   d. pupil

   ANS: C   DIF: B   OBJ: 16-3

7. The sense organ that is designed to detect the motion of air molecules is the _____.
   a. tongue
   b. nose
   c. throat
   d. ear

   ANS: D   DIF: A   OBJ: 16-5

8. The message of smell is carried to the brain by the _____.
   a. nasal chamber
   b. auditory nerve
   c. olfactory nerve
   d. nostrils

   ANS: C   DIF: B   OBJ: 16-4

9. The skin has _____ nerve cell types and each detects a different condition.
   a. three
   b. four
   c. five
   d. six

   ANS: C   DIF: B   OBJ: 16-4

10. A sense organ of a snake that is like the sense organ in humans is the _____.
    a. nose
    b. eye
    c. tongue
    d. skin

    ANS: B   DIF: B   OBJ: 16-2

11. The white outer covering that holds the eye together is the _____.
    a. sclera
    b. cornea
    c. retina
    d. vitreous humor

    ANS: A   DIF: B   OBJ: 16-3

12. The ear bone that can be replaced with a piece of plastic is the _____.
    a. anvil
    b. hammer
    c. stirrup
    d. cochlea

    ANS: C   DIF: B   OBJ: 16-8

13. The nose and the tongue detect _____.
    a. light
    b. chemical molecules
    c. sound

    ANS: B   DIF: A   OBJ: 16-4

14. The opening in the center of the iris is the _____.
    a. cornea
    b. retina
    c. lens
    d. pupil

    ANS: D   DIF: B   OBJ: 16-3

15. Knobs on the front end of a planarian can detect _____.
    a. light
    b. water currents and food
    c. sound
    d. pain and pleasure

    ANS: B   DIF: B   OBJ: 16-1

16. Earthworms do not have eyes but yet they can detect _____.
    a. sound
    b. light
    c. food
    d. pressure

    ANS: B   DIF: B   OBJ: 16-1

17. Which statement best describes how an earthworm sees?
    a. eyes are present on its head
    b. nerve cells below its skin detect light
    c. it can see with its tail
    d. its mouth detects light

    ANS: B   DIF: B   OBJ: 16-1

18. A compound eye is usually found in _____.
    a. snakes
    b. insects
    c. humans
    d. planaria

    ANS: B   DIF: B   OBJ: 16-2

19. A person is nearsighted if he or she can only clearly see objects that are _____.
    a. far away
    b. in color
    c. close up
    d. flat or round

    ANS: C   DIF: B   OBJ: 16-6

20. A person may be nearsighted if his or her eye diameter is _____.
    a. too long
    b. too short
    c. upside down
    d. too square in shape

    ANS: A   DIF: B   OBJ: 16-6

21. A nearsighted person shows a path of light that falls _____ the retina.
    a. in front of
    b. directly on
    c. in back of
    d. above or below

    ANS: A   DIF: B   OBJ: 16-6

22. A person may be farsighted if his or her eye diameter is _____.
    a. too long
    b. too short
    c. inside out
    d. too round

    ANS: B   DIF: B   OBJ: 16-6

23. A farsighted person shows a path of light that falls _____ the retina.
    a. in front of
    b. directly on
    c. in back of
    d. above or below

    ANS: C   DIF: B   OBJ: 16-6

24. Most nerve cells in the skin are found in the _____.
    a. epidermis
    b. dermis
    c. surface

    ANS: B   DIF: B   OBJ: 16-4

25. Snakes smell with their _____.
   a. nostrils
   b. tongues
   c. skin
   d. ears

   ANS: B   DIF: B   OBJ: 16-2

26. Animals that can see color have _____ cells in the retina.
   a. rod
   b. cone
   c. hair

   ANS: B   DIF: B   OBJ: 16-3

27. The taste of food is related to its _____.
   a. odor
   b. color
   c. appearance

   ANS: A   DIF: B   OBJ: 16-4

28. A person who can see clearly far away but not close up is _____.
   a. nearsighted
   b. farsighted
   c. normal

   ANS: B   DIF: B   OBJ: 16-6

29. In dim light the pupils become _____.
   a. larger
   b. smaller
   c. flattened

   ANS: A   DIF: A   OBJ: 16-3

30. The part of the eye that is often compared to film in the camera is the _____.
   a. retina
   b. lens
   c. pupil

   ANS: A   DIF: A   OBJ: 16-3

31. An "electronic ear" helps a person if nerve cells in the _____ do not work.
   a. middle ear membrane
   b. cochlea
   c. ear flap

   ANS: B   DIF: A   OBJ: 16-8

32. A cricket has parts for sensing sound on its _____.
   a. antennae
   b. front legs
   c. head

   ANS: B   DIF: B   OBJ: 16-2

33. The special nerve cells of the tongue are called _____.
   a. taste buds
   b. rods
   c. cones

   ANS: A   DIF: B   OBJ: 16-4

34. When the image of an object reaches the retina, it is _____.
   a. upside down
   b. right side up
   c. sideways

   ANS: A   DIF: B   OBJ: 16-3

35. The ear canal carries sound waves to the _____ ear.
   a. middle
   b. inner
   c. outer

   ANS: A   DIF: B   OBJ: 16-5

MATCHING

Examine Figure 16-1. Choose the letter of the structure that best matches each phrase below.

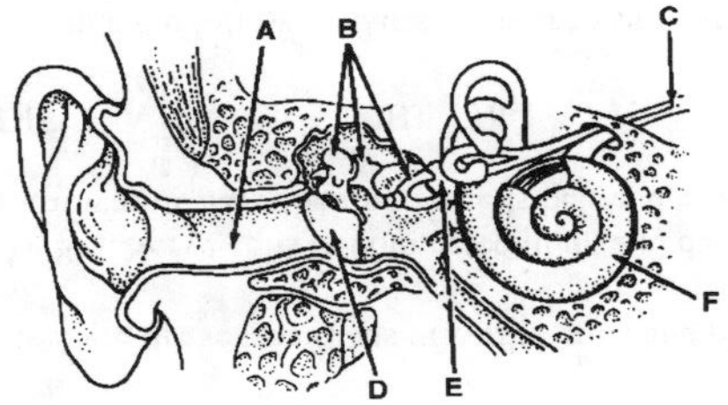

Figure 16-1

1. hammer, anvil, stirrup
2. auditory nerve
3. cochlea
4. ear canal
5. middle ear membrane
6. carries messages to brain
7. eardrum

8. changes vibrations to nerve messages
9. membrane caused to vibrate by vibrating bones
10. pick up eardrum vibrations and pass them to the middle ear membrane
11. sets liquid in cochlea in motion

1. ANS: B   DIF: A   OBJ: 16-5
2. ANS: C   DIF: A   OBJ: 16-5
3. ANS: F   DIF: A   OBJ: 16-5
4. ANS: A   DIF: A   OBJ: 16-5
5. ANS: E   DIF: A   OBJ: 16-5
6. ANS: C   DIF: A   OBJ: 16-5
7. ANS: D   DIF: A   OBJ: 16-5
8. ANS: F   DIF: A   OBJ: 16-5
9. ANS: E   DIF: A   OBJ: 16-5
10. ANS: B   DIF: A   OBJ: 16-5
11. ANS: E   DIF: A   OBJ: 16-5

Examine Figure 16-2. Choose the letter of the structure that best matches each statement below.

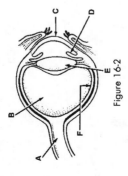

Figure 16-2

12. iris
13. cornea
14. lens
15. retina
16. optic nerve
17. vitreous humor
18. adjusts amount of light entering eye
19. clear outer covering at front of eye
20. carries messages to the brain
21. where the image is formed

12. ANS: D   DIF: A   OBJ: 16-3
13. ANS: C   DIF: A   OBJ: 16-3
14. ANS: E   DIF: A   OBJ: 16-3
15. ANS: F   DIF: A   OBJ: 16-3
16. ANS: A   DIF: A   OBJ: 16-3
17. ANS: B   DIF: A   OBJ: 16-3
18. ANS: D   DIF: A   OBJ: 16-3
19. ANS: C   DIF: A   OBJ: 16-3

20. ANS: A   DIF: A   OBJ: 16-3
21. ANS: F   DIF: A   OBJ: 16-3

SHORT ANSWER

1. Neither an earthworm nor a planarian can actually see objects. What do they actually see? Why might they NOT be able to see objects?

ANS: They detect light. These animals do not have eyes comparable to ours. They have simple nerve cells that can detect changes in light intensity.

DIF: A   OBJ: 16-1

2. How are the sense organs of earthworms and planaria alike? How do they differ?

ANS: Nerve cells in both detect light and dark. Planaria have eyespots that are in the head. Earthworms have their nerve cells below the skin along their entire body length.

DIF: A   OBJ: 16-1

3. Arrange the following parts in order to show the pathway that light takes as it passes through the eye and to the brain: vitreous humor, retina, pupil, optic nerve, lens, cornea.

ANS: cornea, pupil, lens, vitreous humor, optic nerve

DIF: A   OBJ: 16-3

4. What are the two jobs of the brain as it receives light messages?

ANS: The brain interprets or decodes the message and it flips the message right side up.

DIF: A   OBJ: 16-3

5. Explain how the brain helps with the senses of smell, taste, and touch.

ANS: All senses are interpreted in the brain.

DIF: A   OBJ: 16-4

6. What is the location of the semicircular canals?

ANS: inner ear above the cochlea   DIF: A   OBJ: 16-5

7. What is the job of the semicircular canals?

ANS: to help us keep our balance   DIF: A   OBJ: 16-5

MULTIPLE CHOICE

1. Frogs and crickets making sounds is an example of _____ behavior.
   a. courting
   b. protective
   c. learned
   d. food-finding

   ANS: A   DIF: A   OBJ: 17-4

2. All behavior starts with a _____.
   a. stimulus
   b. reward
   c. response
   d. smell

   ANS: A   DIF: A   OBJ: 17-1

3. A behavior that needs practice is usually _____.
   a. innate
   b. a response
   c. fast
   d. learned

   ANS: D   DIF: B   OBJ: 17-3

4. Many animals use this type of behavior to attract a mate.
   a. flying
   b. migration
   c. courting
   d. parental care

   ANS: C   DIF: A   OBJ: 17-4

5. Usually, a stimulus will lead to a _____.
   a. response
   b. problem
   c. change in diet
   d. reward

   ANS: A   DIF: A   OBJ: 17-1

6. A dog's fetching a paper is an example of _____ behavior.
   a. innate
   b. learned
   c. parental care
   d. migration

   ANS: B   DIF: A   OBJ: 17-3

---

8. What is the reason for motion sickness?

   ANS: eyes and semicircular canals receive conflicting messages

   DIF: A   OBJ: 16-5

9. Explain what the numbers 20/20 and 20/40 mean for vision.

   ANS: 20/20 means normal vision--seeing an object clearly (1-cm tall letters) at a distance of 20 feet. 20/40 means seeing an object clearly at 20 feet that a person with normal vision can see at 40 feet.

   DIF: A   OBJ: 16-6

10. Explain the role of lenses in correcting vision problems.

    ANS: Lenses will bend light before it enters the eye so that light rays will meet correctly on the retina.

    DIF: A   OBJ: 16-6

11. Give several sounds that have decibel values below 85 and several sounds that have decibel values over 85.

    ANS: Below 85: air conditioner, television, vacuum cleaner, loud talk. Over 85: motorcycle at 10 meters, power mower, thunderclap, rock concert, shotgun.

    DIF: A   OBJ: 16-7

12. Why is damage to hearing from loud noise not repairable?

    ANS: Hairlike cells within the cochlea become flattened due to loud noise. Once flattened, they are unable to send messages to the auditory nerve and are also unable to repair themselves.

    DIF: A   OBJ: 16-7

7. A flash from a camera startles you. The flash is an example of a _____.
   a. response
   b. pheromone
   c. stimulus
   d. behavior
   ANS: C   DIF: A   OBJ: 17-1

8. Which animal group usually does NOT give parental care?
   a. cats
   b. wolves
   c. those with many offspring
   d. those with few offspring
   ANS: C   DIF: B   OBJ: 17-6

9. The movement of animals from one place to another is _____.
   a. courting
   b. feeding
   c. migration
   d. parental care
   ANS: C   DIF: B   OBJ: 17-5

10. Remove the antennae of a male silk moth and it will no longer be able to _____.
    a. find a mate
    b. fly
    c. see
    d. feed
    ANS: A   DIF: A   OBJ: 17-4

11. Female bees that CANNOT reproduce are _____.
    a. drones
    b. queens
    c. workers
    d. housekeepers
    ANS: C   DIF: B   OBJ: 17-5

12. Adelie penguins can find their way home by using _____ as a guide.
    a. the sun
    b. the stars
    c. humans
    d. waves
    ANS: A   DIF: B   OBJ: 17-5

13. Certain seals will swim to warmer waters when ready to _____.
    a. feed
    b. reproduce
    c. protect the adults
    d. become more social
    ANS: B   DIF: A   OBJ: 17-5

14. Which gives parental care?
    a. frog
    b. insect
    c. all fish
    d. birds
    ANS: D   DIF: B   OBJ: 17-6

MATCHING

Choose the phrase from the following list that best matches each statement below.
   a. innate behavior
   b. learned behavior
   c. innate and learned behaviors

1. An instinct is an example.
2. The behavior can be changed.
3. You are born with it.
4. You must be taught how to do it.
5. It cannot be changed.
6. It is the way that a living thing acts.
7. The same type of behavior will always result from the same stimulus.
8. This behavior must be practiced.
9. writing your name
10. studying a foreign language
11. coughing
12. memorizing the lines to a play
13. sneezing
14. a baby crying when hungry
15. a dog wagging its tail

1. ANS: A   DIF: A   OBJ: 17-2
2. ANS: B   DIF: A   OBJ: 17-3
3. ANS: A   DIF: A   OBJ: 17-2
4. ANS: B   DIF: A   OBJ: 17-3
5. ANS: A   DIF: A   OBJ: 17-2
6. ANS: C   DIF: A   OBJ: 17-3
7. ANS: A   DIF: A   OBJ: 17-2
8. ANS: B   DIF: A   OBJ: 17-3
9. ANS: B   DIF: A   OBJ: 17-3

10. ANS: B DIF: A OBJ: 17-3
11. ANS: A DIF: A OBJ: 17-2
12. ANS: B DIF: A OBJ: 17-3
13. ANS: A DIF: A OBJ: 17-2
14. ANS: A DIF: A OBJ: 17-2
15. ANS: A DIF: A OBJ: 17-2

Choose the phrase from the following list that best matches each statement below.
a. behavior that helps in reproduction
b. behavior that helps to gather food
c. behavior that helps protect
d. behavior that helps in finding a place to live

16. following a migration path
17. musk oxen surrounding their young when attacked by wolves
18. bees "talking" to one another
19. silk moths giving off a pheromone
20. courting of one animal by another
21. a frog making its croaking sound
22. soldier ants defending their nest
23. Adelie penguins using the sun to find their way
24. a spider trapping a fly in its web

16. ANS: D DIF: B OBJ: 17-5
17. ANS: C DIF: B OBJ: 17-5
18. ANS: B DIF: B OBJ: 17-5
19. ANS: A DIF: B OBJ: 17-4
20. ANS: A DIF: B OBJ: 17-4
21. ANS: A DIF: B OBJ: 17-4
22. ANS: C DIF: B OBJ: 17-5
23. ANS: D DIF: B OBJ: 17-5
24. ANS: B DIF: B OBJ: 17-5

Choose the phrase from the following list that best matches each statement below.
a. parental care is given
b. no parental care is given

25. Most mammals provide this type.
26. Food and protection is given to offspring.
27. Hundreds of offspring are produced at one time.
28. Offspring's chance to survive is good.
29. Offspring's chance to survive is poor.

25. ANS: A DIF: A OBJ: 17-6
26. ANS: A DIF: A OBJ: 17-6
27. ANS: B DIF: A OBJ: 17-6
28. ANS: A DIF: A OBJ: 17-6
29. ANS: B DIF: A OBJ: 17-6

SHORT ANSWER

1. How can innate behavior be compared to playing a prerecorded tape?

   ANS: Each time a specific tape is played, the same sounds are heard. Each time the same stimulus is detected, the same response occurs.

   DIF: A OBJ: 17-2

2. Are rewards provided after an innate behavior is carried out? Why or why not?

   ANS: No; the behavior taking place is innate and is something that the organism is born with. It cannot be changed with a reward.

   DIF: A OBJ: 17-2

3. How can learned behavior be compared to recording on a blank tape?

   ANS: A blank tape may be recorded on and may be changed once recorded. Learned behavior is something that is acquired and can therefore be changed depending on the stimulus.

   DIF: A OBJ: 17-3

4. Are rewards provided after a learned behavior is carried out? Why or why not?

   ANS: Yes, rewards tend to reinforce the correct response. They help the learning of a response.

   DIF: A OBJ: 17-3

5. What do pheromones, croaking sounds, and courting behavior all have in common?

   ANS: All are behaviors that aid in reproduction or finding a mate.

   DIF: A OBJ: 17-4

6. Describe how bees are able to tell other bees the direction to find food.

   ANS: Bees form a figure eight when "talking" to other bees. The direction that the bee faces while in the middle of the eight indicates the direction.

   DIF: A OBJ: 17-5

7. How are bees able to tell other bees the distance needed to find food?

   ANS: The number of abdomen wags indicates the distance of food.

   DIF: A OBJ: 17-5

TRUE/FALSE

1. Psychedelic drugs include marijuana, PCP, and LSD.

   ANS: T   DIF: A   OBJ: 18-5

2. Drugs taken by injection enter the bloodstream in order to work.

   ANS: T   DIF: A   OBJ: 18-3

3. If one person is not allergic to a drug, you will not be allergic to it either.

   ANS: F   DIF: A   OBJ: 18-8

4. A drug that encourages sleep usually contains a stimulant.

   ANS: F   DIF: A   OBJ: 18-4

5. You may use another person's drugs if you are both about the same age and weight.

   ANS: F   DIF: A   OBJ: 18-8

6. Labels on drug packages usually include proper dosage and warnings about use.

   ANS: T   DIF: A   OBJ: 18-2

7. Chemicals in nasal sprays prevent leaking of blood plasma from capillaries.

   ANS: T   DIF: B   OBJ: 18-6

8. Many cough medicines contain depressants.

   ANS: T   DIF: B   OBJ: 18-6

9. Beer and whiskey contain the same drug.

   ANS: T   DIF: A   OBJ: 18-9

10. Coughing gets rid of whatever is blocking your esophagus.

    ANS: F   DIF: B   OBJ: 18-6

11. A cough suppressant actually works on the brain's cough control center.

    ANS: T   DIF: B   OBJ: 18-6

---

8. How does the protective behavior of forming a ring help to protect all musk oxen against wolves?

   ANS: Young musk oxen are in the center of the circle and are protected from the wolves by the adults. The adults are protected because it is difficult for wolves to attack an entire group at one time.

   DIF: A   OBJ: 17-5

9. An animal produces 10 000 eggs. Does this animal provide parental care to its offspring? Why or why not?

   ANS: No; animals that produce large numbers of eggs usually provide no parental care.

   DIF: A   OBJ: 17-6

10. An animal produces 5 eggs. Does this animal provide parental care to its offspring? Why or why not?

    ANS: Yes; animals that produce small numbers of offspring usually provide parental care.

    DIF: A   OBJ: 17-6

11. Is the smell of bread baking a response or stimulus?

    ANS: stimulus   DIF: A   OBJ: 17-1

12. Is the heat of a hot pan on a stove a response or stimulus?

    ANS: stimulus   DIF: A   OBJ: 17-1

13. Is quickly removing a hand from a hot pan a response or stimulus?

    ANS: response   DIF: A   OBJ: 17-1

14. Is a robin grabbing a worm a response or stimulus?

    ANS: response   DIF: A   OBJ: 17-1

15. Is saliva collecting in the mouth in reaction to cooking odors a response or stimulus?

    ANS: response   DIF: A   OBJ: 17-1

16. Is coughing a response or stimulus?

    ANS: response   DIF: A   OBJ: 17-1

MULTIPLE CHOICE

1. The correct amount of a drug to take and how often to take it is called the drug _____.
   a. overdose
   b. amount
   c. dosage
   d. time

   ANS: C   DIF: B   OBJ: 18-2

2. _____ are used to treat hay fever.
   a. Antacids
   b. Antihistamines
   c. Stimulants
   d. Barbiturates

   ANS: B   DIF: B   OBJ: 18-6

3. Drugs that speed up activities controlled by the nervous system are _____ drugs.
   a. stimulant
   b. all prescription
   c. depressant
   d. antacid

   ANS: A   DIF: B   OBJ: 18-4

4. An unexpected change caused by a drug is a(n) _____ effect.
   a. frontal
   b. abuse
   c. withdrawal
   d. side

   ANS: D   DIF: B   OBJ: 18-2

5. A drug used as an antacid is _____.
   a. heroin
   b. morphine
   c. barbiturates
   d. sodium bicarbonate

   ANS: D   DIF: B   OBJ: 18-7

6. A drug found in tobacco is _____.
   a. nicotine
   b. cocaine
   c. caffeine
   d. alcohol

   ANS: A   DIF: B   OBJ: 18-9

7. Too much of a drug in the body is _____.
   a. a side effect
   b. an overdose
   c. dependence
   d. tolerance

   ANS: B   DIF: B   OBJ: 18-2

8. A person who needs a drug in order to carry on normal activities has drug _____.
   a. depression
   b. overdose
   c. tolerance
   d. dependence

   ANS: B   DIF: B   OBJ: 18-8

9. Drugs that can change stomach acid to salt and water are _____.
   a. antihistamines
   b. stimulants
   c. antacids
   d. illegal

   ANS: D   DIF: B   OBJ: 18-7

10. If you need a controlled drug for medical reasons, you can get it _____.
    a. over-the-counter
    b. with a prescription
    c. without a prescription

    ANS: C   DIF: B   OBJ: 18-1

11. Drugs taken by mouth will work _____ than those injected.
    a. faster
    b. slower
    c. better
    d. poorer

    ANS: B   DIF: B   OBJ: 18-3

12. Drugs obtained legally without a prescription are _____.
    a. controlled drugs
    b. harmful drugs
    c. over-the-counter drugs
    d. abused drugs

    ANS: C   DIF: B   OBJ: 18-1

13. A drug that first stimulates and then may depress breathing and heart rate is _____.
a. morphine
b. caffeine
c. cocaine
d. LSD
ANS: C   DIF: B   OBJ: 18-9

14. A drug taken for pain in a person's toe actually stops the pain by acting on the _____.
a. toe
b. brain
c. blood
d. stomach
ANS: B   DIF: B   OBJ: 18-3

15. A drug that is swallowed may pass first into the _____ and then into the _____.
a. bloodstream, stomach
b. mouth, brain
c. stomach, bloodstream
ANS: C   DIF: B   OBJ: 18-3

16. A psychedelic drug can change the signals we receive from our _____.
a. skin
b. heart
c. sense organs
d. liver
ANS: C   DIF: B   OBJ: 18-5

17. An inhalant is a drug that is _____.
a. taken by mouth
b. injected
c. breathed in
d. not harmful
ANS: C   DIF: B   OBJ: 18-5

18. A source of inhalants would include _____.
a. aspirin
b. glue and paint
c. cough medicine
d. mushrooms
ANS: B   DIF: B   OBJ: 18-5

MATCHING

Match each term in the following list with its OPPOSITE.
a. acid
b. controlled drug
c. over-the-counter drug
d. drug abuse
e. depressant

1. proper drug use
2. antacid
3. stimulant
4. legal drug
5. prescription drug

1. ANS: D   DIF: A   OBJ: 18-8
2. ANS: A   DIF: A   OBJ: 18-7
3. ANS: E   DIF: A   OBJ: 18-4
4. ANS: B   DIF: A   OBJ: 18-1
5. ANS: C   DIF: A   OBJ: 18-1

Choose the word from the following list that best matches each statement below.
a. stimulant
b. depressant
c. synthetic psychedelic
d. natural psychedelic

6. These drugs block movement of chemical messengers across a synapse.
7. Examples of this type are drugs from mushrooms and cactus plants.
8. Examples of this type are LSD and PCP.
9. These drugs speed up body activities.

6. ANS: B   DIF: A   OBJ: 18-4
7. ANS: D   DIF: A   OBJ: 18-5
8. ANS: C   DIF: A   OBJ: 18-5
9. ANS: A   DIF: A   OBJ: 18-4

Choose the phrase from the following list that best matches each statement below.
a. proper drug use
b. drug abuse

10. using drugs that were prescribed by a doctor for someone else
11. using a drug to which you are allergic
12. using drugs that were prescribed by a doctor for you
13. using controlled drugs for recreation

10. ANS: B   DIF: A   OBJ: 18-8
11. ANS: B   DIF: A   OBJ: 18-8
12. ANS: A   DIF: A   OBJ: 18-8

13. ANS: B DIF: A OBJ: 18-8

Choose the phrase from the following list that best matches each statement below.
a. nicotine
b. caffeine
c. both nicotine and caffeine
d. ethyl alcohol

14. found in beer, wine, and whiskey
15. accompanies other chemicals that cause lung and throat cancers
16. causes loss of memory and muscle control
17. acts as a stimulant
18. made by a plant
19. made by yeast
20. present in cigarettes, chewing tobacco, and snuff
21. acts as a depressant

14. ANS: D DIF: A OBJ: 18-9
15. ANS: A DIF: A OBJ: 18-9
16. ANS: D DIF: A OBJ: 18-9
17. ANS: C DIF: A OBJ: 18-9
18. ANS: C DIF: A OBJ: 18-9
19. ANS: D DIF: A OBJ: 18-9
20. ANS: A DIF: A OBJ: 18-9
21. ANS: D DIF: A OBJ: 18-9

Choose the phrase from the following list that best matches each statement below.
a. found on a drug label
b. not found on a drug label

22. the correct dosage
23. how to use it for mind-altering purposes
24. warnings about side effects
25. name of the drug's discoverer

22. ANS: A DIF: A OBJ: 18-2
23. ANS: B DIF: A OBJ: 18-2
24. ANS: A DIF: A OBJ: 18-2
25. ANS: B DIF: A OBJ: 18-2

SHORT ANSWER

1. Give three reasons why a doctor should tell you which drug to take.

ANS: A doctor will know what drug to use for a specific illness, the proper dose to take, and any problems that may result from the drug use.

DIF: A OBJ: 18-1

2. What is the major reason why controlled drugs are used illegally?

ANS: They are used to change behavior.

DIF: A OBJ: 18-1

3. Why does drug dose vary with body size?

ANS: There must be enough of the drug present in the body to make up for the amount leaving. This amount varies with body size.

DIF: A OBJ: 18-2

4. Use a sink being filled with water to compare how the body normally balances the amount of drug entering and leaving it with how the body reacts to a drug overdose.

ANS: A sink being filled with water and having the same amount of water leaving by way of the drain will not overflow. This is similar to drug use that is balanced. A sink filled with water with no water leaving by way of the drain will overflow. This is similar to a drug overdose.

DIF: A OBJ: 18-2

5. Why do injected drugs work faster than those taken by mouth?

ANS: Injected drugs go directly into the bloodstream and do not have to pass first through the digestive system.

DIF: A OBJ: 18-3

6. Give the different body systems used by a person when swallowing a drug to be used for stopping pain.

ANS: digestive, circulatory, nervous system

DIF: A OBJ: 18-3

7. What are two ways in which a stimulant may affect the normal events that take place in a synapse between neurons?

ANS: It may cause the axon end of the neuron to give off more chemical messenger into the synapse or it may prevent the messenger from being destroyed when it reaches the next neuron.

DIF: A OBJ: 18-4

8. What are two ways in which a depressant may affect the normal events that take place in a synapse between neurons?

ANS: It may block the movement of the messenger across the synapse or it may prevent the axon end of the neuron from giving off its chemical messenger into the synapse.

DIF: A   OBJ: 18-4

9. Name the two general groups of psychedelic drugs and give examples of each group.

ANS: Found in nature: mushrooms, marijuana, cactus plants; synthetic: PCP, LSD, paint, glue.

DIF: A   OBJ: 18-5

10. What are some of the effects on the body when using PCP and when using inhalants?

ANS: PCP: raises blood pressure, affects walking and standing, may cause violence, person may harm him or herself. Inhalant: causes irregular heartbeat and liver damage, may stop heartbeat.

DIF: A   OBJ: 18-5

11. An antihistamine is used to control symptoms from a stuffy nose. Use the word "antihistamine" to determine the name of the chemical that causes the swelling of a stuffy nose.

ANS: histamine (a chemical released from damaged body cells)

DIF: A   OBJ: 18-6

12. Predict what forms chemically when vinegar is added to sodium bicarbonate.

ANS: water, salt, and carbon dioxide gas

DIF: A   OBJ: 18-7

13. Describe the effect of the following drugs on heart rate: caffeine, nicotine, alcohol, and first taking cocaine.

ANS: Heart rate speeds up.   DIF: A   OBJ: 18-9

14. What is the effect of the following drugs on blood pressure: nicotine, and first taking cocaine?

ANS: Blood pressure rises.   DIF: A   OBJ: 18-9

15. What is the effect of the following drugs on the heart: large doses of cocaine, crack?

ANS: Heart may stop.   DIF: A   OBJ: 18-9

18-8

16. Describe the changes that may occur to the body as BAC (blood alcohol concentration) increases.

ANS: Heart and breathing rate increase; alertness decreases; reaction time slows; loss of awareness, stupor, unconsciousness, and death occur.

DIF: A   OBJ: 18-9

17. What are three problems that result to a child born to a mother who was drinking alcohol during her pregnancy?

ANS: Baby is smaller than normal, may be mentally retarded, may have heart defects, and may be dependent on alcohol.

DIF: A   OBJ: 18-9

Write the letter S for stimulant or D for depressant for each of the following drugs.

18. codeine

ANS: D   DIF: B   OBJ: 18-4

19. morphine

ANS: D   DIF: B   OBJ: 18-4

20. cocaine

ANS: S   DIF: B   OBJ: 18-4

21. amphetamines

ANS: S   DIF: B   OBJ: 18-4

22. barbiturates

ANS: D   DIF: B   OBJ: 18-4

23. caffeine

ANS: S   DIF: B   OBJ: 18-4

24. sleep aids

ANS: D   DIF: B   OBJ: 18-4

25. nicotine

ANS: S   DIF: B   OBJ: 18-4

18-9

CHAPTER 19—THE IMPORTANCE OF LEAVES

TRUE/FALSE

1. The thin, flat part of a leaf is called a stalk.

    ANS: F   DIF: B   OBJ: 19-1

2. Stems are the main plant parts that make food.

    ANS: F   DIF: B   OBJ: 19-7

3. Transpiration is the loss of food from a plant.

    ANS: F   DIF: B   OBJ: 19-3

4. Carbon dioxide enters the leaf through the stomata.

    ANS: T   DIF: B   OBJ: 19-2

5. Xylem and phloem connect leaves to roots.

    ANS: T   DIF: B   OBJ: 19-1

6. Most plants are green because of carbon dioxide.

    ANS: F   DIF: B   OBJ: 19-9

7. Many leaves are attached to stems by a midrib.

    ANS: F   DIF: B   OBJ: 19-1

8. Wax is a nonliving layer of the leaf.

    ANS: T   DIF: B   OBJ: 19-2

9. Humans use food and oxygen produced by green plants.

    ANS: T   DIF: B   OBJ: 19-8

10. Xylem cells carry water to leaf cells for photosynthesis.

    ANS: T   DIF: B   OBJ: 19-1

11. Water leaves the leaf through the air space.

    ANS: F   DIF: B   OBJ: 19-2

12. Most guard cells are found on the top of a leaf.

    ANS: F   DIF: B   OBJ: 19-2

13. Plant-eating animals are energy sources for animal eaters.

    ANS: T   DIF: B   OBJ: 19-8

14. There are three epidermis layers in a leaf.

    ANS: F   DIF: B   OBJ: 19-2

15. All cells in a leaf contain chlorophyll.

    ANS: F   DIF: B   OBJ: 19-2

16. The waxy layer is found outside the epidermis.

    ANS: T   DIF: B   OBJ: 19-2

17. Phloem and xylem carry water to all cells in a leaf.

    ANS: F   DIF: B   OBJ: 19-2

18. Stomata are surrounded by guard cells.

    ANS: T   DIF: B   OBJ: 19-2

19. Sugar cannot be used by the plant to form other molecules.

    ANS: F   DIF: B   OBJ: 19-6

20. Leaves that do not get light will not be green.

    ANS: T   DIF: B   OBJ: 19-9

21. Photosynthesis is like the building of a house because both use raw materials.

    ANS: T   DIF: B   OBJ: 19-4

22. Waste materials result from the process of photosynthesis.

    ANS: T   DIF: B   OBJ: 19-4

23. Carbon dioxide enters a plant through its roots.

    ANS: F   DIF: B   OBJ: 19-4

24. Water moves from root to stem to leaf in a plant.

ANS: T   DIF: B   OBJ: 19-4

25. An animal such as a deer that feeds only on plant material would die if all photosynthesis were to stop.

ANS: T   DIF: B   OBJ: 19-7

26. The energy you use for running or cycling has come from the energy trapped in plants.

ANS: T   DIF: B   OBJ: 19-7

27. Plants supply us with needed carbon dioxide.

ANS: T   DIF: B   OBJ: 19-7

MULTIPLE CHOICE

1. All sugars are made up of ____.
   a. oxygen and carbon only
   b. hydrogen and carbon only
   c. oxygen and hydrogen only
   d. oxygen, hydrogen, and carbon

ANS: D   DIF: A   OBJ: 19-5

2. The raw materials used in photosynthesis are ____.
   a. carbon dioxide and water
   b. oxygen and sugar
   c. sugar and carbon dioxide
   d. oxygen and carbon dioxide

ANS: A   DIF: A   OBJ: 19-5

3. The end products of photosynthesis are ____.
   a. sugar and water
   b. oxygen and sugar
   c. carbon dioxide and sugar
   d. water and oxygen

ANS: B   DIF: A   OBJ: 19-5

4. Energy used in photosynthesis is obtained from ____.
   a. food
   b. soil
   c. water
   d. light

ANS: D   DIF: B   OBJ: 19-4

5. The energy needed for photosynthesis is stored in ____.
   a. food
   b. stems
   c. chlorophyll
   d. water

ANS: C   DIF: A   OBJ: 19-4

6. Leaves are arranged on stems in such a way that each receives ____.
   a. water
   b. food
   c. sunlight
   d. carbon dioxide

ANS: C   DIF: B   OBJ: 19-1

7. Photosynthesis takes place in which cells of a leaf?
   a. palisade
   b. xylem
   c. epidermis
   d. stomata

ANS: A   DIF: B   OBJ: 19-2

8. Which is not an element found in sugar?
   a. carbon
   b. nitrogen
   c. oxygen
   d. hydrogen

ANS: B   DIF: B   OBJ: 19-5

9. The size of the stomata is controlled by ____.
   a. the epidermis
   b. the waxy layer
   c. guard cells
   d. palisade cells

ANS: C   DIF: A   OBJ: 19-2

10. The teeth of a leaf could be ____.
   a. rounded
   b. pointed
   c. neither rounded nor pointed
   d. either rounded or pointed

ANS: D   DIF: A   OBJ: 19-1

11. Chlorophyll is made in smaller amounts when _____ is present.
   a. more sunlight
   b. less sunlight
   c. more carbon dioxide
   d. less sugar
   ANS: B   DIF: A   OBJ: 19-9

12. Which of the following leaf parts is NOT made of cells?
   a. palisade
   b. phloem
   c. stoma
   d. epidermis
   ANS: C   DIF: B   OBJ: 19-2

13. Chlorophyll in a leaf _____.
   a. traps light energy
   b. is yellow in color
   c. traps carbon dioxide
   ANS: A   DIF: B   OBJ: 19-4

14. Water loss from a plant can take place through its _____.
   a. guard cells
   b. epidermis
   c. stomata
   d. roots
   ANS: C   DIF: B   OBJ: 19-3

15. On cool damp days, water loss from a plant usually _____.
   a. speeds up
   b. slows down
   c. reaches 100 percent
   d. occurs for 1 hour
   ANS: B   DIF: B   OBJ: 19-3

16. In addition to raw materials needed for photosynthesis, a plant must also _____.
   a. have chlorophyll
   b. receive light
   c. neither a nor b
   d. both a and b
   ANS: D   DIF: B   OBJ: 19-5

17. The sugar made during photosynthesis is _____.
   a. not pure
   b. glucose
   c. made of elements
   d. both b and c
   ANS: D   DIF: B   OBJ: 19-5

18. The final products of photosynthesis can be used as raw materials by _____.
   a. only plants
   b. only animals
   c. only protists
   d. all life forms
   ANS: D   DIF: B   OBJ: 19-6

19. Energy taken in during photosynthesis is stored in the plant as energy _____.
   a. that is wasted
   b. in sugar
   c. that is lost
   d. in oxygen
   ANS: D   DIF: B   OBJ: 19-6

20. The raw materials of photosynthesis are the waste products of _____.
   a. transpiration
   b. cellular respiration
   c. diffusion
   d. chemicals
   ANS: B   DIF: B   OBJ: 19-6

21. Most leaves contain pigments that are green as well as those that are _____.
   a. blue
   b. red
   c. yellow
   d. both b and c
   ANS: D   DIF: B   OBJ: 19-9

22. The green of _____ blocks most other leaf pigments from showing.
   a. flavorings
   b. chlorophyll
   c. spices
   d. photosynthesis
   ANS: B   DIF: B   OBJ: 19-9

MATCHING

Examine Figure 19-1. Choose the letter that best matches each statement.

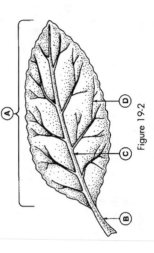

Figure 19-1

1. cells that protect leaf
2. air space
3. epidermis
4. where carbon dioxide enters
5. spongy layer
6. palisade layer
7. guard cell
8. part that has nonliving layer attached
9. cells that surround stomata

1.	ANS:	A	DIF:	A	OBJ: 19-2
2.	ANS:	D	DIF:	A	OBJ: 19-2
3.	ANS:	A	DIF:	A	OBJ: 19-2
4.	ANS:	F	DIF:	A	OBJ: 19-2
5.	ANS:	C	DIF:	A	OBJ: 19-2
6.	ANS:	B	DIF:	A	OBJ: 19-2
7.	ANS:	E	DIF:	A	OBJ: 19-2
8.	ANS:	A	DIF:	A	OBJ: 19-2
9.	ANS:	E	DIF:	A	OBJ: 19-2

Examine Figure 19-2. Choose the letter of the leaf part that best matches each statement below.

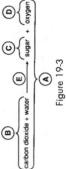

Figure 19-2

10. main part of leaf that makes food
11. connects leaf to stem
12. main vein of leaf blade
13. will appear needle-like in a pine

10.	ANS:	A	DIF:	A	OBJ: 19-1
11.	ANS:	B	DIF:	A	OBJ: 19-1
12.	ANS:	C	DIF:	A	OBJ: 19-1
13.	ANS:	A	DIF:	A	OBJ: 19-1

Use Figure 19-3 to answer the following questions about photosynthesis.

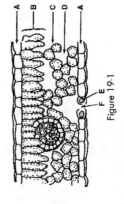

Figure 19-3

14. shows the final product formed
15. shows a waste product formed
16. shows the raw materials needed
17. could be chlorophyll
18. could represent light energy
19. shows the process of photosynthesis

14.	ANS:	C	DIF:	A	OBJ: 19-5
15.	ANS:	D	DIF:	A	OBJ: 19-5
16.	ANS:	B	DIF:	A	OBJ: 19-5
17.	ANS:	E	DIF:	A	OBJ: 19-5
18.	ANS:	E	DIF:	A	OBJ: 19-5
19.	ANS:	A	DIF:	A	OBJ: 19-5

2. Why does a plant left in the dark turn yellow?

ANS: Once light is removed, a plant will fail to form green chlorophyll. The yellow pigment that was present in the leaf will now be visible.

DIF: A   OBJ: 19-9

3. Why do leaves of certain trees change color in the autumn?

ANS: As temperatures drop and day length shortens in autumn, chlorophyll begins to break down, allowing the other colored pigments to show through.

DIF: A   OBJ: 19-9

4. You discover a wilted plant. Why has it wilted and what can you do to correct the problem?

ANS: The plant has lost water faster than it can be replaced. As a result, its cells have also lost water and are no longer firm. Adding water will restore the plant to its original condition.

DIF: A   OBJ: 19-3

5. You wish to bake some cookies from scratch. What do the following compare to in the process of photosynthesis? a) an electric mixer, b) the bowl for mixing, c) flour, eggs, butter, d) egg shells and a dirty cookie sheet after baking

ANS: a) energy needs, b) the leaf, c) raw materials, d) waste chemicals

DIF: A   OBJ: 19-4

6. How are the two processes of photosynthesis and cellular respiration different in terms of what happens to energy?

ANS: During photosynthesis, energy is needed and is stored in sugar. During cellular respiration, energy stored in sugar is released or given off.

DIF: A   OBJ: 19-6

7. "If there were no plants on Earth for food, we could survive by eating only meat such as beef or pork." Explain what is wrong with this statement.

ANS: Animals such as cows and pigs, which are our source of beef and pork, also depend on plants for their food. With no plants, there would be no other animals for us to use as food.

DIF: A   OBJ: 19-7

Choose the word from the following list that best matches each statement below.

a. stomata
b. guard cells
c. palisade cells
d. waxy layer
e. phloem

20. Gases enter the leaf through these parts.
21. long, thin cells beneath epidermis
22. a nonliving part of the leaf
23. cells that control opening and closing of leaf
24. cells that carry food

20. ANS: A   DIF: A   OBJ: 19-2
21. ANS: C   DIF: A   OBJ: 19-2
22. ANS: D   DIF: A   OBJ: 19-2
23. ANS: B   DIF: A   OBJ: 19-2
24. ANS: E   DIF: A   OBJ: 19-1

Choose the word from the following list that best matches each statement below.

a. wilting
b. photosynthesis
c. leaf
d. transpiration
e. blade

25. the thin, flat part of a leaf
26. a plant loses water faster than it can be replaced
27. a process in which a plant makes food
28. the process by which a plant loses water
29. the part of a plant that makes food

25. ANS: E   DIF: A   OBJ: 19-1
26. ANS: A   DIF: A   OBJ: 19-3
27. ANS: B   DIF: A   OBJ: 19-4
28. ANS: D   DIF: A   OBJ: 19-3
29. ANS: C   DIF: A   OBJ: 19-2

SHORT ANSWER

1. A walk through the aisles of a grocery or drug store would show a number of plant leaves that are used by us in our daily life. Give several examples of these leaves.

ANS: Leaves used as food and seasoning include tea, lettuce, spinach, sage, and spearmint. Leaves used as medicine include foxglove.

DIF: A   OBJ: 19-8

8. Which of the following items come from a plant leaf? sage spice, tea, wood, potato, peppermint flavoring, cabbage and spinach, wool or nylon, parsley

ANS: sage spice, tea, peppermint flavoring, cabbage and spinach, parsley

DIF: B   OBJ: 19-8

CHAPTER 20—PLANT SUPPORT AND TRANSPORT

TRUE/FALSE

1. Large amounts of food are stored in fibrous roots.

   ANS: F   DIF: B   OBJ: 20-11

2. You would expect to find many food storage cells in the roots of carrots.

   ANS: T   DIF: B   OBJ: 20-11

3. Plants store food in their roots so that humans have something to eat.

   ANS: F   DIF: B   OBJ: 20-11

4. Cortex cells of roots hold large amounts of minerals.

   ANS: F   DIF: B   OBJ: 20-11

5. The most important product humans get from stems is wood.

   ANS: T   DIF: B   OBJ: 20-6

6. All paper products are from the leaves of plants.

   ANS: F   DIF: B   OBJ: 20-6

7. Maple sugar and turpentine are products made or stored in stems.

   ANS: T   DIF: B   OBJ: 20-6

8. Asparagus and broccoli are foods that come from the root of the plant.

   ANS: F   DIF: B   OBJ: 20-6

MULTIPLE CHOICE

1. Which of the following is NOT an important function of roots?
   a. make food
   b. absorb materials
   c. anchor plants
   d. hold soil in place

   ANS: A   DIF: A   OBJ: 20-11

2. _____ has fibrous roots.
   a. A dandelion
   b. A carrot
   c. A beet
   d. Grass

   ANS: D   DIF: B   OBJ: 20-7

3. Most of the water that enters a plant enters through the _____.
   a. primary root
   b. taproot
   c. root hairs
   d. cortex

   ANS: C   DIF: B   OBJ: 20-10

4. The roots of clover help make the soil rich in _____.
   a. food
   b. water
   c. nitrogen
   d. carbon dioxide

   ANS: C   DIF: B   OBJ: 20-12

5. Herbaceous stems do NOT grow tall because they do not have enough _____ cells.
   a. cambium
   b. xylem
   c. phloem
   d. cortex

   ANS: B   DIF: A   OBJ: 20-1

6. New root growth occurs mainly from the root _____.
   a. hairs
   b. tip
   c. xylem
   d. epidermis

   ANS: B   DIF: B   OBJ: 20-9

7. Some stems store food as _____.
   a. paraffin
   b. wood
   c. starch
   d. sugar

   ANS: C   DIF: B   OBJ: 20-5

8. The two types of herbaceous stems differ in arrangement of _____.
   a. bark and xylem
   b. phloem and xylem
   c. cortex and cambium
   d. bark and phloem

   ANS: B   DIF: A   OBJ: 20-1

9. One product that comes from stems is _____.
   a. plastic
   b. aluminum
   c. rubber
   d. glass

   ANS: C   DIF: B   OBJ: 20-6

10. Herbaceous stems are usually _____ and _____.
    a. very tall, green
    b. green, soft
    c. woody, short

    ANS: B   DIF: B   OBJ: 20-1

11. Which of the following are NOT herbaceous stems?
    a. bean
    b. tree
    c. corn
    d. wheat

    ANS: B   DIF: B   OBJ: 20-1

12. A woody stem is NOT _____.
    a. living
    b. tall
    c. dark in color
    d. green

    ANS: D   DIF: B   OBJ: 20-2

13. Woody stems have an outer covering called _____.
    a. phloem
    b. xylem
    c. bark
    d. cambium

    ANS: C   DIF: B   OBJ: 20-2

14. Found at the tip end of a stem is a _____ bud.
    a. terminal
    b. lateral
    c. flower
    d. dead

    ANS: A   DIF: B   OBJ: 20-3

15. Found along the sides of a stem are _____ buds.
    a. terminal
    b. lateral
    c. dead
    d. no answer is correct

    ANS: B   DIF: B   OBJ: 20-3

16. Which shows the correct pathway of water up through a plant?
    a. root, leaf, stem
    b. stem, root, leaf
    c. root, stem, leaf

    ANS: C   DIF: B   OBJ: 20-4

17. Which shows the correct pathway of food down through a plant?
    a. root, leaf, stem
    b. leaf, stem, root
    c. stem, leaf, root

    ANS: B   DIF: B   OBJ: 20-4

18. The three processes used by a plant to move water through it are _____.
    a. diffusion, osmosis, circulation
    b. transpiration, perspiration, osmosis
    c. osmosis, diffusion, transpiration

    ANS: C   DIF: B   OBJ: 20-4

19. Water is lost from the _____ of leaves and is replaced by water coming in from the _____.
    a. stomata, epidermis
    b. epidermis, bark
    c. stomata, stem

    ANS: C   DIF: B   OBJ: 20-4

20. A plant that stores water in its stem would be _____.
    a. a serious problem
    b. a cactus
    c. a tree
    d. corn

    ANS: B   DIF: B   OBJ: 20-5

21. Stored food in a stem is often used by the plant as _____.
    a. a mineral
    b. xylem and phloem
    c. an anchor
    d. a reserve supply

    ANS: D   DIF: B   OBJ: 20-5

22. The first root to appear from a seed is the _____ root.
    a. secondary
    b. epidermis
    c. primary
    d. hair

    ANS: C   DIF: B   OBJ: 20-9

23. Roots branching from a primary root are _____ roots.
    a. secondary
    b. thick
    c. useless
    d. storage

    ANS: A   DIF: B   OBJ: 20-9

24. A primary root is usually _____ than all other roots.
    a. thinner
    b. greener
    c. thicker
    d. more compact

    ANS: C   DIF: B   OBJ: 20-9

25. Tiny threadlike parts on secondary roots are _____.
    a. stems
    b. xylem
    c. endodermis
    d. root hairs

    ANS: D   DIF: B   OBJ: 20-9

26. Root hairs increase surface area of the root and thus _____ water taken in.
    a. increase
    b. decrease
    c. slow
    d. block

    ANS: A   DIF: B   OBJ: 20-10

27. Minerals are used by a plant for the forming of _____.
    a. water
    b. oxygen
    c. carbon dioxide
    d. protein

    ANS: D   DIF: B   OBJ: 20-10

28. Needed plant minerals are present in _____.
    a. air
    b. soil
    c. food
    d. starch

    ANS: B   DIF: B   OBJ: 20-10

29. Water is lost from the surface of a leaf through _____.
    a. diffusion
    b. osmosis
    c. transpiration

    ANS: C   DIF: A   OBJ: 20-4

30. Water is taken up by root cells through _____.
    a. diffusion
    b. osmosis
    c. transpiration

    ANS: B   DIF: A   OBJ: 20-4

31. Water moves upward through the stem by _____.
    a. diffusion
    b. osmosis
    c. transpiration

    ANS: A   DIF: A   OBJ: 20-4

MATCHING

Choose a letter from Figure 20-1 to match with the following questions.

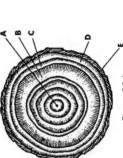

Figure 20-1

1. Which is the ring growing now?
2. Which ring grew during the most rain?
3. Which letter points out the bark?
4. Growth takes place under which layer of the tree?
5. Which layer contains cork?
6. Which is the oldest ring of xylem?
7. Which layer contains phloem?

1. ANS: D   DIF: A   OBJ: 20-3
2. ANS: B   DIF: A   OBJ: 20-3
3. ANS: E   DIF: A   OBJ: 20-2
4. ANS: E   DIF: A   OBJ: 20-2
5. ANS: E   DIF: A   OBJ: 20-2
6. ANS: A   DIF: A   OBJ: 20-2
7. ANS: E   DIF: A   OBJ: 20-3

Examine Figure 20-2. Choose the letter of the root that best matches each statement below.

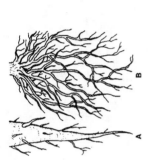

Figure 20-2

8. taproot

9. fibrous root
10. grass
11. beet or carrot
12. collects materials from a large area
13. more likely to contain stored food
14. found in oak and hickory trees
15. easy to pull from the ground

8. ANS: A DIF: B OBJ: 20-7
9. ANS: B DIF: B OBJ: 20-7
10. ANS: B DIF: B OBJ: 20-7
11. ANS: A DIF: B OBJ: 20-7
12. ANS: B DIF: A OBJ: 20-7
13. ANS: A DIF: A OBJ: 20-7
14. ANS: A DIF: B OBJ: 20-7
15. ANS: A DIF: A OBJ: 20-7

Examine Figure 20-3. Choose the letter of the structure that best matches each statement below.

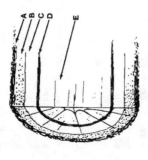

Figure 20-3

16. carries water
17. where new cells are formed
18. where food is stored
19. transports water up from the roots
20. protects the stem
21. moves food down the stem
22. provides most support for plant
23. made up of dead cells
24. causes tree to become wider with age
25. thickest part of old tree

16. ANS: E DIF: A OBJ: 20-2
17. ANS: D DIF: A OBJ: 20-2
18. ANS: B DIF: A OBJ: 20-2
19. ANS: E DIF: A OBJ: 20-4
20. ANS: A DIF: A OBJ: 20-2
21. ANS: C DIF: A OBJ: 20-2

22. ANS: E DIF: A OBJ: 20-2
23. ANS: A DIF: A OBJ: 20-2
24. ANS: D DIF: A OBJ: 20-2
25. ANS: E DIF: A OBJ: 20-2

Examine Figure 20-4. Choose the letter of the structure that best matches each statement below.

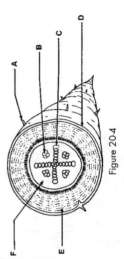

Figure 20-4

26. epidermis
27. cortex
28. xylem
29. phloem
30. root hair
31. endodermis
32. part that carries water
33. absorbs water
34. protects root
35. stores food
36. carries food
37. retains water in root

26. ANS: D DIF: B OBJ: 20-8
27. ANS: E DIF: B OBJ: 20-8
28. ANS: C DIF: B OBJ: 20-8
29. ANS: B DIF: B OBJ: 20-8
30. ANS: A DIF: B OBJ: 20-8
31. ANS: F DIF: B OBJ: 20-8
32. ANS: C DIF: A OBJ: 20-8
33. ANS: A DIF: A OBJ: 20-8
34. ANS: D DIF: A OBJ: 20-8
35. ANS: E DIF: A OBJ: 20-8
36. ANS: B DIF: A OBJ: 20-8
37. ANS: F DIF: A OBJ: 20-8

SHORT ANSWER

1. Why is an annual ring made up of a light and dark band?

   ANS: The light band forms when there is plenty of water and growth is rapid, forming large cells of xylem. Dark bands form when there is less water and growth is slower, forming small cells of xylem.

   DIF: A   OBJ: 20-3

2. When do the light and dark bands of an annual ring form?

   ANS: Light bands form during spring. Dark bands form during summer.

   DIF: A   OBJ: 20-3

3. How are minerals in the soil able to reach the leaves of plants?

   ANS: Minerals are dissolved in the water of soil. They are carried through the plant along with water.

   DIF: A   OBJ: 20-4

4. A plant stem may store food and water. Where does the water and food being stored originally come from?

   ANS: Water came from the soil; food was made by the plant during photosynthesis.

   DIF: A   OBJ: 20-5

5. Rope is a product that comes from the stems of certain plants. What specific stem tissue might this product actually be?

   ANS: vascular bundles (xylem cells)   DIF: A   OBJ: 20-6

6. Place the following root parts in order as a molecule of water passes from the soil into a root: epidermis, endodermis, xylem, root hair, cortex.

   ANS: root hair, epidermis, cortex, endodermis, xylem

   DIF: A   OBJ: 20-8

7. A scientist removes the tip end from all secondary roots of a young bean plant. Predict what may happen to the roots.

   ANS: All future growth of the roots lengthwise will stop.

   DIF: A   OBJ: 20-9

Choose the word from the following list that best matches each statement below.

a. cortex
b. xylem
c. phloem
d. cambium
e. epidermis

38. cell layer from which root hairs grow
39. forms woody tissue in a stem
40. stores food in a plant
41. produces new xylem and phloem
42. protective layer of cells
43. cell with the thickest cell walls in a stem
44. carries food to cells of plants
45. outermost layer of cells in roots and stems
46. xylem plus this tissue are in scattered bundles in corn stems

38. ANS: E	DIF: A	OBJ: 20-8
39. ANS: B	DIF: A	OBJ: 20-2
40. ANS: A	DIF: A	OBJ: 20-2
41. ANS: D	DIF: A	OBJ: 20-2
42. ANS: E	DIF: A	OBJ: 20-2
43. ANS: B	DIF: A	OBJ: 20-2
44. ANS: C	DIF: A	OBJ: 20-2
45. ANS: E	DIF: A	OBJ: 20-8
46. ANS: C	DIF: A	OBJ: 20-1

Choose the phrase from the following list that best matches each statement below.

a. helpful use of roots
b. harmful result of root growth

47. breaking of sidewalks
48. used for making medicines
49. used as a seasoning
50. blocking of water pipes
51. food as in beets
52. supplying nitrogen to soil
53. keeping soil from washing away

47. ANS: B	DIF: A	OBJ: 20-12
48. ANS: A	DIF: A	OBJ: 20-12
49. ANS: A	DIF: A	OBJ: 20-12
50. ANS: B	DIF: A	OBJ: 20-12
51. ANS: A	DIF: A	OBJ: 20-12
52. ANS: A	DIF: A	OBJ: 20-12
53. ANS: A	DIF: A	OBJ: 20-12

8. How does food storage by roots help a plant the following spring?

ANS: Food is used for future growth by the plant in the spring following a winter when it is not capable of carrying on photosynthesis or food production.

DIF: A   OBJ: 20-11

9. Grass growing on a hill helps to keep the soil from washing away. Why does this happen?

ANS: The roots hold the soil together as they grow into the soil.

DIF: A   OBJ: 20-12

10. A farmer plants a field of clover. The following year, corn is planted where the clover was growing. The farmer sees that the corn is growing faster and healthier than ever before. Why?

ANS: Clover helps to supply nitrogen to the soil. The nitrogen was used by the corn plants and improved their growth. Nitrogen acts as a natural fertilizer.

DIF: A   OBJ: 20-12

11. How do the patterns of xylem and phloem in corn and bean stems differ?

ANS: A bean shows a ring or circle of xylem and phloem around the inside of the stem. Phloem forms a circle toward the outside and xylem is toward the inside. Corn shows scattered bundles of xylem and phloem throughout the stem.

DIF: A   OBJ: 20-1

12. Is cardboard a stem product?

ANS: yes   DIF: A   OBJ: 20-6

13. Are dollar bills stem products?

ANS: yes   DIF: A   OBJ: 20-6

14. Is chewing gum a stem product?

ANS: yes   DIF: A   OBJ: 20-6

15. Are plastic spoons stem products?

ANS: no   DIF: A   OBJ: 20-6

16. Is dill for seasoning a stem product?

ANS: yes   DIF: A   OBJ: 20-6

17. Is writing paper a stem product?

ANS: yes   DIF: A   OBJ: 20-6

18. Are a football or a tennis ball stem products?

ANS: no   DIF: A   OBJ: 20-6

19. Is young bamboo as food a stem product?

ANS: yes   DIF: A   OBJ: 20-6

20. Is bamboo for chop sticks a stem product?

ANS: yes   DIF: A   OBJ: 20-6

CHAPTER 21—PLANT RESPONSE, GROWTH, AND DISEASE

TRUE/FALSE

1. Insects that feed on plant tissues can spread plant diseases.

   ANS: T   DIF: B   OBJ: 21-8

2. The movement of leaves of an insect-trapping plant is a tropism.

   ANS: F   DIF: A   OBJ: 21-3

3. A stem grows toward light when the cells on the dark side of the stem become longer.

   ANS: T   DIF: A   OBJ: 21-3

4. Hormones do NOT control growth.

   ANS: F   DIF: B   OBJ: 21-1

5. The underground parts of an annual plant do NOT die at the end of the growing season.

   ANS: F   DIF: B   OBJ: 21-4

6. Plants grown in less light than normal will have a stem that is tall and pale green.

   ANS: T   DIF: B   OBJ: 21-5

7. You can increase air spaces in soil by adding dead organic matter.

   ANS: T   DIF: A   OBJ: 21-5

8. Hormones near terminal buds cause roots to grow longer.

   ANS: F   DIF: A   OBJ: 21-1

9. Diseases in plants are caused by protozoans.

   ANS: F   DIF: B   OBJ: 21-6

10. Removing terminal buds from a shrub causes the shrub to produce side branches.

    ANS: T   DIF: A   OBJ: 21-1

11. An increase in the number of cells causes plant parts to become larger or thicker.

    ANS: T   DIF: A   OBJ: 21-1

12. In short-day plants, long periods of light cause the needed amount of hormone to be produced for flowering.

    ANS: F   DIF: A   OBJ: 21-2

13. Hormones are chemicals made in the soil that affect parts of plants.

    ANS: F   DIF: B   OBJ: 21-1

14. Plant diseases may be caused by bacteria.

    ANS: T   DIF: B   OBJ: 21-6

15. Plant diseases are caused by the same kinds of organisms that cause disease in humans.

    ANS: T   DIF: B   OBJ: 21-6

16. The same type of virus that causes yellow spots on a leaf can cause yellow spots on your skin.

    ANS: F   DIF: B   OBJ: 21-6

MULTIPLE CHOICE

1. Thigmotropism is a response to ____.
   a. contact
   b. gravity
   c. light
   d. water

   ANS: A   DIF: B   OBJ: 21-3

2. An oak tree is a ____.
   a. perennial
   b. annual
   c. triennial
   d. biennial

   ANS: A   DIF: B   OBJ: 21-4

3. Clay soil is hard because the soil particles ____.
   a. are packed closely together
   b. are packed loosely
   c. are all large
   d. have large air spaces

   ANS: A   DIF: A   OBJ: 21-5

4. The amount of light a plant gets has no effect on ____.
   a. development of buds
   b. response to gravity
   c. time of flowering
   d. normal growth

   ANS: B   DIF: A   OBJ: 21-5

5. Short-day plants bloom during ____.
   a. summer
   b. autumn
   c. both a and b
   d. the whole year

   ANS: B   DIF: B   OBJ: 21-2

6. Plants use minerals for making chlorophyll and ____.
   a. energy
   b. fertilizer
   c. water
   d. cell walls

   ANS: D   DIF: B   OBJ: 21-5

7. Environmental factors needed by a plant for proper growth are ____.
   a. tropisms
   b. raw materials
   c. hormones
   d. growth requirements

   ANS: D   DIF: B   OBJ: 21-5

8. Roots grow downward into the soil as a result of ____.
   a. phototropism
   b. gravitropism
   c. thigmotropism
   d. pressure

   ANS: B   DIF: B   OBJ: 21-3

9. Plants easily absorb which of the following from the soil?
   a. energy
   b. dissolved minerals
   c. undissolved minerals
   d. light

   ANS: B   DIF: B   OBJ: 21-5

10. Gravitropism is a response to ____.
    a. light
    b. gravity
    c. minerals
    d. water

    ANS: B   DIF: B   OBJ: 21-3

11. Long-day plants bloom during ____.
    a. summer
    b. autumn
    c. spring
    d. all year

    ANS: A   DIF: B   OBJ: 21-2

12. Phototropism is a response to ____.
    a. water
    b. gravity
    c. light
    d. minerals

    ANS: C   DIF: B   OBJ: 21-3

13. Plants that complete their life cycle in one year are ____.
    a. biennial
    b. perennial
    c. woody
    d. annual

    ANS: D   DIF: B   OBJ: 21-4

14. Plants that do NOT die after one or two years are ____.
    a. perennial
    b. annual
    c. costly
    d. biennial

    ANS: A   DIF: B   OBJ: 21-4

15. Plants that grow for two years and form seeds the second year are ____.
    a. poisonous
    b. annual
    c. biennial
    d. perennial

    ANS: C   DIF: B   OBJ: 21-4

16. An example of an annual plant is ____.
a. daffodil
b. corn
c. onions
d. cabbage
ANS: B   DIF: B   OBJ: 21-4

17. A fungus disease that destroys American elms does so by ____.
a. eating leaves
b. eating roots
c. plugging xylem
d. rotting bark
ANS: C   DIF: B   OBJ: 21-7

18. Fungus diseases are spread by the ____ of the organism.
a. seeds
b. runners
c. tubers or bulbs
d. spores
ANS: D   DIF: B   OBJ: 21-7

19. Insects carry plant diseases caused by ____.
a. viruses
b. bacteria
c. fungi
d. choices a, b, and c
ANS: D   DIF: B   OBJ: 21-8

20. Insects usually transfer disease through their ____.
a. abdomen
b. pores
c. mouthparts
d. wings
ANS: C   DIF: B   OBJ: 21-8

COMPLETION

Use Figure 21-1 to answer the following questions.

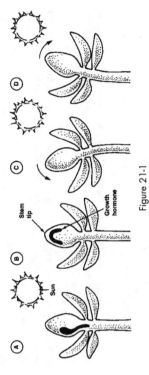

Figure 21-1

1. Stem tip(s) ____ has equal growth hormone on all sides.
ANS: B   DIF: A   OBJ: 21-3

2. Stem tip(s) ____ shows growth hormone moving away from the sun.
ANS: A   DIF: A   OBJ: 21-3

3. Stem tip(s) ____ will have cells along the left side lengthening.
ANS: A, D   DIF: A   OBJ: 21-3

4. Stem tip(s) ____ shows a tropism response.
ANS: A, C, D   DIF: A   OBJ: 21-3

5. Diagram(s) ____ shows a stimulus.
ANS: A, C, D   DIF: A   OBJ: 21-3

MATCHING

Choose the growth requirement that best matches each statement below.
a. light
b. minerals
c. water
d. soil
e. temperature

1. Geranium plants will freeze if planted too early.
2. Corn grows best in direct sun.
3. Rice grows well in a flooded field.

4. Plants do NOT grow well in packed clay.
5. Fertilizing the lawn makes it green and healthy.

1. ANS: E   DIF: A   OBJ: 21-5
2. ANS: A   DIF: A   OBJ: 21-5
3. ANS: C   DIF: A   OBJ: 21-5
4. ANS: D   DIF: A   OBJ: 21-5
5. ANS: B   DIF: A   OBJ: 21-5

Choose the phrase from the following list that best matches each statement below. Some phrases will be used more than once.

a. short-day plant
b. long-day plant
c. day-neutral plant
d. gravitropism
e. phototropism

6. mayapple (blooms in summer)
7. ragweed (blooms in autumn)
8. marigold (does not depend on length of day)
9. response of plant to gravity
10. more light causes flowering
11. plant blooms in autumn
12. plant blooms from late spring to late fall
13. plant blooms in summer
14. response of a plant to light
15. less light causes flowering

6. ANS: B   DIF: A   OBJ: 21-2
7. ANS: A   DIF: A   OBJ: 21-2
8. ANS: C   DIF: A   OBJ: 21-2
9. ANS: D   DIF: A   OBJ: 21-3
10. ANS: B   DIF: A   OBJ: 21-2
11. ANS: A   DIF: A   OBJ: 21-2
12. ANS: C   DIF: A   OBJ: 21-2
13. ANS: B   DIF: A   OBJ: 21-2
14. ANS: E   DIF: A   OBJ: 21-3
15. ANS: A   DIF: A   OBJ: 21-2

Choose the word from the following list that best matches each plant disease below. Some words may be used more than once.

a. virus
b. bacterium
c. fungus
d. insect

16. mosaic disease
17. corn smut
18. Dutch elm disease

19. blister spots
20. eats leaves
21. wheat rust
22. tumors

16. ANS: A   DIF: B   OBJ: 21-6
17. ANS: C   DIF: B   OBJ: 21-7
18. ANS: C   DIF: B   OBJ: 21-7
19. ANS: B   DIF: B   OBJ: 21-6
20. ANS: D   DIF: B   OBJ: 21-8
21. ANS: C   DIF: B   OBJ: 21-7
22. ANS: A   DIF: B   OBJ: 21-6

Choose the word from the following list that best matches each statement below.

a. temperature
b. soil
c. fertilizer

23. improves the soil
24. affects the rate of photosynthesis
25. determines the best time to plant seeds
26. made of clay and sand
27. contains minerals
28. contains air spaces

23. ANS: C   DIF: A   OBJ: 21-5
24. ANS: A   DIF: A   OBJ: 21-5
25. ANS: B   DIF: A   OBJ: 21-5
26. ANS: C   DIF: A   OBJ: 21-5
27. ANS: B   DIF: A   OBJ: 21-5
28. ANS: B   DIF: A   OBJ: 21-5

SHORT ANSWER

1. Name the three plant processes that are controlled by hormones.

ANS: growth, flowering, branching   DIF: A   OBJ: 21-1

2. Each hormone may cause a different change to take place in the plant. Give an example of a plant hormone that causes cells to increase their growth, and an example of a plant hormone that causes cells to slow their growth.

ANS: Increase growth: stem tip cells result in tall growth, root tip cells result in roots growing longer. Slow growth: high levels of hormone present in terminal buds slow down growth of lateral branches.

DIF: A   OBJ: 21-1

3. Plants respond to stimuli. Define stimulus and give an example.

ANS: anything that causes a change; light, gravity, touch

DIF: A   OBJ: 21-3

4. Plants respond to stimuli. Define tropism and give three examples.

ANS: movement of a plant caused by a change in growth as a response to a stimulus; phototropism, gravitropism, thigmotropism

DIF: A   OBJ: 21-3

5. Explain why it may be to a plant's advantage to a) have its leaves grow toward light, and b) have its roots grow downward into the soil.

ANS: a. more light means more food production b. water is present in the soil

DIF: A   OBJ: 21-3

6. Explain how certain perennials such as trees and spring wildflowers differ as to their stem type.

ANS: Trees are woody and not green while wild flowers are herbaceous and green.

DIF: A   OBJ: 21-4

7. How is a disease organism able to enter a plant?

ANS: The disease organism enters the plant through stoma or cuts in the plant leaf.

DIF: A   OBJ: 21-6

8. Give three different ways in which a fungus disease may be spread from plant to plant.

ANS: wind, water, insects   DIF: A   OBJ: 21-7

9. Fungus diseases are rare among desert plants. Why might this be?

ANS: Fungi require a lot of moisture to survive and grow. Cactus plants grow in areas with little moisture.

DIF: A   OBJ: 21-7

10. Fungus diseases are common among plants growing in areas that receive a lot of rain. Why might this be?

ANS: Fungi require a lot of moisture to survive and grow. Thus, they will grow in areas with high rainfall.

DIF: A   OBJ: 21-7

11. Give two reasons why farmers spend millions of dollars trying to destroy insect pests.

ANS: Insects will destroy crops by eating plant leaves. Insects spread many plant diseases from one plant to another as they feed.

DIF: A   OBJ: 21-8

12. How might farmers be harming their crops by spraying to rid them of insects?

ANS: Insects are needed for pollinating flowers of crop plants. No pollination will mean no fruit or seed formation.

DIF: A   OBJ: 21-8

CHAPTER 22—CELL REPRODUCTION

TRUE/FALSE

1. Puberty is a period in life when sex cells begin to develop.

ANS: T   DIF: B   OBJ: 22-6

2. Only females form polar bodies.

ANS: T   DIF: B   OBJ: 22-5

3. After mitosis, each new cell has an equal number of chromosomes.

ANS: T   DIF: A   OBJ: 22-3

4. Cancer cells form by meiosis only.

ANS: F   DIF: B   OBJ: 22-8

5. When a sperm and an egg unite, one cell is formed.

ANS: T   DIF: B   OBJ: 22-6

6. Mitosis is complete when two identical cells are formed.

ANS: T   DIF: B   OBJ: 22-3

7. The result of meiosis is two new cells.

ANS: F   DIF: B   OBJ: 22-4

8. Centrioles are always found in plant cells.

ANS: F   DIF: B   OBJ: 22-3

9. Compared with sperm cells, egg cells are larger.

ANS: T   DIF: B   OBJ: 22-6

10. Egg cells are formed by fertilization.

ANS: F   DIF: B   OBJ: 22-4

11. Skin and muscle cells are examples of body cells.

ANS: T   DIF: B   OBJ: 22-1

12. A human male forms four sperm cells from each original cell.

ANS: T   DIF: B   OBJ: 22-4

13. Body growth and repair usually takes place through meiosis.

ANS: F   DIF: A   OBJ: 22-1

MULTIPLE CHOICE

1. During mitosis, sister chromatids are pulled apart _____.
   a. by the centrioles
   b. in the nucleus
   c. by the fibers
   d. two times

ANS: C   DIF: B   OBJ: 22-3

2. Before the first step of mitosis, chromosomes _____.
   a. move to the end of the cell.
   b. separate
   c. make two copies
   d. make exact copies of themselves

ANS: D   DIF: B   OBJ: 22-2

3. You grow mainly because your cells _____.
   a. get larger
   b. divide
   c. join together
   d. get shorter

ANS: B   DIF: B   OBJ: 22-1

4. The sex cell of an animal has 20 chromosomes. A body cell of this same animal has how many chromosomes?
   a. 40
   b. 30
   c. 20
   d. 10

ANS: A   DIF: A   OBJ: 22-4

5. During mitosis, which of the following does NOT occur?
   a. cells divide; 2 cells form
   b. sister chromatids double
   c. centrioles move
   d. fibers attach to chromosomes

ANS: B   DIF: A   OBJ: 22-3

6. Cancer cells undergo mitosis at a(n) _____ rate.
   a. normal
   b. abnormally slow
   c. abnormally fast
   d. decreased

   ANS: C   DIF: B   OBJ: 22-8

7. Which cells are formed by meiosis?
   a. sperm only
   b. egg only
   c. sperm and egg
   d. body cells

   ANS: C   DIF: B   OBJ: 22-4

8. Excessive exposure to sunlight may cause cancer of the _____.
   a. lungs
   b. mouth
   c. skin
   d. liver

   ANS: C   DIF: B   OBJ: 22-8

9. A human female forms how many eggs from one original cell?
   a. one
   b. two
   c. three
   d. four

   ANS: A   DIF: B   OBJ: 22-4

10. A cell has 4 chromosomes. After mitosis, each new cell will have _____ chromosomes.
    a. 2
    b. 4
    c. 8
    d. 26

    ANS: B   DIF: A   OBJ: 22-3

11. Which of the statements is NOT true about fertilization?
    a. chromosomes separate
    b. sperm and egg cells meet
    c. chromosome number doubles
    d. a new organism begins to form

    ANS: A   DIF: A   OBJ: 22-6

22-3

12. In cell division chromosomes make copies of themselves _____.
    a. before Step 1
    b. as they separate
    c. on the fibers
    d. after division

    ANS: A   DIF: B   OBJ: 22-2

13. A typical animal cell shows all the following parts before mitosis EXCEPT _____.
    a. centrioles
    b. a nuclear membrane
    c. chloroplasts
    d. chromosomes

    ANS: C   DIF: B   OBJ: 22-2

14. What is a chromosome called after it has made a copy of itself?
    a. brother chromosomes
    b. sister chromosomes
    c. sister chromatids
    d. cousin chromosomes

    ANS: C   DIF: B   OBJ: 22-2

15. Common signs of human aging include all the following EXCEPT _____.
    a. loss of hair
    b. muscle cell increase
    c. calcium loss
    d. skin wrinkling

    ANS: B   DIF: B   OBJ: 22-7

16. Fingernail growth slows due to a slowing down of _____.
    a. mitosis
    b. meiosis
    c. centriole copying
    d. fertilization

    ANS: A   DIF: B   OBJ: 22-7

17. A 20 year old would show a _____ lung volume compared to a 70 year old.
    a. smaller
    b. greater
    c. equal
    d. reduced

    ANS: B   DIF: B   OBJ: 22-7

22-4

18. Possible causes of cancer include _____.
   a. chemicals and viruses
   b. viruses and plastic
   c. radiation and water

   ANS: A   DIF: B   OBJ: 22-8

19. Which of the following is a known cause of cancer of the mouth?
   a. purified water
   b. raw food
   c. vitamin B
   d. chewing tobacco

   ANS: D   DIF: B   OBJ: 22-8

20. Which of the following may cause bone cancer?
   a. X rays
   b. too much calcium
   c. cigarettes
   d. too little calcium

   ANS: A   DIF: B   OBJ: 22-8

21. Cancer cells cause problems by _____ normal cells.
   a. eating
   b. crowding out
   c. destroying
   d. increasing

   ANS: B   DIF: B   OBJ: 22-8

22. The body cell of a cat has 38 chromosomes. A sperm from this cat will have _____.
   a. 19 chromosomes
   b. 38 chromosomes
   c. 76 chromosomes

   ANS: A   DIF: A   OBJ: 22-4

23. A human egg cell has 23 chromosomes. A fertilized human egg cell will have _____.
   a. 23 chromosomes
   b. 45 chromosomes
   c. 46 chromosomes

   ANS: C   DIF: A   OBJ: 22-6

24. The body cell of a chicken has 78 chromosomes. A body cell of its parent had _____.
   a. 39 chromosomes
   b. 78 chromosomes
   c. 156 chromosomes

   ANS: B   DIF: A   OBJ: 22-3

25. Humans have 46 chromosomes. Human sperm cells contain _____.
   a. 46 chromosomes
   b. 23 chromosomes
   c. no chromosomes

   ANS: B   DIF: A   OBJ: 22-4

26. The stem cells of rye grass contain 14 chromosomes. A sex cell of this plant will have _____ of chromosomes as the stem cells.
   a. the same number
   b. half the number
   c. twice the number

   ANS: B   DIF: A   OBJ: 22-4

27. Cell reproduction in which two identical cells are made is _____.
   a. mitosis
   b. meiosis
   c. sexual

   ANS: A   DIF: B   OBJ: 22-1

28. The strand of protein that attaches to the chromosome is a _____.
   a. polar body
   b. fiber
   c. chromatid

   ANS: B   DIF: B   OBJ: 22-3

29. _____ occurs when mitosis slows down in the body.
   a. Aging
   b. Cancer
   c. Growth

   ANS: A   DIF: B   OBJ: 22-7

30. The _____ is the body organ that produces sperm.
   a. ovary
   b. testis
   c. uterus

   ANS: B   DIF: B   OBJ: 22-6

31. Body cells are produced by _____.
   a. mitosis
   b. meiosis
   c. aging

   ANS: A   DIF: B   OBJ: 22-1

MATCHING

Choose the phrase from the following list that best matches each statement below.

a. mitosis only
b. meiosis only
c. mitosis and meiosis
d. neither mitosis nor meiosis

1. nucleus and nuclear membrane break down
2. matching pairs of sister chromatids move to opposite ends of the cell
3. six new cells formed
4. each chromosome copies itself
5. each new cell has twice as many chromosomes as the original cell
6. centrioles form fibers
7. two new cells formed
8. makes sperm and egg cells
9. centrioles move away from each other
10. each new cell has one half the number of chromosomes as the original cell
11. makes new body cells
12. matching sister chromatids pair together
13. each new cell has the same number of chromosomes as the original cell
14. polar bodies formed
15. lung cells form new cells

1.	ANS: C	DIF: A	OBJ: 22-3
2.	ANS: B	DIF: A	OBJ: 22-5
3.	ANS: D	DIF: A	OBJ: 22-3
4.	ANS: C	DIF: A	OBJ: 22-2
5.	ANS: D	DIF: A	OBJ: 22-3
6.	ANS: C	DIF: A	OBJ: 22-3
7.	ANS: A	DIF: A	OBJ: 22-3
8.	ANS: B	DIF: A	OBJ: 22-5
9.	ANS: C	DIF: A	OBJ: 22-3
10.	ANS: B	DIF: A	OBJ: 22-5
11.	ANS: A	DIF: A	OBJ: 22-1
12.	ANS: B	DIF: A	OBJ: 22-5
13.	ANS: A	DIF: A	OBJ: 22-3
14.	ANS: B	DIF: A	OBJ: 22-5
15.	ANS: A	DIF: A	OBJ: 22-1

Choose the word or phrase from the following list that best matches each statement below.

a. egg
b. sperm
c. both egg and sperm
d. neither sperm nor egg

16. often called a sex cell
17. formed through meiosis

18. has a tail
19. has the full chromosome number for a living thing
20. has no tail
21. formed in the ovaries of a living thing
22. formed through mitosis
23. After the first division, one cell is much smaller than the other.
24. Polar bodies are formed.
25. contain only half the original chromosome number found in body cells
26. often called a body cell
27. four result from each original cell

16.	ANS: C	DIF: A	OBJ: 22-6
17.	ANS: C	DIF: A	OBJ: 22-6
18.	ANS: B	DIF: A	OBJ: 22-6
19.	ANS: D	DIF: A	OBJ: 22-6
20.	ANS: A	DIF: A	OBJ: 22-6
21.	ANS: A	DIF: A	OBJ: 22-6
22.	ANS: D	DIF: A	OBJ: 22-6
23.	ANS: A	DIF: A	OBJ: 22-6
24.	ANS: A	DIF: A	OBJ: 22-6
25.	ANS: C	DIF: A	OBJ: 22-6
26.	ANS: D	DIF: A	OBJ: 22-6
27.	ANS: B	DIF: A	OBJ: 22-6

Examine Figure 22-1. Choose the letter of the step that best matches each statement below. NOTE: the steps are NOT in the correct order for mitosis.

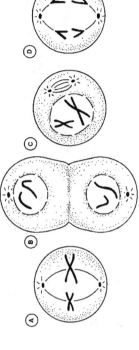

Figure 22-1

28. Step 1
29. Centrioles have just moved to opposite cell ends.
30. Nuclear membrane begins to reform.
31. Nuclear membrane begins to disappear.
32. Step 2
33. Chromosomes are at the cell's center.
34. Step 3
35. Sister chromatids are being pulled apart.
36. Fibers pull chromatids toward centrioles.

37. Step 4
38. Two new cells are formed.
39. Fibers begin to form.
40. Fibers begin to disappear.

28.	ANS: C	DIF: A	OBJ:	22-3
29.	ANS: A	DIF: A	OBJ:	22-3
30.	ANS: B	DIF: A	OBJ:	22-3
31.	ANS: C	DIF: A	OBJ:	22-3
32.	ANS: A	DIF: A	OBJ:	22-3
33.	ANS: A	DIF: A	OBJ:	22-3
34.	ANS: D	DIF: A	OBJ:	22-3
35.	ANS: D	DIF: A	OBJ:	22-3
36.	ANS: D	DIF: A	OBJ:	22-3
37.	ANS: B	DIF: A	OBJ:	22-3
38.	ANS: B	DIF: A	OBJ:	22-3
39.	ANS: C	DIF: A	OBJ:	22-3
40.	ANS: B	DIF: A	OBJ:	22-3

Examine Figure 22-2. Choose the letter of the step that best matches each statement below. NOTE: all steps are NOT being shown for meiosis.

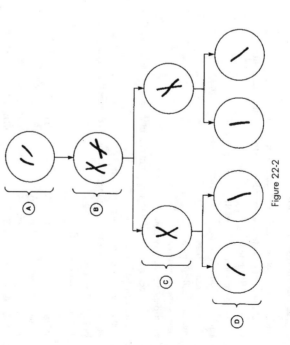

Figure 22-2

41. Matching chromosomes come together.
42. Original cell has two chromosomes before sister chromatids are formed.
43. Sister chromatids are pulled apart.
44. Sister chromatids are still together after cell divides for first time.

45. Four new cells are formed.
46. Chromosome number has been reduced by half from original number.

41.	ANS: B	DIF: A	OBJ:	22-5
42.	ANS: A	DIF: A	OBJ:	22-5
43.	ANS: D	DIF: A	OBJ:	22-5
44.	ANS: C	DIF: A	OBJ:	22-5
45.	ANS: D	DIF: A	OBJ:	22-5
46.	ANS: C	DIF: A	OBJ:	22-5

SHORT ANSWER

1. Why is an older person not as strong as a younger person?

ANS: Muscle cells are lost as a person ages.

DIF: A   OBJ: 22-7

2. Why does an older person heal slower from an injury than a younger person?

ANS: Healing of an injury occurs through mitosis and this process slows with age.

DIF: A   OBJ: 22-7

3. Why are the treatment and cure for cancer difficult?

ANS: Cancer is caused by many different things. Scientists have not yet discovered all possible causes.

DIF: A   OBJ: 22-8

4. Use specific examples to show that different human body cells carry on different rates of mitosis.

ANS: Red blood cells form every 120 days. Liver cells form every 200 days. Intestine lining cells form every 3 days. Brain cells form every 30 to 50 years.

DIF: A   OBJ: 22-1

5. Name two cell parts that double just before mitosis begins and two cell parts that do not double before mitosis begins.

ANS: Centrioles and chromosomes double before mitosis begins; nuclear membrane, cytoplasm, cell membrane do not double before mitosis begins.

DIF: A   OBJ: 22-2

CHAPTER 23—PLANT REPRODUCTION AND DEVELOPMENT

MULTIPLE CHOICE

1. A stem that grows along the ground and forms a new plant at its tip is a _____.
   a. cutting
   b. root
   c. graft
   d. runner

   ANS: D   DIF: B   OBJ: 23-3

2. In _____ reproduction the offspring will have the same features as the parent.
   a. asexual
   b. sexual
   c. flower
   d. seed

   ANS: A   DIF: A   OBJ: 23-9

3. An ovary with ten ovules before fertilization could have ten _____ after fertilization.
   a. seeds
   b. flowers
   c. fruits
   d. spores

   ANS: A   DIF: A   OBJ: 23-7

4. A white potato is a _____.
   a. bulb
   b. stem
   c. root
   d. runner

   ANS: B   DIF: B   OBJ: 23-3

5. During fertilization, a sperm combines with a nucleus in the ovule to form _____
   a. an egg
   b. stored food
   c. an ovary
   d. a pollen grain

   ANS: B   DIF: B   OBJ: 23-6

6. During germination the _____ is the first structure to grow out of the seed.
   a. stem
   b. leaf
   c. flower
   d. root

   ANS: D   DIF: B   OBJ: 23-8

7. In a flower, sperm are able to reach the egg by means of _____.
   a. water
   b. a pollen tube
   c. the stamen
   d. a runner

   ANS: B   DIF: B   OBJ: 23-6

8. Pollen may be carried to a flower by _____.
   a. wind
   b. insects
   c. birds
   d. any of these

   ANS: D   DIF: B   OBJ: 23-5

9. Insects are attracted to the _____ of a flower.
   a. sepals
   b. fruits
   c. leaves
   d. petals

   ANS: D   DIF: B   OBJ: 23-4

10. Sepals are used by the flower for _____.
    a. beauty
    b. protection
    c. making food
    d. storing food

    ANS: B   DIF: B   OBJ: 23-4

11. Which of the following is NOT a fruit?
    a. cucumber
    b. tomato
    c. carrot
    d. apple

    ANS: C   DIF: A   OBJ: 23-7

12. A plant embryo is found in a _____.
    a. stamen
    b. bulb
    c. sepal
    d. seed

    ANS: D   DIF: A   OBJ: 23-7

13. Dandelion seeds are scattered by _____ .
   a. water
   b. animals
   c. wind
   d. fruits

   ANS: C   DIF: B   OBJ: 23-8

14. Tulips, daffodils, and hyacinths grow from _____ .
   a. runners
   b. tubers
   c. bulbs
   d. cuttings

   ANS: C   DIF: B   OBJ: 23-3

15. A new plant forming from a root is an example of _____ reproduction.
   a. asexual
   b. sexual
   c. incorrect
   d. abnormal

   ANS: A   DIF: B   OBJ: 23-1

16. An example of a plant that can reproduce through its roots is a(n) _____ .
   a. African violet
   b. strawberry
   c. onion
   d. sweet potato

   ANS: D   DIF: B   OBJ: 23-1

17. Begonias and dahlias usually can be grown rapidly by using their _____ .
   a. flowers
   b. leaves
   c. bulbs
   d. root tubers

   ANS: D   DIF: B   OBJ: 23-1

18. A new plant forming from a leaf is an example of _____ reproduction.
   a. abnormal
   b. impossible
   c. sexual
   d. asexual

   ANS: D   DIF: B   OBJ: 23-2

19. A new plant may be grown from the leaf of a(n) _____ .
   a. sweet potato
   b. snake plant
   c. rose
   d. onion

   ANS: B   DIF: B   OBJ: 23-2

20. Examples of plants that reproduce through runners include _____ .
   a. roses
   b. clover and spider plants
   c. dahlias
   d. both a and c

   ANS: B   DIF: B   OBJ: 23-3

21. Onion bulbs and potato stem tubers are both said to be _____ .
   a. leaf parts
   b. flowers
   c. underground stems
   d. roots

   ANS: C   DIF: B   OBJ: 23-3

22. The part of the onion bulb that we eat as food is actually the plant's _____ .
   a. roots
   b. stem
   c. leaves
   d. flower

   ANS: C   DIF: B   OBJ: 23-3

23. Transfer of pollen from male to female flower parts is _____ .
   a. transformation
   b. germination
   c. pollination
   d. transpiration

   ANS: C   DIF: B   OBJ: 23-5

24. Pollen from the stamen of one flower is carried to the pistil of a flower on a different plant in _____ .
   a. self pollination
   b. cross pollination
   c. fertilization
   d. ovulation

   ANS: B   DIF: B   OBJ: 23-5

25. Pollen from the stamen of a flower is carried to the pistil of the same flower in _____.
   a. reproduction
   b. fertilization
   c. self pollination
   d. both a and b

   ANS: C   DIF: B   OBJ: 23-5

26. The first step in plant fertilization is the trapping of pollen onto the tip of the _____.
   a. anther
   b. ovary
   c. flower
   d. pistil

   ANS: D   DIF: B   OBJ: 23-6

27. Two nuclei within the _____ will form sperm nuclei.
   a. ovary
   b. sepal
   c. pistil
   d. pollen grain

   ANS: D   DIF: B   OBJ: 23-6

28. New growth of a young plant from a seed is _____.
   a. evaporation
   b. germination
   c. transpiration
   d. fertilization

   ANS: B   DIF: B   OBJ: 23-8

29. What conditions are needed for new plant growth from a seed?
   a. moisture and soil
   b. proper temperature and moisture
   c. proper temperature and soil
   d. soil and fertilizer

   ANS: B   DIF: B   OBJ: 23-8

30. As a young plant grows from a seed, the first leaves to appear will _____.
   a. turn brown
   b. turn green
   c. enter the soil
   d. wither and die

   ANS: B   DIF: B   OBJ: 23-8

31. Food within _____ will get used up and finally _____ the plant.
   a. seed halves, damage
   b. roots, harm
   c. seed halves, drop off

   ANS: C   DIF: B   OBJ: 23-8

32. A group of living things identical to the parents are _____.
   a. clowns
   b. clones
   c. twins
   d. offspring

   ANS: B   DIF: B   OBJ: 23-9

33. Reproduction by this method takes a short time.
   a. sexual
   b. asexual
   c. using egg and sperm cells
   d. using flowers

   ANS: B   DIF: B   OBJ: 23-9

34. A plant that does NOT form seeds can carry out only _____ reproduction.
   a. sexual
   b. slow
   c. asexual
   d. meiosis

   ANS: C   DIF: B   OBJ: 23-9

MATCHING

Examine Figure 23-1. Choose the letter of the structure that best matches each statement below.

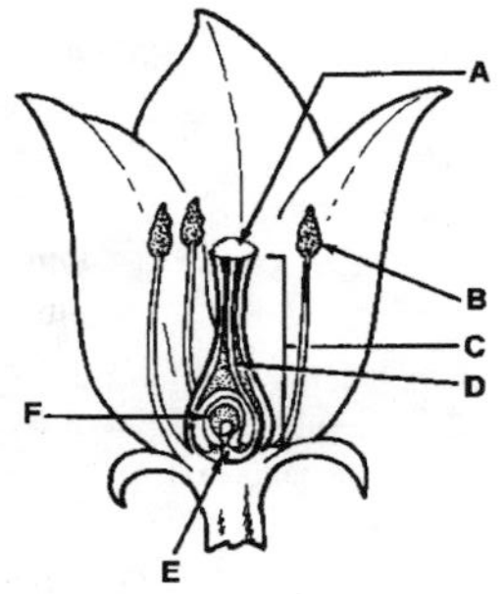

Figure 23-1

1. ovule
2. sperm

Choose the word or phrase from the following list that best matches each statement below.

a. male
b. female
c. neither male nor female

20. ovary
21. pistil
22. petal
23. showy flower part
24. stamen
25. sepal
26. ovule
27. pollen

20.	ANS: B	DIF: A	OBJ: 23-4
21.	ANS: B	DIF: A	OBJ: 23-4
22.	ANS: C	DIF: A	OBJ: 23-4
23.	ANS: C	DIF: A	OBJ: 23-4
24.	ANS: A	DIF: A	OBJ: 23-4
25.	ANS: C	DIF: A	OBJ: 23-4
26.	ANS: B	DIF: A	OBJ: 23-4
27.	ANS: A	DIF: A	OBJ: 23-4

Choose the word from the following list that best matches each statement below.

a. ovule
b. ovary
c. egg
d. stamen

28. will become a new embryo after fertilization
29. will become a fruit after fertilization
30. will wither and dry up after fertilization
31. will form the pollen cells needed for fertilization
32. will become a seed after fertilization
33. will form the cells that produce sperm
34. will form the cells that produce a pollen tube
35. will contain stored food for the embryo after fertilization

28.	ANS: C	DIF: A	OBJ: 23-6
29.	ANS: B	DIF: A	OBJ: 23-7
30.	ANS: D	DIF: A	OBJ: 23-7
31.	ANS: D	DIF: A	OBJ: 23-4
32.	ANS: A	DIF: A	OBJ: 23-7
33.	ANS: D	DIF: A	OBJ: 23-4
34.	ANS: D	DIF: A	OBJ: 23-4
35.	ANS: A	DIF: A	OBJ: 23-7

3. place where pollen is produced
4. female reproductive organ
5. male sex cell
6. becomes a seed
7. is sticky and traps pollen grains
8. pollen tube
9. tip of pistil
10. stamen

1.	ANS: F	DIF: B	OBJ: 23-4
2.	ANS: E	DIF: B	OBJ: 23-4
3.	ANS: B	DIF: A	OBJ: 23-4
4.	ANS: C	DIF: A	OBJ: 23-4
5.	ANS: E	DIF: B	OBJ: 23-4
6.	ANS: F	DIF: A	OBJ: 23-6
7.	ANS: A	DIF: A	OBJ: 23-4
8.	ANS: D	DIF: B	OBJ: 23-4
9.	ANS: A	DIF: A	OBJ: 23-4
10.	ANS: B	DIF: B	OBJ: 23-4

Choose the word or phrase from the following list that best matches each statement below.

a. root
b. stem
c. leaf
d. root, stem, or leaf
e. no root, stem, or leaf

11. plant part used when making a cutting
12. plant part that is a tuber of a sweet potato
13. plant part used for grafting
14. plant part that uses only one parent to reproduce
15. plant part that uses sperm and egg cells to reproduce
16. easy way to grow new African violets
17. plant part used in reproduction
18. plant part that uses meiosis during reproduction
19. plant part that uses mitosis during reproduction

11.	ANS: B	DIF: A	OBJ: 23-3
12.	ANS: A	DIF: A	OBJ: 23-1
13.	ANS: B	DIF: A	OBJ: 23-3
14.	ANS: D	DIF: A	OBJ: 23-1
15.	ANS: E	DIF: A	OBJ: 23-1
16.	ANS: C	DIF: A	OBJ: 23-2
17.	ANS: D	DIF: A	OBJ: 23-1
18.	ANS: E	DIF: A	OBJ: 23-1
19.	ANS: D	DIF: A	OBJ: 23-1

Choose the phrase from the following list that best matches each statement below.

a. true or helpful to plants with asexual reproduction
b. true or helpful to plants with sexual reproduction
c. true or helpful to plants with both asexual and sexual reproduction

36. This is a way for a plant to form offspring.
37. Fertilization is not needed.
38. Banana plants depend on this type of reproduction.
39. The plant does NOT have to depend on fertilization or seed formation.
40. Plants have features that are exactly the same as those of the parent.
41. Two parents are needed.
42. Meiosis must take place.
43. Seeds can be kept alive for long periods of time.
44. Offspring may have features that are better than those in either parent.
45. Plants are exact copies of one another.

36. ANS: C   DIF: A   OBJ: 23-9
37. ANS: A   DIF: A   OBJ: 23-9
38. ANS: A   DIF: A   OBJ: 23-9
39. ANS: A   DIF: A   OBJ: 23-9
40. ANS: A   DIF: A   OBJ: 23-9
41. ANS: B   DIF: A   OBJ: 23-9
42. ANS: B   DIF: A   OBJ: 23-9
43. ANS: B   DIF: A   OBJ: 23-9
44. ANS: B   DIF: A   OBJ: 23-9
45. ANS: A   DIF: A   OBJ: 23-9

SHORT ANSWER

1. Predict the number of pollen grains needed to fertilize a flower with 1 egg, with 10 eggs, and with 25 eggs. Explain your answers.

   ANS: 1, 10, 25; each egg requires its own sperm nucleus for fertilization. Thus, 10 eggs would need 10 sperm nuclei.

   DIF: A   OBJ: 23-6

2. How can you tell that a tomato and pumpkin are fruits?

   ANS: They contain seeds within. Any plant part with seeds is a fruit.

   DIF: A   OBJ: 23-7

3. What are three different ways in which seeds may be carried away from the parent plant?

   ANS: Seeds may be carried by wind, by birds that eat the fruit containing the seeds, by the fruit bursting and throwing out the seeds, or by clinging to animal fur.

   DIF: A   OBJ: 23-8

4. Describe the changes that can be seen over several weeks in a sweet potato when it is placed into a beaker of water.

   ANS: New green shoots appear and continue to grow, forming leaves, stems, and new roots while still attached to the original parent tuber.

   DIF: A   OBJ: 23-1

5. Give the three main characteristics of asexual reproduction in plants.

   ANS: Mitosis is used, egg and sperm cells are not used, and no fertilization is needed.

   DIF: A   OBJ: 23-1

6. Why will a new plant formed from a leaf resemble the parent exactly?

   ANS: Plants formed this way are the result of asexual reproduction. All plants formed this way will resemble the parent exactly.

   DIF: A   OBJ: 23-2

7. Explain what is meant by grafting.

   ANS: joining a stem of one plant type to the stem of another plant type

   DIF: A   OBJ: 23-3

8. What are three different ways in which the design of a flower aids in its pollination?

   ANS: Some petals give off strong scents that attract insect pollinators, others form a nectar or food that attracts insects, some have long hanging flowers that allow wind to carry the pollen away.

   DIF: A   OBJ: 23-5

9. The following steps describe the events that occur after fertilization. Arrange the steps in correct order from 1 to 4 by numbering each statement.
   a. _____ Petals, stamens, and pistil wither and die.
   b. _____ Ovules form seeds and ovary forms a fruit.
   c. _____ All eggs within ovules have been fertilized by sperm cells.
   d. _____ Ovules and ovary begin to grow.

   ANS: 2, 4, 1, 3   DIF: A   OBJ: 23-7

CHAPTER 24—ANIMAL REPRODUCTION

TRUE/FALSE

1. Asexual reproduction occurs mainly in complex animals.

   ANS: F   DIF: A   OBJ: 24-1

2. External fertilization occurs when a female releases eggs in the water to be fertilized.

   ANS: T   DIF: A   OBJ: 24-4

3. The bud on a hydra is a clone.

   ANS: T   DIF: A   OBJ: 24-2

4. An egg is released from a human female ovary every 14 days.

   ANS: F   DIF: A   OBJ: 24-6

5. Deer, bear, and other large mammals breed during the autumn.

   ANS: T   DIF: A   OBJ: 24-5

6. Sperm and egg meet by chance during external fertilization.

   ANS: T   DIF: A   OBJ: 24-4

7. Special organs are needed in sexual reproduction.

   ANS: T   DIF: A   OBJ: 24-3

8. The uterus thickens after the ovary releases an egg.

   ANS: T   DIF: A   OBJ: 24-7

9. When offspring look different from their parents, they were asexually reproduced.

   ANS: F   DIF: A   OBJ: 24-1

10. Hormones cause an egg in the ovary to mature.

    ANS: T   DIF: A   OBJ: 24-7

11. Animals that mate at a certain time of the year have a breeding season.

    ANS: T   DIF: A   OBJ: 24-5

12. Eggs are produced in the oviducts.

    ANS: F   DIF: B   OBJ: 24-6

13. Sexually transmitted diseases can damage the reproductive system.

    ANS: T   DIF: B   OBJ: 24-8

14. The menstrual cycle is started by the pituitary gland.

    ANS: T   DIF: B   OBJ: 24-7

15. Sex cells are produced by the testes and ovaries.

    ANS: T   DIF: B   OBJ: 24-3

MULTIPLE CHOICE

1. Offspring look exactly like the parents if they were _____.
   a. asexually reproduced
   b. sexually reproduced
   c. internally fertilized
   d. externally fertilized

   ANS: A   DIF: B   OBJ: 24-1

2. Most fish and birds breed at what time of the year?
   a. autumn
   b. summer
   c. spring
   d. all seasons

   ANS: C   DIF: B   OBJ: 24-5

3. Which of the following is true about internal fertilization?
   a. cloning takes place
   b. mating takes place
   c. sperm are not released
   d. two eggs are needed

   ANS: B   DIF: A   OBJ: 24-4

4. When an egg and sperm join outside the body, the process is _____ fertilization.
   a. internal
   b. external
   c. budding type of
   d. in vitro

   ANS: B   DIF: B   OBJ: 24-4

5. Sperm cells are produced in the _____.
   a. glands
   b. urethra
   c. testes
   d. tube

   ANS: C   DIF: B   OBJ: 24-3

6. Which of these animals CANNOT reproduce asexually?
   a. sponge
   b. bird
   c. flatworm
   d. hydra

   ANS: B   DIF: B   OBJ: 24-3

7. In humans, embryos develop in the _____.
   a. uterus
   b. vagina
   c. testes
   d. ovary

   ANS: A   DIF: B   OBJ: 24-6

8. Sperm and egg joining inside the body is _____.
   a. internal fertilization
   b. external fertilization
   c. cloning
   d. menstruation

   ANS: A   DIF: B   OBJ: 24-4

9. The menstrual cycle occurs _____.
   a. only in cows and humans
   b. once a year
   c. about once a month in humans
   d. in all mammals

   ANS: C   DIF: A   OBJ: 24-7

10. Changes in the reproductive system during the menstrual cycle are controlled by _____.
    a. a breeding season
    b. an estrous cycle
    c. mating
    d. hormones

    ANS: D   DIF: B   OBJ: 24-7

11. Which type of fertilization can occur during sexual reproduction?
    a. internal only
    b. external only
    c. both internal and external
    d. budding

    ANS: C   DIF: A   OBJ: 24-4

12. An example of an animal that reproduces by regeneration is a(n) _____.
    a. flatworm
    b. fish
    c. frog
    d. insect

    ANS: A   DIF: B   OBJ: 24-2

13. Croaking frogs are really _____.
    a. clearing their throat
    b. calling a mate
    c. singing
    d. fertilizing

    ANS: B   DIF: B   OBJ: 24-5

14. Female animals that allow mating only at certain times have _____ cycle.
    a. a menstrual
    b. a yearly
    c. an estrous
    d. a monthly

    ANS: C   DIF: B   OBJ: 24-5

15. The hormone _____ is given off by the human ovary.
    a. estrogen
    b. progesterone
    c. both a and b
    d. neither a nor b

    ANS: C   DIF: B   OBJ: 24-7

16. During days 5-13 of the menstrual cycle, the uterus lining _____.
    a. thickens
    b. is lost
    c. thins
    d. receives a fertilized egg

    ANS: A   DIF: B   OBJ: 24-7

17. During days 15-28, the uterus lining thickens by a hormone called _____.
   a. estrogen
   b. endocrine
   c. thyroxine
   d. progesterone
   ANS: D   DIF: B   OBJ: 24-7

18. During days 1-4 of the menstrual cycle, if no fertilization occurs, the uterus lining _____.
   a. thickens
   b. is lost
   c. thins
   d. forms a new egg
   ANS: B   DIF: B   OBJ: 24-7

19. On about day 14 of the menstrual cycle, a(n) _____ is released from an ovary.
   a. uterus
   b. egg
   c. oviduct
   d. sperm cell
   ANS: B   DIF: B   OBJ: 24-7

20. If fertilization occurs, which event in the menstrual cycle will NOT occur following day 28?
   a. mating
   b. mitosis
   c. menstruation
   d. regeneration
   ANS: C   DIF: B   OBJ: 24-7

21. During days 1-4 of the menstrual cycle, the uterus lining and unfertilized egg are _____.
   a. formed
   b. strengthened
   c. regenerated
   d. lost
   ANS: D   DIF: B   OBJ: 24-7

22. Which of the following sexually transmitted diseases is NOT caused by bacteria?
   a. AIDS
   b. gonorrhea
   c. chlamydia
   d. syphilis
   ANS: A   DIF: B   OBJ: 24-8

23. Antibiotics can work against those diseases caused by _____.
   a. genital herpes
   b. sexual contact
   c. bacteria
   d. the AIDS virus
   ANS: C   DIF: B   OBJ: 24-8

24. A disease that may result in a female becoming sterile would be _____.
   a. AIDS
   b. genital herpes
   c. syphilis
   d. gonorrhea
   ANS: D   DIF: B   OBJ: 24-8

25. A pus discharge from the penis may indicate _____.
   a. syphilis
   b. gonorrhea
   c. AIDS
   d. genital herpes
   ANS: B   DIF: B   OBJ: 24-8

MATCHING

Choose the phrase from the following list that best matches each statement below.
   a. asexual reproduction
   b. sexual reproduction

1. meiosis takes place
2. internal fertilization
3. estrous cycle
4. reproduction by one parent
5. no meiosis
6. mating never needed
7. complex animals such as birds
8. regeneration
9. external fertilization
10. budding

1. ANS: B   DIF: A   OBJ: 24-3
2. ANS: B   DIF: A   OBJ: 24-4
3. ANS: B   DIF: A   OBJ: 24-5
4. ANS: A   DIF: A   OBJ: 24-1
5. ANS: A   DIF: A   OBJ: 24-1
6. ANS: A   DIF: A   OBJ: 24-1
7. ANS: B   DIF: A   OBJ: 24-3
8. ANS: A   DIF: A   OBJ: 24-2

9. ANS: B   DIF: A   OBJ: 24-4
10. ANS: A   DIF: A   OBJ: 24-2

Choose the phrase from the following list that best matches each statement below.
 a. external fertilization
 b. internal fertilization

11. animal lives in water all of its life
12. animal produces only 5 eggs each year
13. animal produces 10 000 eggs each season
14. animal mates
15. animal protects and cares for young
16. animal does not protect or care for young

11. ANS: A   DIF: A   OBJ: 24-4
12. ANS: B   DIF: A   OBJ: 24-4
13. ANS: A   DIF: A   OBJ: 24-4
14. ANS: B   DIF: A   OBJ: 24-4
15. ANS: B   DIF: A   OBJ: 24-4
16. ANS: A   DIF: A   OBJ: 24-4

Examine Figure 24-1. Choose the letter of the male reproductive structure that best matches each statement below.

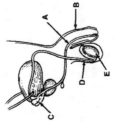

Figure 24-1

17. vas deferens
18. penis
19. place where sperm cells are found after they leave the testes
20. found in scrotum
21. carries sperm to urethra
22. provides liquid for sperm cells to swim
23. testis
24. carries sperm out of body
25. urethra
26. produces sperm cells
27. glands

17. ANS: D   DIF: B   OBJ: 24-6
18. ANS: B   DIF: B   OBJ: 24-6

19. ANS: D   DIF: A   OBJ: 24-6
20. ANS: E   DIF: B   OBJ: 24-6
21. ANS: D   DIF: A   OBJ: 24-6
22. ANS: C   DIF: A   OBJ: 24-6
23. ANS: E   DIF: B   OBJ: 24-6
24. ANS: A   DIF: A   OBJ: 24-6
25. ANS: A   DIF: B   OBJ: 24-6
26. ANS: E   DIF: A   OBJ: 24-6
27. ANS: C   DIF: B   OBJ: 24-6

Examine Figure 24-2. Choose the letter of the female reproductive structure that best matches each statement below.

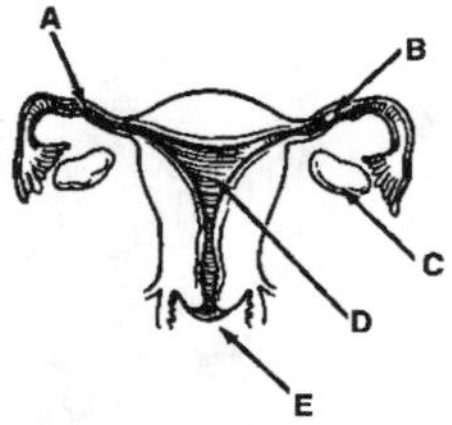

Figure 24-2

28. released once a month
29. oviduct
30. uterus
31. vagina
32. ovary
33. carries egg to uterus from ovary
34. egg
35. fertilized egg develops here
36. place where egg is produced
37. where sperm is released during mating

28. ANS: B   DIF: A   OBJ: 24-6
29. ANS: A   DIF: B   OBJ: 24-6
30. ANS: D   DIF: B   OBJ: 24-6
31. ANS: E   DIF: B   OBJ: 24-6
32. ANS: C   DIF: B   OBJ: 24-6
33. ANS: A   DIF: A   OBJ: 24-6
34. ANS: B   DIF: B   OBJ: 24-6
35. ANS: D   DIF: A   OBJ: 24-6
36. ANS: C   DIF: A   OBJ: 24-6
37. ANS: E   DIF: A   OBJ: 24-6

SHORT ANSWER

1. Give five features of asexual reproduction in animals.

   ANS: 1. Egg and sperm cells are not used. 2. Ovaries and testes are not used to form sex cells. 3. Mitosis is the cell reproduction type used. 4. Body cells undergo mitosis to form offspring. 5. Offspring are clones of the parent.

   DIF: A   OBJ: 24-1

2. Give three ways that one reduces the chance of getting a sexually transmitted disease.

   ANS: 1. Avoid sexual contact. 2. Use a condom during sexual contact. 3. Have sexual contact with only one partner.

   DIF: A   OBJ: 24-8

3. A mother infects her newborn child with a sexually transmitted disease. Explain how this is possible.

   ANS: The bacterium or virus are present in the birth canal of the mother and are passed to the offspring as it moves through the birth canal during birth.

   DIF: A   OBJ: 24-8

4. Describe the symptoms and problems that result from AIDS.

   ANS: fever, dry cough, weight loss, swollen glands, constant tiredness; problems: destruction of immune system, pneumonia, cancer, death

   DIF: A   OBJ: 24-8

5. Give five features of sexual reproduction in animals.

   ANS: 1. Egg and sperm are used. 2. Testes in male and ovaries in female form sex cells. 3. Meiosis is the type of cell reproduction used. 4. Mating may take place. 5. Offspring will not look alike and will not look exactly like either parent.

   DIF: A   OBJ: 24-3

6. Why must animals that show external fertilization deposit their sex cells in water?

   ANS: Sperm must be able to swim to the egg for fertilization. This can only take place if the sex cells are in water.

   DIF: A   OBJ: 24-4

7. Explain how a breeding season and an estrous cycle help the chance for fertilization.

   ANS: A breeding season makes sure that young are born at the right time of the year. With an estrous cycle, the female will make sure that her eggs are being fertilized.

   DIF: A   OBJ: 24-5

8. Arrange the following steps in correct order from days 5-28 and back to days 1-4 of the menstrual cycle. NO fertilization has taken place.
   a. _____ Unfertilized egg moves into oviduct and then uterus.
   b. _____ Uterus lining begins to thicken.
   c. _____ An egg is released from the ovary.
   d. _____ Unfertilized egg and uterus lining leave body by way of vagina.
   e. _____ A hormone causes continued thickening of the uterus lining.

   ANS: 3, 1, 2, 5, 4   DIF: A   OBJ: 24-7

9. Arrange the following steps in correct order from days 5-27 of the menstrual cycle. Fertilization has taken place.
   a. _____ Fertilized egg develops into newborn during next nine months.
   b. _____ An egg is released from the ovary.
   c. _____ Uterus lining begins to thicken.
   d. _____ Fertilized egg moves into uterus and attaches to lining.
   e. _____ Egg is fertilized in the oviduct.

   ANS: 5, 2, 1, 4, 3   DIF: A   OBJ: 24-7

PROBLEM

Figure 24-3

1. Describe the process that is occurring in Figure 24-3, name the animal shown, describe the future appearance of the young animal compared to its parent, and explain why.

   ANS: Budding in a hydra is shown. The young animal is identical to the parent because mitosis is being used to form the offspring from body cells of the parent. This is asexual reproduction.

   DIF: A   OBJ: 24-2

TRUE/FALSE

1. A nymph forms during complete metamorphosis.

    ANS: F   DIF: A   OBJ: 25-7

2. A fetus is the same as an embryo.

    ANS: F   DIF: A   OBJ: 25-3

3. Animals that develop within eggs have no need for waste removal.

    ANS: F   DIF: A   OBJ: 25-5

4. The sac of liquid around a fetus supplies oxygen to the fetus.

    ANS: F   DIF: A   OBJ: 25-2

5. Wastes are carried away from a fetus by its lungs and kidneys.

    ANS: F   DIF: A   OBJ: 25-2

6. All eggs that are laid must be laid in water.

    ANS: F   DIF: A   OBJ: 25-4

7. All animals develop from eggs that attach within a uterus.

    ANS: F   DIF: A   OBJ: 25-4

8. Yolk is very high in fat and protein.

    ANS: T   DIF: B   OBJ: 25-5

9. Food is delivered from mother to fetus through a placenta and cord.

    ANS: T   DIF: B   OBJ: 25-2

10. Much human development occurs in the first three months after fertilization.

    ANS: T   DIF: A   OBJ: 25-3

11. Development of a human in the uterus lasts about 6 months.

    ANS: F   DIF: B   OBJ: 25-3

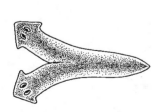

Figure 24-4

2. Describe the process that is occurring in Figure 24-4, name the animal shown, describe the future appearance of the two animals compared to each other, and explain why.

    ANS: Regeneration in a planarian is shown. The two offspring are identical to each other because in asexual reproduction, mitosis is being used to form the offspring. All offspring are clones of each other.

    DIF: A   OBJ: 24-2

12. The things needed by a fetus within the uterus come from the mother.

    ANS: T   DIF: A   OBJ: 25-2

13. Frogs lay eggs on land.

    ANS: F   DIF: B   OBJ: 25-4

14. As time passes, a fetus changes into an embryo.

    ANS: F   DIF: B   OBJ: 25-3

15. In frogs, the larva looks different from the adult.

    ANS: T   DIF: A   OBJ: 25-6

16. Once an egg is fertilized, it undergoes mitosis to form an embryo.

    ANS: T   DIF: A   OBJ: 25-1

17. Some animals have fertilized eggs that develop outside the female's body.

    ANS: T   DIF: A   OBJ: 25-4

18. The navel was part of your amniotic sac.

    ANS: F   DIF: B   OBJ: 25-3

19. Contractions of the vagina are called labor.

    ANS: F   DIF: B   OBJ: 25-3

20. Normal human birth occurs about 38 weeks or 266 days after fertilization.

    ANS: T   DIF: B   OBJ: 25-3

21. The cells of an embryo produce carbon dioxide and urea.

    ANS: T   DIF: A   OBJ: 25-2

22. It takes 120 hours for a human fertilized egg to develop into sixteen cells.

    ANS: F   DIF: B   OBJ: 25-1

MULTIPLE CHOICE

1. A dividing fertilized egg can be called a(n) _____.
   a. juvenile
   b. embryo
   c. larva
   d. fetus

   ANS: B   DIF: B   OBJ: 25-1

2. A caterpillar is another name for a _____.
   a. pupa
   b. nymph
   c. larva
   d. cocoon

   ANS: C   DIF: B   OBJ: 25-8

3. The change in appearance between hatching and the adult stage in some animals is _____.
   a. metamorphosis
   b. development
   c. larva
   d. cleavage

   ANS: A   DIF: A   OBJ: 25-6

4. Oxygen gets into a chicken egg through the _____.
   a. albumen
   b. placenta
   c. sac within egg
   d. eggshell

   ANS: D   DIF: A   OBJ: 25-5

5. Which of the following has incomplete metamorphosis?
   a. butterfly
   b. grasshopper
   c. frog
   d. moth

   ANS: B   DIF: B   OBJ: 25-7

6. Embryos attached to the mother get their food by way of the _____.
   a. uterus
   b. fetus
   c. vagina
   d. placenta

   ANS: D   DIF: A   OBJ: 25-2

7. The bag filled with liquid around a developing embryo is a(n) _____.
   a. eggshell
   b. fetus
   c. amniotic sac
   d. placenta

   ANS: C   DIF: B   OBJ: 25-2

8. The afterbirth is made of the _____.
   a. amniotic sac
   b. placenta
   c. uterus
   d. yolk

   ANS: B   DIF: B   OBJ: 25-3

9. Wastes produced by an embryo are _____.
   a. urea and oxygen
   b. carbon dioxide only
   c. carbon dioxide and urea
   d. oxygen only

   ANS: C   DIF: B   OBJ: 25-2

10. A pupa is sometimes called a _____.
    a. butterfly
    b. cocoon
    c. larva
    d. nymph

    ANS: B   DIF: B   OBJ: 25-8

11. The umbilical cord connects the embryo to the _____.
    a. uterus
    b. fetus
    c. placenta
    d. vagina

    ANS: C   DIF: A   OBJ: 25-2

12. At birth, a human fetus weighs about _____ grams.
    a. 2000
    b. 3000
    c. 2500
    d. 2850

    ANS: B   DIF: A   OBJ: 25-3

13. What supplies food to a chick embryo?
    a. yolk
    b. albumen
    c. both yolk and albumen
    d. sac within the egg

    ANS: C   DIF: A   OBJ: 25-5

14. Forming of bones, muscle, and skin tissues is _____.
    a. growth
    b. fertilization
    c. cleavage
    d. development

    ANS: D   DIF: B   OBJ: 25-1

15. A series of changes from a fertilized egg to a hollow ball is _____.
    a. development
    b. reproduction
    c. cleavage
    d. fetus formation

    ANS: C   DIF: B   OBJ: 25-1

16. Most changes that occur during cleavage take place within the female _____.
    a. oviduct
    b. uterus
    c. vagina
    d. amniotic sac

    ANS: A   DIF: B   OBJ: 25-1

17. Time for a fertilized egg to move through the oviduct and attach to the uterus takes about _____.
    a. 120 minutes
    b. 120 hours
    c. 120 days
    d. 120 seconds

    ANS: B   DIF: B   OBJ: 25-1

18. A frog larva uses _____ to breathe while an adult uses _____.
    a. lungs, gills
    b. its mouth, gills
    c. gills, lungs
    d. skin, its mouth

    ANS: C   DIF: B   OBJ: 25-6

19. A frog larva has _____ while an adult has _____.
a. legs, a tail
b. a tail, legs
c. lungs, gills
d. a mouth, no mouth
ANS: B   DIF: B   OBJ: 25-6

20. Another name for a frog larva is _____.
a. adult
b. embryo
c. egg
d. tadpole
ANS: D   DIF: B   OBJ: 25-6

21. Changes in an insect from nymph to adult is _____ metamorphosis.
a. complete
b. incomplete
c. total
d. typical
ANS: B   DIF: B   OBJ: 25-7

22. A nymph is a young insect that looks like _____.
a. the adult
b. a larva
c. a pupa
d. an egg
ANS: B   DIF: B   OBJ: 25-7

23. Which shows the correct order in cricket metamorphosis?
a. egg-larva-adult
b. egg-adult-pupa
c. egg-nymph-adult
d. nymph-egg-adult
ANS: C   DIF: B   OBJ: 25-7

24. The type of insect metamorphosis that includes a pupa is _____ metamorphosis.
a. abnormal
b. complete
c. incomplete
d. incorrect
ANS: B   DIF: A   OBJ: 25-8

25. Which of the following insects has a pupa stage?
a. grasshopper
b. moth
c. cricket
d. both a and c
ANS: B   DIF: A   OBJ: 25-8

26. Which shows the correct order in a butterfly's metamorphosis?
a. egg-nymph-adult-larva
b. adult-egg-nymph-pupa
c. egg-larva-adult-pupa
d. egg-larva-pupa-adult
ANS: D   DIF: A   OBJ: 25-8

27. The stage of a butterfly that feeds on plant material is the _____.
a. larva
b. pupa
c. egg
d. adult
ANS: A   DIF: A   OBJ: 25-8

MATCHING

Choose the word or phrase from the following list that best matches each statement below.
a. amphibian
b. human
c. reptile and bird
d. amphibian, reptile, bird
e. amphibian, reptile, bird, human

1. development occurs outside body of female
2. development occurs inside body of female
3. egg is laid outside body of female
4. undergo changes called cleavage
5. egg contains a shell
6. egg contains no shell and is laid in water

1. ANS: D   DIF: A   OBJ: 25-4
2. ANS: B   DIF: A   OBJ: 25-4
3. ANS: D   DIF: A   OBJ: 25-4
4. ANS: E   DIF: A   OBJ: 25-4
5. ANS: C   DIF: A   OBJ: 25-4
6. ANS: A   DIF: A   OBJ: 25-4

Choose the word from the following list that best matches each statement below.

a. egg
b. embryo
c. larva
d. adult

7. This stage develops directly from an embryo.
8. This stage will turn into the adult.
9. This stage will lay eggs.
10. This stage develops directly from a fertilized egg.
11. This stage will turn into the larva.
12. This stage will turn into the embryo.
13. This stage has legs and no tail.
14. This stage has a jellylike covering for protection.

7. ANS: C DIF: A OBJ: 25-6
8. ANS: C DIF: A OBJ: 25-6
9. ANS: D DIF: A OBJ: 25-6
10. ANS: B DIF: A OBJ: 25-6
11. ANS: B DIF: A OBJ: 25-6
12. ANS: A DIF: A OBJ: 25-6
13. ANS: D DIF: A OBJ: 25-6
14. ANS: A DIF: A OBJ: 25-6

Examine Figure 25-1. Choose the letter of the structure that best matches each statement below.

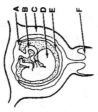

Figure 25-1

15. fetus
16. liquid-filled sac
17. placenta
18. uterus
19. passageway where fetus leaves the mother's body
20. umbilical cord
21. where wastes from developing young are exchanged for food and oxygen from the mother
22. helps protect the developing young from injury

15. ANS: D DIF: A OBJ: 25-3
16. ANS: E DIF: A OBJ: 25-2
17. ANS: A DIF: A OBJ: 25-2
18. ANS: C DIF: A OBJ: 25-2

19. ANS: F DIF: A OBJ: 25-3
20. ANS: B DIF: A OBJ: 25-3
21. ANS: A DIF: A OBJ: 25-2
22. ANS: E DIF: A OBJ: 25-2

SHORT ANSWER

1. Name the three jobs of an egg shell.

ANS: 1. protection; 2. oxygen supply; 3. waste removal

DIF: A OBJ: 25-5

2. Why must the food supply for a developing chick be present as yolk and albumen within the egg?

ANS: There is no other food source available to the developing chick except what is already within the shell.

DIF: A OBJ: 25-5

3. Describe how the nymph stage of an insect a.) differs from the adult; b.) is like the adult.

ANS: a. It is smaller, sexually immature, and lacks wings; b. it has many of the same parts and looks almost like the adult.

DIF: A OBJ: 25-7

4. How does the larva stage differ from the pupa stage in a butterfly?

ANS: The larva stage moves about, feeds, has legs, antennae, and a segmented body. The pupa stage does not move about or feed, remains attached to a tree limb or burrows into the ground, and does not look like either adult or larval stage.

DIF: A OBJ: 25-8

5. How does the pupa stage differ from the adult stage in a butterfly?

ANS: The pupa is a quiet stage that undergoes major change and looks nothing like an adult insect. The adult flies, reproduces, and may feed.

DIF: A OBJ: 25-8

6. How is the larva stage different from and similar to the adult stage in a butterfly?

ANS: Differences: larva looks more wormlike than insectlike, lacks wings, cannot reproduce. Similarities: eyes, legs, and antennae present, feeds, moves about, parts of adult body (abdomen) and all of larva are segmented.

DIF: A OBJ: 25-8

TRUE/FALSE

1. Chromosomes are found in the nucleus of a cell.

   ANS: T   DIF: B   OBJ: 26-1

2. A human cell with 46 chromosomes is a sex cell.

   ANS: F   DIF: A   OBJ: 26-1

3. A gene is a section of a chromosome.

   ANS: T   DIF: B   OBJ: 26-3

4. A heterozygous individual has a dominant and a recessive gene for a trait.

   ANS: T   DIF: B   OBJ: 26-2

5. A mother with Dd genes can make only D eggs.

   ANS: F   DIF: A   OBJ: 26-3

6. A father with Dd genes can make D or d sperm.

   ANS: T   DIF: A   OBJ: 26-3

7. Mendel reported results of genetic crosses.

   ANS: T   DIF: B   OBJ: 26-6

8. Genes are passed from parents to offspring in the joining of the body cells.

   ANS: F   DIF: B   OBJ: 26-3

9. A living thing that shows a dominant trait may be pure dominant or pure recessive for the trait.

   ANS: F   DIF: A   OBJ: 26-2

MULTIPLE CHOICE

1. When Mendel crossed tall plants with tall plants, he sometimes got short plants. This can be explained by saying what about the parents?
   a. One was pure dominant.
   b. Both were pure recessive.
   c. One was heterozygous.
   d. Both were heterozygous.

   ANS: D   DIF: A   OBJ: 26-5

PROBLEM

1. Arrange the following steps of a normal birth in correct order from 1 to 6 by numbering each statement.
   a. _____ The uterus contracts.
   b. _____ The fetus is born.
   c. _____ The amniotic sac breaks.
   d. _____ The head of fetus is in downward position.
   e. _____ The placenta is pushed out.
   f. _____ Contractions push fetus through vagina.

   ANS: 2, 5, 3, 1, 6, 4   DIF: A   OBJ: 25-3

2. Arrange the following steps of development of a human embryo in correct order from 1 to 5 by numbering each statement.
   a. _____ all body organs present
   b. _____ 500 millimeters long
   c. _____ arms and legs form
   d. _____ stomach and brain present
   e. _____ kicking begins

   ANS: 3, 5, 2, 1, 4   DIF: A   OBJ: 25-3

3. The following list gives the changes that occur to a fertilized egg as it moves through an oviduct. Arrange the steps in correct order from 1 to 6 by numbering each statement.
   a. _____ Two cells form by mitosis.
   b. _____ Egg is fertilized.
   c. _____ A hollow ball of cells forms.
   d. _____ A solid ball of cells forms.
   e. _____ Embryo attaches to uterus.
   f. _____ Two cells form four, eight, and then sixteen cells.

   ANS: 2, 1, 5, 4, 6, 3   DIF: A   OBJ: 25-1

2. Genes that do not show their traits even though they are present are _____.
   a. pure
   b. dominant
   c. recessive
   d. heterozygous

   ANS: C   DIF: B   OBJ: 26-2

3. Genetics is the study of _____.
   a. how traits are passed to offspring
   b. chromosomes
   c. cell parts
   d. cell parts and chromosomes

   ANS: A   DIF: B   OBJ: 26-3

4. Mendel noticed that short plants mated to short plants always produced _____.
   a. short plants
   b. tall plants
   c. both tall and short plants
   d. mostly short plants

   ANS: A   DIF: B   OBJ: 26-6

5. Observed results of genetic traits _____.
   a. can be predicted
   b. are those that can be seen
   c. are always the same as expected results
   d. are always dominant traits

   ANS: B   DIF: A   OBJ: 26-5

6. Genes are found on which parts of a cell?
   a. ribosomes
   b. proteins
   c. chromosomes
   d. centrioles

   ANS: C   DIF: B   OBJ: 26-3

7. Genes that prevent other genes from showing traits are _____.
   a. pure
   b. dominant
   c. recessive
   d. heterozygous

   ANS: B   DIF: B   OBJ: 26-2

8. When both parents have attached earlobes, you could expect the children to be _____.
   a. 1/4 with free earlobes
   b. 2/4 with free earlobes
   c. 3/4 with free earlobes
   d. none with free earlobes

   ANS: D   DIF: A   OBJ: 26-3

9. Each sex cell has how many chromosomes of each kind?
   a. two
   b. three
   c. one
   d. four

   ANS: C   DIF: B   OBJ: 26-1

10. Which cell part is the smallest?
   a. cell membrane
   b. nucleus
   c. chromosome
   d. gene

   ANS: D   DIF: A   OBJ: 26-3

11. Each body cell has how many genes for each trait?
   a. none
   b. one
   c. two
   d. three

   ANS: C   DIF: B   OBJ: 26-1

12. Expected results _____.
   a. can be predicted
   b. can be observed
   c. cannot be predicted
   d. are always visible

   ANS: A   DIF: B   OBJ: 26-5

13. Each body cell has how many chromosomes of each kind?
   a. one
   b. two
   c. three
   d. four

   ANS: B   DIF: B   OBJ: 26-1

14. Dominant genes are always written as a ____.
   a. small letter
   b. large letter
   c. trait
   d. Punnett square
   ANS: B   DIF: B   OBJ: 26-2

15. Recessive genes are always written as a ____.
   a. combination
   b. trait
   c. large letter
   d. small letter
   ANS: D   DIF: B   OBJ: 26-2

16. A Punnett square shows which genes will combine when ____ join.
   a. egg
   b. sperm
   c. both a and b
   d. neither a nor b
   ANS: C   DIF: B   OBJ: 26-4

17. Each small box of a Punnett square represents genes in a(n) ____.
   a. egg cell
   b. sperm cell
   c. new organism
   d. parent cell
   ANS: C   DIF: B   OBJ: 26-4

18. Letters across the top of a Punnett square represent ____ of one parent.
   a. sex cells
   b. traits
   c. genes for one trait
   d. genes for all traits
   ANS: C   DIF: B   OBJ: 26-4

19. Letters along the side of a Punnett square are ____ when you complete it.
   a. brought down
   b. brought across
   c. crossed off
   d. doubled
   ANS: B   DIF: B   OBJ: 26-4

20. Results from a Punnett square are always ____.
   a. expected results
   b. observed results
   c. wrong
   d. changing
   ANS: A   DIF: B   OBJ: 26-5

21. The more results you observe, the closer the ____ results will be to the expected.
   a. predicted
   b. corrected
   c. observed
   d. expected
   ANS: C   DIF: B   OBJ: 26-5

22. Two black mice have produced 24 black and 8 white offspring in several litters. Black hair B is dominant to white hair b. What can you say about the genes of the parents?
   a. They are pure black.
   b. Both are heterozygous.
   c. One is pure; the other is heterozygous.
   d. You cannot make a conclusion.
   ANS: B   DIF: B   OBJ: 26-5

23. After mating several times, a white mouse and a black mouse have produced 42 black and 45 white offspring. Black hair B is dominant to white hair b. What can you say about the parents?
   a. Both are pure dominant.
   b. Both are heterozygous.
   c. One is pure dominant; the other is heterozygous.
   d. Both are pure recessive.
   ANS: B   DIF: A   OBJ: 26-5

24. A mouse with genes BB would have ____ hair. Black hair B is dominant to white hair b.
   a. black
   b. white
   c. mixed black and white
   d. cannot be determined
   ANS: A   DIF: A   OBJ: 26-2

25. A mouse with genes Bb would have ____ hair. Black hair B is dominant to white hair b.
   a. black
   b. white
   c. mixed black and white
   d. cannot be determined
   ANS: A   DIF: A   OBJ: 26-2

26. A mouse with genes bb would have _____ hair. Black hair B is dominant to white hair b.
a. black
b. white
c. mixed black and white
d. cannot be determined

ANS: B   DIF: A   OBJ: 26-2

MATCHING

Work out the genetic crosses of peas in Figure 26-1. Then choose the letter of the diagram that best matches each statement below. T = tall pea plant, t = short pea plant

T = tall pea plant   t = short pea plant

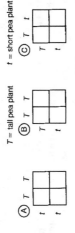

Figure 26-1

1. Which cross is between a pure dominant parent and a pure recessive parent?
2. Which cross is between two heterozygous parents?
3. Which cross will produce all tall pea plants with some being pure dominant?
4. Which cross will produce two short pea plants?
5. Which cross is between a pure dominant parent and a heterozygous parent?
6. Which cross is between a pure recessive parent and a heterozygous parent?

1. ANS: A   DIF: A   OBJ: 26-4
2. ANS: C   DIF: A   OBJ: 26-4
3. ANS: B   DIF: A   OBJ: 26-5
4. ANS: D   DIF: A   OBJ: 26-5
5. ANS: B   DIF: A   OBJ: 26-4
6. ANS: D   DIF: A   OBJ: 26-4

Choose the word or phrase from the following list that best matches each statement below.
a. pure dominant
b. heterozygous
c. pure recessive
d. cannot be determined

7. Suppose a black mouse and a white mouse are mated several times. They produce all black offspring. Black hair is dominant to white hair. The black parent is _____.
8. What is the gene makeup of a white mouse parent if it produces all black offspring when mated with a black mouse? Black hair is dominant.
9. What is the gene makeup of black offspring resulting from the mating of a pure recessive white parent and a pure recessive black parent?
10. The term used to describe a bb combination of genes is _____.
11. The term used to describe a Bb combination of genes is _____.
12. The term used to describe a BB combination of genes is _____.

7. ANS: A   DIF: A   OBJ: 26-5
8. ANS: C   DIF: A   OBJ: 26-5
9. ANS: B   DIF: A   OBJ: 26-5
10. ANS: C   DIF: A   OBJ: 26-2
11. ANS: B   DIF: A   OBJ: 26-2
12. ANS: A   DIF: A   OBJ: 26-2

PROBLEM

1. An animal has a total of 14 chromosomes in its body cells. A specific chromosome, which is called Z, has 300 different genes located on it. Use these numbers to answer the following questions: 14, 7, 300, 600, 150. a.) number of chromosomes found in the sperm cells of this animal b.) number of chromosomes found in skin cells of this animal c.) number of genes on chromosomes pair Z in a body cell d.) number of genes on chromosomes Z in an egg cell

ANS: a. 7, b. 14, c. 600, d. 300   DIF: A   OBJ: 26-1

2. A pure dominant tall pea plant is mated with a pure short pea plant. Use the results observed by Mendel to answer the following questions. a.) How many offspring out of four will be pure tall? b.) How many offspring out of four will be short? c.) How many out of four will be pure dominant? d.) How many out of four offspring will be pure recessive? e.) How many out of eight offspring are expected to be pure short? g.) How many out of eight offspring are expected to be pure tall? h.) How many out of eight offspring are expected to be heterozygous?

ANS: a. 4, b. 0, c. 0, d. 0, e. 4, f. 0, g. 0, h. 8

DIF: A   OBJ: 26-6

3. A heterozygous tall pea plant is mated with a pure short pea plant. Use the results observed by Mendel to answer the following questions. a.) How many offspring out of four will be tall? b.) How many offspring out of four will be short? c.) How many out of four will be pure dominant? d.) How many out of four offspring will be pure recessive? e.) How many out of four offspring will be heterozygous? f.) How many out of eight offspring are expected to be pure short? g.) How many out of eight offspring are expected to be pure tall? h.) How many out of eight offspring are expected to be heterozygous?

ANS: a. 2, b. 2, c. 0, d. 2, e. 2, f. 4, g. 0, h. 4

DIF: A   OBJ: 26-6

6. Use Figure 26-2 to match the following choices with the questions below: free earlobes, attached earlobes, pure dominant, pure recessive, heterozygous. a.) What will child 1 look like for earlobe shape? b.) What will child 2 look like for earlobe shape? c.) What will child 3 look like for earlobe shape? d.) What will child 4 look like for earlobe shape? e.) What gene combination will child 1 have? f.) What gene combination will child 2 have? g.) What gene combination will child 3 have? h.) What gene combination will child 4 have?

ANS: a. free earlobes, b. free earlobes, c. free earlobes, d. attached earlobes, e. pure dominant, f. heterozygous, g. heterozygous, h. pure recessive

DIF: A   OBJ: 26-3

4. A heterozygous tall pea plant is mated with a heterozygous tall pea plant. Use the results observed by Mendel to answer the following questions. a.) How many offspring out of four will be tall? b.) How many offspring out of four will be short? c.) How many offspring out of four will be pure dominant? d.) How many out of four offspring will be pure recessive? e.) How many out of four offspring will be heterozygous? f.) How many out of eight offspring are expected to be pure tall? g.) How many out of eight offspring are expected to be pure short? g.) How many out of eight offspring are expected to be heterozygous?

ANS: a. 3, b. 1, c. 1, d. 1, e. 2, f. 2, g. 2, h. 4

DIF: A   OBJ: 26-6

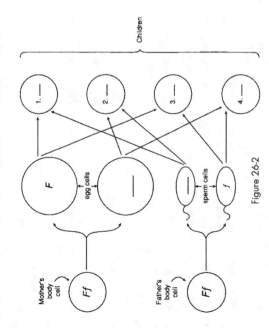

Figure 26-2

5. The gene for free earlobes is shown in Figure 26-2 as F. The gene for attached earlobes is shown as f. Use the following choices to answer the questions below: F, f, FF, ff, Ff. a.) What is the missing gene for the second egg cell? b.) What is the missing gene for the first sperm cell? c.) What are the genes for child 1? d.) What are the genes for child 2? e.) What are the genes for child 3? f.) What are the genes for child 4?

ANS: a. f, b. F, c. FF, d. Ff, e. Ff, f. ff   DIF: A   OBJ: 26-3

CHAPTER 27—HUMAN GENETICS

TRUE/FALSE

1. It is possible for a female to have red-green color blindness.

   ANS: T   DIF: A   OBJ: 27-5

2. PKU is a genetic disorder that harms brain cells.

   ANS: T   DIF: B   OBJ: 27-7

3. Down syndrome is caused by an extra autosome.

   ANS: T   DIF: B   OBJ: 27-7

4. Dyslexia is caused by a dominant gene on an autosome.

   ANS: T   DIF: B   OBJ: 27-6

5. Autosomes are chromosomes that determine sex.

   ANS: F   DIF: B   OBJ: 27-3

6. A mistake in chromosome number can occur during meiosis.

   ANS: T   DIF: A   OBJ: 27-6

7. Each living organism has the same number of chromosomes.

   ANS: F   DIF: A   OBJ: 27-1

8. Each human egg has 46 chromosomes and the sperm has no chromosomes.

   ANS: F   DIF: B   OBJ: 27-1

9. Amniocentesis is used to test the cells of the skin of an unborn baby.

   ANS: F   DIF: B   OBJ: 27-2

10. Amniotic fluid contains skin cells that have rubbed off a fetus.

    ANS: T   DIF: B   OBJ: 27-2

11. Amniocentesis allows a doctor to tell if a child has the correct number of chromosomes even before it is born.

    ANS: T   DIF: B   OBJ: 27-2

12. Removing cells from the placenta will tell a doctor if the mother has the correct number of chromosomes.

    ANS: F   DIF: B   OBJ: 27-2

13. All human male sperm cells have an X chromosome.

    ANS: F   DIF: B   OBJ: 27-3

14. The sex of a child is determined by the mother.

    ANS: F   DIF: B   OBJ: 27-3

15. According to a Punnett square, the chance of a child being born male in a family of four is 3 to 1.

    ANS: F   DIF: B   OBJ: 27-3

16. According to a Punnett square, the chance of a child being born female in a family of four is 1 to 1.

    ANS: T   DIF: B   OBJ: 27-3

17. A person with the genes RR will have all sickled red blood cells.

    ANS: F   DIF: B   OBJ: 27-4

18. All red blood cells will be round in a person with RR' genes.

    ANS: F   DIF: B   OBJ: 27-4

19. A person with RR' genes may not be as active as a person with all round red blood cells.

    ANS: T   DIF: B   OBJ: 27-4

20. A person with sickle-cell anemia may have serious health problems.

    ANS: T   DIF: B   OBJ: 27-4

21. The gene for color vision is found on the sex chromosome.

    ANS: T   DIF: B   OBJ: 27-5

22. A female with genes Cc for color vision would be color blind.

    ANS: F   DIF: B   OBJ: 27-5

23. A male with gene C for color vision would be able to see colors.

    ANS: T   DIF: B   OBJ: 27-5

24. A male with the gene c for color vision would be able to see colors.

ANS: F   DIF: B   OBJ: 27-5

25. Males have only one gene for color vision.

ANS: T   DIF: B   OBJ: 27-5

26. Females have only one gene for color vision.

ANS: F   DIF: B   OBJ: 27-5

27. A child born with the wrong chromosome number will always die.

ANS: F   DIF: B   OBJ: 27-6

28. A male child with a missing X sex chromosome will die before birth.

ANS: T   DIF: B   OBJ: 27-6

29. A female child born with only one X chromosome will die before birth.

ANS: F   DIF: B   OBJ: 27-6

30. Down syndrome results from having too few autosomes.

ANS: F   DIF: B   OBJ: 27-6

31. Males born with sex chromosomes XXY cannot make sperm cells.

ANS: T   DIF: B   OBJ: 27-6

32. A genetic counselor can tell parents how their child got a genetic disorder.

ANS: T   DIF: B   OBJ: 27-7

33. A genetic counselor cannot tell parents the chances that future children will have of receiving a genetic disorder.

ANS: F   DIF: B   OBJ: 27-7

34. Both parents are Ff for cystic fibrosis. All children will have the disorder.

ANS: F   DIF: B   OBJ: 27-7

35. Genetic counselors know which traits are dominant and recessive.

ANS: T   DIF: B   OBJ: 27-7

MULTIPLE CHOICE

1. A trait that is inherited on sex chromosomes is _____.
   a. eye color
   b. dyslexia
   c. color vision
   d. hair color

ANS: C   DIF: B   OBJ: 27-5

2. A human male has sex chromosomes _____.
   a. XX
   b. X only
   c. XY
   d. Y only

ANS: C   DIF: B   OBJ: 27-3

3. There are _____ main blood types.
   a. 2
   b. 3
   c. 4
   d. 5

ANS: C   DIF: B   OBJ: 27-4

4. There are _____ genes that determine blood type.
   a. 2
   b. 3
   c. 4
   d. 5

ANS: B   DIF: B   OBJ: 27-4

5. A trait that shows lack of dominance is _____.
   a. dyslexia
   b. PKU
   c. hemophilia
   d. sickle-cell anemia

ANS: D   DIF: B   OBJ: 27-4

6. A male who has normal blood clotting would be shown as _____.
   a. HH
   b. hY
   c. HY
   d. hh

ANS: C   DIF: A   OBJ: 27-6

7. A person with type O blood can give genes ____.
   a. AB
   b. AO
   c. BO
   d. OO

   ANS: D   DIF: B   OBJ: 27-4

8. In cows, red hair shows incomplete dominance over white hair. A cow heterozygous for the trait of hair color would have ____ hair.
   a. red
   b. white
   c. black
   d. mixed red and white

   ANS: D   DIF: A   OBJ: 27-4

9. Genes for color vision are on which chromosomes?
   a. X only
   b. Y only
   c. X and Y
   d. autosomes

   ANS: A   DIF: B   OBJ: 27-5

10. A person with blood type A has the following genes:
    a. AO
    b. BO
    c. AB
    d. OO

    ANS: A   DIF: B   OBJ: 27-4

11. Sex cells in a female have the following chromosomes:
    a. X
    b. XX
    c. Y
    d. X or Y

    ANS: A   DIF: B   OBJ: 27-3

12. Which is true about the Y chromosome when compared to the X chromosome?
    a. It is longer than the X.
    b. It is smaller than the X.
    c. It has more parts than the X.
    d. It has the same parts as the X.

    ANS: B   DIF: B   OBJ: 27-3

13. A human liver cell would have how many pairs of chromosomes present?
    a. 46
    b. none
    c. 23
    d. 2

    ANS: C   DIF: B   OBJ: 27-1

14. A human sperm cell would have how many chromosomes present?
    a. 46
    b. 23
    c. 92
    d. none

    ANS: B   DIF: B   OBJ: 27-1

15. A human sperm would have how many pairs of chromosomes present?
    a. 23
    b. 46
    c. 2
    d. none

    ANS: D   DIF: B   OBJ: 27-1

Use the following information to answer the questions below. In Family A, the father has hemophilia and the mother is heterozygous for hemophilia.

16. The correct gene(s) for the father are ____.
    a. HH
    b. hh
    c. HY
    d. hY

    ANS: D   DIF: A   OBJ: 27-7

17. The correct gene(s) for the mother are ____.
    a. Hh
    b. HH
    c. hh
    d. HY

    ANS: A   DIF: A   OBJ: 27-7

18. Out of four children, the expected number of girls with hemophilia is ____.
    a. none
    b. one
    c. two
    d. four

    ANS: B   DIF: A   OBJ: 27-7

19. Out of four children, the expected number of boys with hemophilia is _____.
   a. none
   b. one
   c. two
   d. four
   ANS: B   DIF: A   OBJ: 27-7

20. Hemophilia is a disease in which blood _____.
   a. does not clot properly
   b. does not reproduce
   c. moves too rapidly through veins
   d. cannot be typed
   ANS: A   DIF: B   OBJ: 27-7

21. The correct genes for a female with normal clotting are _____.
   a. HH only
   b. Hh only
   c. HH or Hh
   d. hh
   ANS: C   DIF: A   OBJ: 27-7

22. The correct genes for a male with normal clotting are _____.
   a. HY
   b. hY
   c. HY and hY
   d. hh
   ANS: A   DIF: A   OBJ: 27-7

Use the following information to answer the questions below. In Family B, a heterozygous father and a pure recessive mother for the trait of freckles have four children. Freckling is a dominant trait.

23. The correct genes for the father are _____.
   a. FF
   b. Ff
   c. ff
   d. FY
   ANS: B   DIF: A   OBJ: 27-5

24. The correct genes for the mother are _____.
   a. FF
   b. Ff
   c. ff
   d. FY
   ANS: C   DIF: A   OBJ: 27-5

25. A daughter is born and has no freckles. The correct genes for this daughter are _____.
   a. FF
   b. Ff
   c. ff
   d. fY
   ANS: C   DIF: A   OBJ: 27-5

26. Her brother is born with freckles. The correct genes for him are _____.
   a. FF
   b. Ff
   c. ff
   d. FY
   ANS: B   DIF: A   OBJ: 27-5

27. How many children in this family can be expected to have freckles?
   a. none
   b. one
   c. two
   d. four
   ANS: C   DIF: A   OBJ: 27-5

SHORT ANSWER

1. Choose the correctly worked Punnett square in Figure 27-1. (A) (B) (C)

(a)
	D	d
D	DD	Dd
D	DD	Dd

(b)
	D	d
d	dd	dd
d	Dd	dd

(c)
	d	d
d	Dd	dd
d	Dd	dd

Figure 27-1

ANS: A   DIF: A   OBJ: 27-5

2. Choose the correctly worked Punnett square in Figure 27-2. (A) (B) (C)

(a)
	X	Y
x	XX	XY
x	XX	XY

(b)
	X	Y
x	XX	XY
x	XX	XX

(c)
	X	Y
x	XX	XX
x	XY	XX

Figure 27-2

ANS: A   DIF: A   OBJ: 27-5

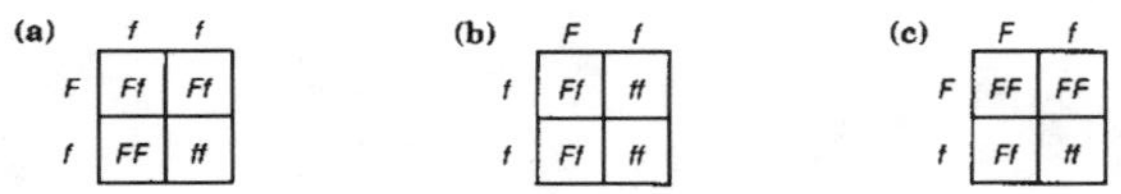

Page 27-9

(a)

(b)

(c)

Figure 27-3

3. Choose the correctly worked Punnett square in Figure 27-3. (A) (B) (C)

ANS: B   DIF: A   OBJ: 27-5

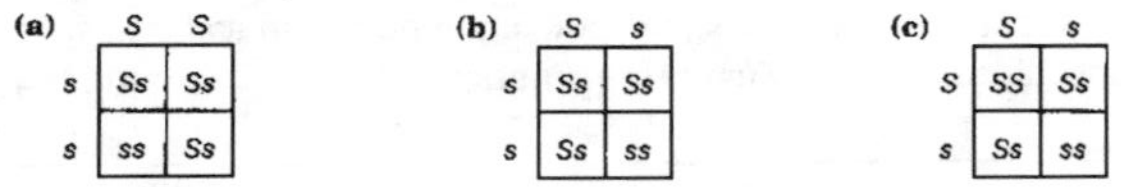

(a)

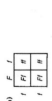

(b)

(c)

Figure 27-4

4. Choose the correctly worked Punnett square in Figure 27-4. (A) (B) (C)

ANS: C   DIF: A   OBJ: 27-5

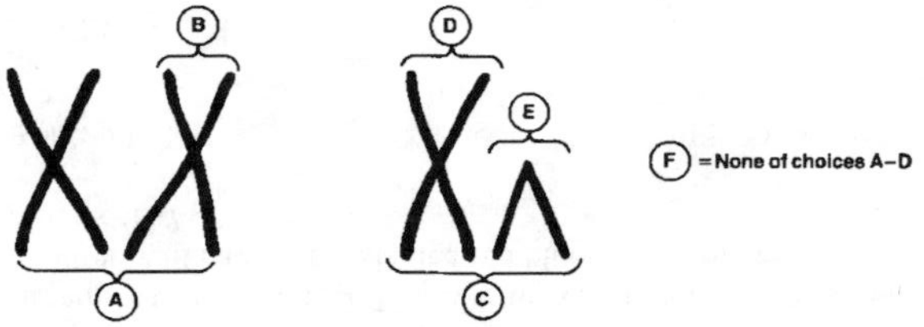

F = None of choices A–D

Figure 27-5

5. Choose the letter of Figure 27-5 that shows each of the following chromosomes: a.) sex chromosomes present in a female's body cells; b.) autosomes; c.) sex chromosomes present in a male's body cells; d.) sex chromosome present in an egg cell; e.) sex chromosome present in a sperm cell.

ANS: a. A; b. F; c. C; d. B; e. D or E   DIF: A   OBJ: 27-3

6. Explain how the wrong chromosome number may end up in a sex cell.

ANS: An error during meiosis occurs. Sister chromatids do not pull apart, causing the wrong number to end up in a sex cell.

DIF: A   OBJ: 27-6

Page 27-10

7. Explain what dyslexia and hemophilia are, and where the genes causing these problems are located.

ANS: Dyslexia is a genetic disorder that results in seeing words or letters backwards. The gene is on an autosome. Hemophilia is a genetic disorder in which a person's blood does not clot. The gene is located on the X sex chromosome.

DIF: A   OBJ: 27-6

8. What are two ways that a doctor can study the cells of a child before it is born?

ANS: One method removes cells from the amniotic fluid of a pregnant mother, while the other method removes a sample of the placenta.

DIF: A   OBJ: 27-2

Blood Types

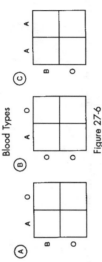

Figure 27-6

9. In family A in Figure 27-6, how many children will have blood type A, how many children will have blood type B, how many children will have blood type AB, and how many children will have blood type O?

ANS: 1, 1, 1, 1   DIF: A   OBJ: 27-4

10. In family B in Figure 27-6, how many children will have blood type A, how many children will have blood type B, how many children will have blood type AB, and how many children will have blood type O?

ANS: 2, 0, 0, 2   DIF: A   OBJ: 27-4

11. In family C in Figure 27-6, how many children will have blood type A, how many children will have blood type B, how many children will have blood type AB, and how many children will have blood type O?

ANS: 2, 0, 2, 0   DIF: A   OBJ: 27-4

CHAPTER 28—DNA–LIFE'S CODE

TRUE/FALSE

1. DNA is found in the cytoplasm.

   ANS: F   DIF: B   OBJ: 28-1

2. The chemical that controls traits is RNA.

   ANS: F   DIF: B   OBJ: 28-2

3. DNA is copied exactly when new chromosomes form during mitosis.

   ANS: T   DIF: B   OBJ: 28-3

4. Mutations can cause harmful traits to appear.

   ANS: T   DIF: A   OBJ: 28-4

5. A fraternal twin is a clone.

   ANS: F   DIF: A   OBJ: 28-5

6. Mutations may be caused by certain chemicals and radiation.

   ANS: T   DIF: B   OBJ: 28-4

7. Harmless living bacteria injected into a mouse should kill the mouse.

   ANS: F   DIF: B   OBJ: 28-2

8. Harmful dead pneumonia bacteria injected into a mouse should NOT kill it.

   ANS: T   DIF: B   OBJ: 28-2

9. Dead pneumonia bacteria and living harmless bacteria when injected together into a mouse caused a mouse to die.

   ANS: T   DIF: B   OBJ: 28-2

10. Harmless living bacteria can change into harmful living bacteria if they pick up the DNA from harmless living bacteria.

    ANS: F   DIF: B   OBJ: 28-2

11. Ribosomes are located in the nucleus of a cell.

    ANS: F   DIF: B   OBJ: 28-3

28-1

Solve the Punnett squares in Figure 27-7 for sickle-cell anemia and then answer the following questions.

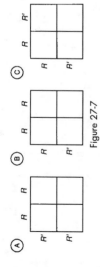

Figure 27-7

12. In family A in Figure 27-7, how many children will have all normal red blood cells, how many children will have some sickled red blood cells, and how many children will have all sickled red blood cells?

    ANS: 0, 4, 0   DIF: A   OBJ: 27-4

13. In family B in Figure 27-7, how many children will have all normal red blood cells, how many children will have some sickled red blood cells, and how many children will have all sickled red blood cells?

    ANS: 2, 2, 0   DIF: A   OBJ: 27-4

14. In family C in Figure 27-7, how many children will have all normal red blood cells, how many children will have some sickled red blood cells, and how many children will have all sickled red blood cells?

    ANS: 1, 2, 1   DIF: A   OBJ: 27-4

PROBLEM

Table 27-1	
Living Thing	**Body Chromosome Number**
Pea	14
Corn	20
Cat	38
Rabbit	44

1. Examine Table 27-1. Determine how many pairs of chromosomes would be found in the body cells of a pea plant and in the body cells of a cat. How many chromosomes would be found in sperm cells of a corn plant and in egg cells of a rabbit?

   ANS: pea plant - 7 pairs, cat - 19 pairs; corn sperm - 10 chromosomes, rabbit egg - 22 chromosomes

   DIF: A   OBJ: 27-1

27-11

12. Your traits are determined by the kinds of protein you have.

ANS: T   DIF: B   OBJ: 28-3

13. A code of acids controls the different kinds of protein you make.

ANS: F   DIF: B   OBJ: 28-3

MULTIPLE CHOICE

1. The shape of a DNA molecule is _____.
   a. straight
   b. circular
   c. flat
   d. spiral

ANS: D   DIF: B   OBJ: 28-1

2. DNA makes up parts of _____.
   a. proteins
   b. chromosomes
   c. sugars

ANS: B   DIF: B   OBJ: 28-1

3. The DNA message depends on the order of the _____.
   a. nitrogen bases
   b. acids
   c. sugars
   d. genes

ANS: A   DIF: A   OBJ: 28-2

4. Besides the nitrogen bases, DNA contains sugar and _____.
   a. acid
   b. protein
   c. RNA
   d. fat

ANS: A   DIF: B   OBJ: 28-1

5. DNA forms the code for the making of _____.
   a. proteins
   b. genes
   c. fats
   d. chromosomes

ANS: A   DIF: A   OBJ: 28-3

6. _____ are cell parts where proteins are made.
   a. Mitochondria
   b. Ribosomes
   c. Nuclei
   d. Chromosomes

ANS: B   DIF: B   OBJ: 28-3

7. If a change is made when DNA copies itself, a _____ results.
   a. clone
   b. death
   c. mutation
   d. base

ANS: C   DIF: B   OBJ: 28-4

8. A short section of DNA that codes for a trait is a _____.
   a. protein
   b. sugar
   c. chromosome
   d. gene

ANS: D   DIF: B   OBJ: 28-2

9. The messages of the genes of chromosomes are carried to ribosomes by _____.
   a. DNA
   b. protein
   c. RNA
   d. acid

ANS: C   DIF: B   OBJ: 28-3

10. The DNA is identical twins is _____.
    a. different
    b. the same
    c. opposite

ANS: B   DIF: B   OBJ: 28-5

11. An animal that has been cloned in the laboratory is the _____.
    a. cow
    b. pig
    c. frog
    d. bear

ANS: C   DIF: B   OBJ: 28-5

12. A section of DNA with bases ATTCGC will line up with bases _____.
    a. TAAGGC
    b. ATTCGC
    c. TAAGCG
    d. TAAGCC

    ANS: C   DIF: A   OBJ: 28-3

13. When twins have the same DNA, they are _____.
    a. fraternal
    b. clones
    c. identical
    d. b and c

    ANS: D   DIF: A   OBJ: 28-5

14. Recombinant DNA is used in making _____.
    a. insulin
    b. bacteria
    c. diabetes
    d. wires

    ANS: A   DIF: B   OBJ: 28-6

15. Mutations appear in children only if they occur in the parents' _____.
    a. body cells
    b. sex cells
    c. RNA
    d. ribosomes

    ANS: B   DIF: B   OBJ: 28-4

16. Which of the following may cause mutations?
    a. ultraviolet light
    b. x-rays
    c. cloning
    d. both a and b

    ANS: D   DIF: B   OBJ: 28-4

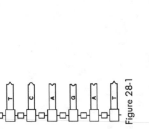

Figure 28-1

17. Figure 28-1 represents a portion of a(n) _____ molecule.
    a. RNA
    b. DNA
    c. acid
    d. protein

    ANS: A   DIF: A   OBJ: 28-1

18. The lettered parts of Figure 28-1 represent _____.
    a. nitrogen bases
    b. acids
    c. sugars
    d. proteins

    ANS: B   DIF: A   OBJ: 28-1

19. The large squares in Figure 28-1 represent _____.
    a. bases
    b. acids
    c. sugars
    d. proteins

    ANS: A   DIF: A   OBJ: 28-1

20. The correct order of lettered parts in Figure 28-1 in the missing half of this molecule from top to bottom, is _____.
    a. TAGACT
    b. AGTCTA
    c. TCAGAT
    d. GACTCG

    ANS: C   DIF: A   OBJ: 28-1

21. The sides of the DNA ladder in Figure 28-1 are made up of _____.
    a. nitrogen bases
    b. acids and sugars
    c. sugars only
    d. proteins

    ANS: B   DIF: A   OBJ: 28-1

14. ANS: D   DIF: B   OBJ: 28-3
15. ANS: B   DIF: B   OBJ: 28-4
16. ANS: F   DIF: B   OBJ: 28-5
17. ANS: A   DIF: B   OBJ: 28-5
18. ANS: G   DIF: B   OBJ: 28-5
19. ANS: E   DIF: B   OBJ: 28-6

SHORT ANSWER

1. How were scientists able to prove that DNA is the chemical that controls traits?

   ANS: Harmless bacteria picked up a cell part from harmful pneumonia bacteria. The cell part, DNA, caused the harmless bacteria to change into harmful bacteria. No other cell part was shown to cause the change.

   DIF: A   OBJ: 28-2

2. A person has skin cells that have undergone a mutation from too much exposure to the sun. Explain why this mutation will not show in a person's children.

   ANS: Skin cells are body cells. Mutations can't be passed to offspring through body cells.

   DIF: A   OBJ: 28-4

3. Where must a mutation occur, if it is to show in a person's children?

   ANS: The mutation must occur in sex cells. Mutations can be passed to offspring only through the sex cells.

   DIF: A   OBJ: 28-4

4. Name and describe three ways that humans have benefited from gene splicing.

   ANS: 1. Gene splicing is used to make insulin for diabetics. 2. This technique is used to make growth hormone for humans who do not produce enough growth hormones. 3. Gene splicing has been used to make certain plants resistant to chemical sprays that ordinarily would kill them.

   DIF: A   OBJ: 28-6

MATCHING

Choose the word or phrase from the following list that best matches each example of how genetics is used.

a. breeding
b. cloning
c. splicing genes

1. involving mitosis only, not meiosis
2. produces more plants of exactly the same kind
3. mating two varieties of hog to produce leaner bacon
4. combining DNA molecules in a laboratory
5. planting a cutting from a decorative houseplant
6. crossing two types of corn to get disease-resistant corn
7. involves formation of sex cells
8. changing bacteria so they will make human proteins
9. producing new planaria from cut pieces
10. mating two varieties of cattle to produce more milk
11. may cure diseases in the future
12. crossing two varieties of cotton plants to get rid of a disease
13. used in making the hormone insulin

1. ANS: B   DIF: A   OBJ: 28-5
2. ANS: B   DIF: A   OBJ: 28-5
3. ANS: A   DIF: A   OBJ: 28-5
4. ANS: C   DIF: A   OBJ: 28-6
5. ANS: B   DIF: A   OBJ: 28-5
6. ANS: A   DIF: A   OBJ: 28-5
7. ANS: A   DIF: A   OBJ: 28-5
8. ANS: C   DIF: A   OBJ: 28-6
9. ANS: B   DIF: A   OBJ: 28-5
10. ANS: A   DIF: A   OBJ: 28-5
11. ANS: C   DIF: A   OBJ: 28-6
12. ANS: A   DIF: A   OBJ: 28-5
13. ANS: C   DIF: A   OBJ: 28-6

Choose the word or phrase from the following list that best matches each statement below.

a. clone
b. mutation
c. gene
d. RNA
e. recombinant
f. breeding
g. identical twins

14. a chemical that acts as a messenger for DNA
15. a change in the DNA code
16. mating two living things
17. an exact copy of a living thing
18. formed from the same fertilized egg
19. the type of DNA that results from gene splicing

PROBLEM

1. The following steps describe how a cell changes DNA messages to protein. Arrange the steps in correct order from 1 to 6 by numbering each statement.
   a. _____ RNA directs the formation of protein according to the translated DNA code.
   b. _____ Chromosomes within the cell nucleus contain a DNA code.
   c. _____ RNA is also present in the nucleus.
   d. _____ RNA acts as a messenger and moves out of the nucleus.
   e. _____ RNA arrives at the ribosomes.
   f. _____ RNA makes a copy of the DNA code in the nucleus.

   ANS: 6, 1, 2, 4, 5, 3   DIF: A   OBJ: 28-3

2. Figure 28-2 shows the events that occur during the formation of recombinant DNA, but NOT IN THEIR CORRECT ORDER. Write the correct letter of the event being described. a.) chromosome of a bacterium b.) bacterial chromosome being opened c.) human section of DNA with genes for making insulin d.) human DNA spliced into bacterial DNA e.) bacterial cell now able to make human insulin f.) cell that now contains recombinant DNA g.) cell with no recombinant DNA

   ANS: a-E, b-C, c-D, d-F, e-B, f-B, g-A

   DIF: A   OBJ: 28-6

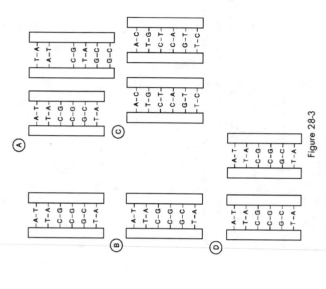

Figure 28-2

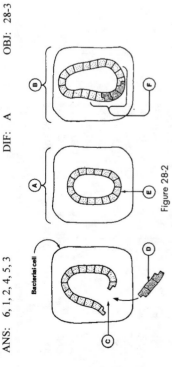

Figure 28-3

3. The unlabeled diagram of Figure 28-3 shows a section of DNA before it has copied itself. Figures 28-3 A-D show the same section of DNA after copying. Explain what is incorrect about diagrams A, B, and C. Explain why diagram D is correct.

   ANS: Diagram A shows incorrect matches between bases and has certain bases out of order on the right-hand DNA molecule. Diagram B shows that only one DNA molecule has formed, not the correct number of two. Diagram C shows incorrect matching of bases. Diagram D shows two DNA molecules that are identical to each other and to the original DNA.

   DIF: A   OBJ: 28-3

CHAPTER 29—EVOLUTION

TRUE/FALSE

1. Hawks eat more dark lizards if they are on dark soil.

   ANS: F   DIF: A   OBJ: 29-1

2. When individuals of different species mate, they produce infertile offspring.

   ANS: T   DIF: A   OBJ: 29-2

3. The organisms that are alive today are best suited to their surroundings.

   ANS: T   DIF: A   OBJ: 29-4

4. Natural selection is a change in the hereditary traits of a species over a period of time.

   ANS: F   DIF: B   OBJ: 29-2

5. Darwin's theory of evolution stated that organisms could develop traits they needed for survival.

   ANS: F   DIF: A   OBJ: 29-4

6. A change in climate may bring about the development of a new species.

   ANS: T   DIF: A   OBJ: 29-2

7. One group of Homo sapiens became extinct. The other group evolved into modern humans.

   ANS: T   DIF: B   OBJ: 29-3

8. Comparing embryos of different animals provides evidence for evolution.

   ANS: T   DIF: B   OBJ: 29-5

9. New-world monkeys have grasping tails.

   ANS: T   DIF: B   OBJ: 29-3

10. Some fossils are found in sedimentary rocks.

    ANS: T   DIF: B   OBJ: 29-5

11. All finches on the Galapagos Islands are the same species.

    ANS: F   DIF: B   OBJ: 29-2

12. Macaws may be of different species when they cannot breed and form fertile offspring.

    ANS: T   DIF: B   OBJ: 29-2

13. New world monkeys include baboons.

    ANS: F   DIF: B   OBJ: 29-3

14. Old world monkeys can grasp with their tails.

    ANS: F   DIF: B   OBJ: 29-3

15. All monkeys and humans belong to the Primate order.

    ANS: T   DIF: B   OBJ: 29-3

16. Primates have eyes that face forward and thumbs that grasp.

    ANS: T   DIF: B   OBJ: 29-3

17. Many chordate embryos look very much alike because their parents shared a common habitat.

    ANS: F   DIF: B   OBJ: 29-5

18. The first life forms were made of cells. Later life forms are not.

    ANS: F   DIF: B   OBJ: 29-5

19. Vestigial structures are body parts that no longer have a job.

    ANS: T   DIF: B   OBJ: 29-5

20. Vestigial structures are evidence of common ancestry.

    ANS: T   DIF: B   OBJ: 29-5

21. Your appendix is an example of a fossil.

    ANS: F   DIF: B   OBJ: 29-5

MULTIPLE CHOICE

1. The structure of a bird's toes is an example of _____.
   a. selection
   b. adaptation
   c. survival
   d. development

   ANS: B   DIF: B   OBJ: 29-1

2. The most important advantage an adaptation gives a living thing is to help it to survive in order that it may ___.
   a. kill
   b. reproduce
   c. eat
   d. grow

   ANS: B   DIF: A   OBJ: 29-1

3. Albino (white-haired) deer that are born in forest surroundings will probably ___.
   a. survive better
   b. reproduce
   c. be eaten
   d. adapt

   ANS: C   DIF: A   OBJ: 29-1

4. A trait that makes an individual different from others in its species is ___.
   a. a variation
   b. competition
   c. an adaptation
   d. selection

   ANS: A   DIF: A   OBJ: 29-4

5. A mutation is helpful depending on whether it makes the living thing ___.
   a. larger
   b. smaller
   c. better adapted
   d. another color

   ANS: C   DIF: A   OBJ: 29-2

6. The theory of evolution by natural selection was developed by ___.
   a. Pasteur
   b. Mendel
   c. Darwin
   d. Hooke

   ANS: C   DIF: B   OBJ: 29-4

7. Many scientists believe that, over time, the horse changed from a small animal to the large one we know today. These scientists would say that the horse ___.
   a. evolved
   b. cloned
   c. fossilized
   d. did not adapt

   ANS: A   DIF: A   OBJ: 29-4

8. Rabbits are rivals for food and shelter. This is an example of ___.
   a. selection
   b. mutation
   c. competition
   d. evolution

   ANS: C   DIF: A   OBJ: 29-4

9. Animals that are most fit for their surroundings usually ___.
   a. are killed
   b. survive
   c. do not reproduce
   d. kill other animals

   ANS: B   DIF: A   OBJ: 29-4

10. A mutation is a change in the ___ of an organism.
    a. color
    b. DNA code
    c. environment
    d. birthrate

    ANS: B   DIF: B   OBJ: 29-2

11. If animals of a species become separated in different environments, the animals in each environment may develop into different ___.
    a. mutations
    b. fossils
    c. species
    d. clones

    ANS: B   DIF: B   OBJ: 29-2

12. One kind of evidence that life existed in the past is a ___.
    a. mutation
    b. fossil
    c. variation
    d. selection

    ANS: C   DIF: A   OBJ: 29-5

13. Living things that are well suited to their surroundings will usually ___.
    a. feed
    b. survive
    c. die off
    d. improve their appearance

    ANS: B   DIF: B   OBJ: 29-2

14. An owl that feeds on certain mice is doing the choosing of who will survive. This is an example of _____
a. natural selection
b. adaptations
c. mutations
d. passing on

ANS: A   DIF: B   OBJ: 29-2

15. Offspring that are fertile can form _____.
a. adaptations
b. environments
c. egg and sperm
d. mutations

ANS: C   DIF: B   OBJ: 29-2

16. Onions, garlic, and leek are all _____.
a. the same species
b. different species
c. mutations
d. adaptations

ANS: B   DIF: B   OBJ: 29-2

MATCHING

Examine the diagram in Figure 29-1 of rock layers with fossils as they might be found. Choose the letter of the layer that best answers each question.

Figure 29-1

1. Which layer has the simplest life forms?
2. Which layer has more life forms still alive today?
3. Which layer is the oldest layer?
4. Which layer has the most complex life forms?
5. Which layer formed last?

1. ANS: D   DIF: A   OBJ: 29-5
2. ANS: A   DIF: A   OBJ: 29-5
3. ANS: D   DIF: A   OBJ: 29-5

4. ANS: A   DIF: A   OBJ: 29-5
5. ANS: A   DIF: A   OBJ: 29-5

Choose one of the four points of Darwin's theory of evolution from the following list that best matches each statement below.
a. Living things overproduce.
b. There is variation among offspring.
c. There is a struggle to survive.
d. Individuals that have desirable traits are more fit.

6. An oyster produces millions of eggs.
7. Wheat seeds sprout and grow into either tall, thin plants or short, thick plants.
8. Foxes use the same food and dens.
9. A pine tree produces more than 100 000 seeds each year.
10. Low-growing plants are able to live on windy seashores.
11. Young plants die when taller plants keep sunlight from them.
12. You are different from your sisters and brothers.
13. Some bacteria cannot be killed with antibiotics.

6. ANS: A   DIF: A   OBJ: 29-4
7. ANS: B   DIF: A   OBJ: 29-4
8. ANS: C   DIF: A   OBJ: 29-4
9. ANS: A   DIF: A   OBJ: 29-4
10. ANS: D   DIF: A   OBJ: 29-4
11. ANS: C   DIF: A   OBJ: 29-4
12. ANS: B   DIF: A   OBJ: 29-4
13. ANS: D   DIF: A   OBJ: 29-4

Choose the word or phrase from the following list that best matches each statement below.
a. adaptation
b. competition
c. natural selection

14. Two robins will struggle over a worm.
15. The long beak of a hummingbird is used to sip nectar.
16. The mud-colored frog will survive and reproduce in a muddy pond.
17. The hollow bones of a bird help it fly.
18. Oak seedlings are rivals for sunlight.
19. The hard, cone-shaped beak of the cardinal is used for eating seeds.
20. The white rabbit will not survive in a forest environment.
21. The flippers of a dolphin are used in swimming.

14. ANS: B   DIF: A   OBJ: 29-4
15. ANS: A   DIF: A   OBJ: 29-1
16. ANS: C   DIF: A   OBJ: 29-4
17. ANS: A   DIF: A   OBJ: 29-1
18. ANS: B   DIF: A   OBJ: 29-4
19. ANS: A   DIF: A   OBJ: 29-1
20. ANS: C   DIF: A   OBJ: 29-4

21. ANS: A   DIF: A   OBJ: 29-1

Choose the type of monkey from the following list that best matches each statement below.

a. new world monkeys
b. old world monkeys
c. both old and new world monkeys

22. belong to the Mammal class
23. are members of the Primate order
24. have no tail or cannot grasp with their tail
25. include howler and spider monkeys
26. have a tail and can grasp with it
27. have a well-developed cerebrum

22. ANS: C   DIF: A   OBJ: 29-3
23. ANS: C   DIF: A   OBJ: 29-3
24. ANS: B   DIF: A   OBJ: 29-3
25. ANS: A   DIF: A   OBJ: 29-3
26. ANS: A   DIF: A   OBJ: 29-3
27. ANS: C   DIF: A   OBJ: 29-3

Choose the phrase from the following list that best matches each statement below.

a. fossil evidence
b. embryo comparison
c. cell makeup
d. vestigial structure

28. pink lump in corner of our eye
29. animal trapped in ice
30. a developing fish looking like a developing bird
31. DNA makes up all chromosomes
32. nitrogen bases in DNA are all the same
33. a footprint of an animal in rock
34. usually an extinct form
35. seeing what life forms in the past looked like
36. a body part that no longer has a needed function

28. ANS: D   DIF: A   OBJ: 29-5
29. ANS: A   DIF: A   OBJ: 29-5
30. ANS: B   DIF: A   OBJ: 29-5
31. ANS: C   DIF: A   OBJ: 29-5
32. ANS: C   DIF: A   OBJ: 29-5
33. ANS: A   DIF: A   OBJ: 29-5
34. ANS: A   DIF: A   OBJ: 29-5
35. ANS: A   DIF: A   OBJ: 29-5
36. ANS: D   DIF: A   OBJ: 29-5

SHORT ANSWER

1. Describe the three events that may lead to the development of new species.

   ANS: A barrier forms and separates members of the species. Separated species live in different environments. Different traits appear as a result of natural selection acting on the different species. In time, they become different species.

   DIF: A   OBJ: 29-2

2. Describe the steps that are needed for a fossil to form in sedimentary rock.

   ANS: Sediments are present at the bottom of bodies of water. Plants and animals die and settle to the bottom of the bodies of water. The plant and animal remains become trapped in the sediments. Over millions of years, the sediments change into rock and the water level drops.

   DIF: A   OBJ: 29-2

CHAPTER 30—POPULATIONS AND COMMUNITIES

TRUE/FALSE

1. Plants compete for space.

   ANS: T   DIF: A   OBJ: 30-3

2. In a community, predators use prey as a food source.

   ANS: T   DIF: A   OBJ: 30-10

3. Food webs connected together are called food chains.

   ANS: F   DIF: B   OBJ: 30-7

4. Habitats are needed by animals and not plants.

   ANS: F   DIF: A   OBJ: 30-4

5. Parasitic relationships are harmful to a host.

   ANS: T   DIF: A   OBJ: 30-10

6. Termites and the protists that live inside them depend on each other.

   ANS: T   DIF: A   OBJ: 30-8

7. Consumers eat other organisms.

   ANS: T   DIF: B   OBJ: 30-5

8. Space is a limiting factor for humans.

   ANS: T   DIF: A   OBJ: 30-3

9. Predator populations decrease if the number of prey increases.

   ANS: F   DIF: A   OBJ: 30-10

10. An orchid is usually harmful to the trees upon which it lives.

    ANS: F   DIF: A   OBJ: 30-9

11. Trees can emigrate but cannot immigrate to an area.

    ANS: F   DIF: A   OBJ: 30-2

12. Energy is transferred through a food chain.

    ANS: T   DIF: B   OBJ: 30-6

13. The movement of animals out of an area is called immigration.

    ANS: F   DIF: B   OBJ: 30-2

14. Clumped populations, such as herds and flocks, provide protection.

    ANS: T   DIF: A   OBJ: 30-1

15. An energy pyramid shows energy loss in a food chain.

    ANS: T   DIF: A   OBJ: 30-6

16. A population can change in size when the number of deaths increases.

    ANS: T   DIF: A   OBJ: 30-2

17. A change in size of one population causes no change in size of other populations.

    ANS: F   DIF: B   OBJ: 30-1

18. Finding the size of a moving population such as mice is always easy.

    ANS: F   DIF: B   OBJ: 30-1

19. A radio transmitter attached to an animal allows one to find the animal's den and then to be able to count offspring.

    ANS: T   DIF: B   OBJ: 30-1

20. Communities are groups of living things in an area that do NOT depend on one another.

    ANS: F   DIF: B   OBJ: 30-4

21. Producers depend on other living things for food.

    ANS: F   DIF: B   OBJ: 30-5

22. A primary consumer eats only other animals.

    ANS: F   DIF: B   OBJ: 30-5

23. Secondary consumers eat only other animals.

    ANS: T   DIF: B   OBJ: 30-5

24. Food chains hold materials together in a community.

ANS: F   DIF: B   OBJ: 30-6

25. All the energy in a primary consumer becomes available to a secondary consumer.

ANS: F   DIF: B   OBJ: 30-6

26. Several different primary consumers can eat the same producer.

ANS: T   DIF: B   OBJ: 30-7

27. Different secondary consumers cannot eat the same primary consumer.

ANS: F   DIF: B   OBJ: 30-7

28. Arrows in a food web show the direction in which waste chemicals move.

ANS: F   DIF: B   OBJ: 30-7

29. Mutualism is found only in the animal kingdom.

ANS: F   DIF: B   OBJ: 30-8

30. Protists are supplied with food and shelter while inside a termite.

ANS: T   DIF: B   OBJ: 30-8

31. A bee visits a flower and gets nectar. In turn, the bee helps the flower with pollination. This is an example of mutualism.

ANS: T   DIF: B   OBJ: 30-8

32. Small birds feed off the insects buried in the skin of a rhinoceros. This is an example of commensalism.

ANS: F   DIF: B   OBJ: 30-9

33. Certain barnacles live on the jaws of whales. They get a free ride and food scraps. They do not bother the whale. This is an example of commensalism.

ANS: T   DIF: B   OBJ: 30-9

MULTIPLE CHOICE

1. Populations of rabbits usually are counted by marking with ____.
   a. paint
   b. transmitters
   c. ear tags
   d. leg bands

   ANS: C   DIF: B   OBJ: 30-1

2. A prey population usually decreases as a predator population ____
   a. increases
   b. decreases
   c. emigrates
   d. stays the same

   ANS: A   DIF: A   OBJ: 30-10

3. Food chains connected together are ____.
   a. competitors
   b. a food web
   c. populations
   d. communities

   ANS: B   DIF: B   OBJ: 30-7

4. A population might be increasing because the ____.
   a. birth rate is decreasing
   b. death rate is decreasing
   c. birth rate is increasing
   d. both b and c

   ANS: D   DIF: A   OBJ: 30-2

5. Which of the following is NOT a limiting factor?
   a. nutrients
   b. emigration
   c. water
   d. space

   ANS: B   DIF: A   OBJ: 30-3

6. Predator-prey relationships ____.
   a. are limiting factors
   b. affect both plants and animals
   c. affect only prey populations
   d. affect only predator populations

   ANS: A   DIF: A   OBJ: 30-10

7. The second link in a food chain could be a _____.
   a. dog
   b. cow
   c. tree
   d. fox

   ANS: B   DIF: A   OBJ: 30-6

8. Food is made in a community by _____.
   a. all consumers
   b. decomposers
   c. producers
   d. both a and b.

   ANS: C   DIF: B   OBJ: 30-5

9. The job of an organism in a community is _____.
   a. limiting factors
   b. a habitat
   c. a niche
   d. competition

   ANS: C   DIF: B   OBJ: 30-4

10. Which of the following causes an increase in population size?
    a. limiting factor
    b. emigration
    c. immigration
    d. competition

    ANS: C   DIF: A   OBJ: 30-2

11. Limiting factors keep populations from _____.
    a. starving
    b. emigrating
    c. increasing
    d. decreasing

    ANS: C   DIF: A   OBJ: 30-3

12. Which level of a food chain has the most food energy available?
    a. producers
    b. primary consumers
    c. decomposers
    d. secondary consumers

    ANS: A   DIF: B   OBJ: 30-6

13. Which of the following correctly shows a food chain pathway?
    a. primary consumer to producer to secondary consumer
    b. primary consumer to secondary consumer to producer
    c. producer to primary consumer to secondary consumer
    d. producer to secondary consumer to primary consumer

    ANS: C   DIF: B   OBJ: 30-6

14. Which level of a food chain has the greatest number of organisms in it?
    a. producer
    b. primary consumer
    c. secondary consumer
    d. top level

    ANS: A   DIF: B   OBJ: 30-6

15. A mouse eats grass and a hawk eats the mouse. A mouse eats corn and a snake eats the mouse. A hawk also eats the snake. This is an example of _____.
    a. a community
    b. a food web
    c. a habitat
    d. immigration

    ANS: B   DIF: B   OBJ: 30-7

16. Your skin is the _____ for millions of bacteria that live there.
    a. community
    b. habitat
    c. population
    d. primary consumer

    ANS: B   DIF: B   OBJ: 30-7

17. An example of a community would be a _____.
    a. pond or lake
    b. rock
    c. forest
    d. both a and c

    ANS: D   DIF: B   OBJ: 30-7

18. A predator is an animal that hunts and finally _____ another animal.
    a. mates with
    b. ignores
    c. kills and eats
    d. helps

    ANS: C   DIF: B   OBJ: 30-10

19. The food of a predator is its _____.
    a. nutrients
    b. habitat
    c. niche
    d. prey

ANS: D   DIF: B   OBJ: 30-10

20. All predators are _____.
    a. producers
    b. primary consumers
    c. secondary consumers
    d. food webs

ANS: C   DIF: B   OBJ: 30-10

21. Using mice and an owl in a food chain, an owl is a _____ and mice are _____.
    a. predator, prey
    b. prey, predators
    c. consumer, producers
    d. producer, consumers

ANS: A   DIF: B   OBJ: 30-10

MATCHING

Choose the word from the following list of relationships in a community that best matches each statement below.
    a. mutualism
    b. commensalism
    c. parasitism

1. One organism is harmed in a relationship.
2. Two organisms benefit from a relationship.
3. A tree with an orchid population is unaffected by the relationship.
4. Bacteria cause strep throat in humans.
5. A protist that lives in a termite intestine digests wood eaten by the termite.
6. A small insect called an aphid harms the stems and leaves of rosebushes.
7. Bacteria make vitamin B12 in the human intestine.
8. Two organisms live together, one benefits and the other is unharmed.

1. ANS: C   DIF: B   OBJ: 30-10
2. ANS: A   DIF: B   OBJ: 30-8
3. ANS: B   DIF: A   OBJ: 30-9
4. ANS: C   DIF: A   OBJ: 30-10
5. ANS: A   DIF: A   OBJ: 30-8
6. ANS: C   DIF: A   OBJ: 30-10
7. ANS: A   DIF: A   OBJ: 30-8
8. ANS: B   DIF: B   OBJ: 30-9

Choose the word from the following list of living parts of an ecosystem that best matches each statement below.
    a. producer
    b. primary consumer
    c. secondary consumer
    d. decomposer

9. a tree
10. a squirrel eating a nut
11. bacteria changing dead plants into nutrients
12. a toad eating a grasshopper
13. a hawk eating a lizard
14. bacteria on a rotting apple
15. a human eating some lettuce
16. a cricket eating grass
17. a tomato plant
18. a mosquito biting a human
19. a fungus growing in decaying matter
20. algae growing on a seashell
21. a bird eating seeds from a fruit
22. bracket fungi decaying a stump
23. a human eating fried chicken
24. a human eating corn and peas

9. ANS: A   DIF: A   OBJ: 30-5
10. ANS: B   DIF: A   OBJ: 30-5
11. ANS: D   DIF: A   OBJ: 30-5
12. ANS: C   DIF: A   OBJ: 30-5
13. ANS: C   DIF: A   OBJ: 30-5
14. ANS: D   DIF: A   OBJ: 30-5
15. ANS: B   DIF: A   OBJ: 30-5
16. ANS: B   DIF: A   OBJ: 30-5
17. ANS: A   DIF: A   OBJ: 30-5
18. ANS: C   DIF: A   OBJ: 30-5
19. ANS: D   DIF: A   OBJ: 30-5
20. ANS: A   DIF: A   OBJ: 30-5
21. ANS: B   DIF: A   OBJ: 30-5
22. ANS: D   DIF: A   OBJ: 30-5
23. ANS: C   DIF: A   OBJ: 30-5
24. ANS: B   DIF: A   OBJ: 30-5

Use the following changes to predict the effect that takes place in a population.
    a. increases
    b. decreases
    c. stays the same

25. animals are dying faster than offspring are being born
26. plants stop producing seeds for 10 years

27. animals produce fewer offspring
28. animals emigrate from an area
29. animals immigrate to a new area
30. birth rate and death rate remain the same
31. a farmer turns a wooded area where rabbits live into farm land
32. a natural reserve for migrating birds is established

25.	ANS:	B	DIF:	A	OBJ:	30-2
26.	ANS:	B	DIF:	A	OBJ:	30-2
27.	ANS:	B	DIF:	A	OBJ:	30-2
28.	ANS:	B	DIF:	A	OBJ:	30-2
29.	ANS:	A	DIF:	A	OBJ:	30-2
30.	ANS:	C	DIF:	A	OBJ:	30-2
31.	ANS:	B	DIF:	A	OBJ:	30-2
32.	ANS:	A	DIF:	A	OBJ:	30-2

Examine Figure 30-1. Choose the letter that best answers each question below.

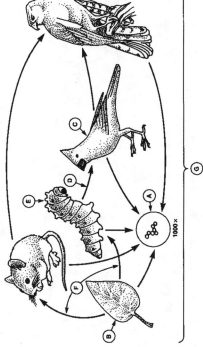

Figure 30-1

33. Which is a producer?
34. Which is a primary consumer?
35. Which shows the movement of energy from primary to secondary consumer?
36. Which shows that more than one consumer can feed off a producer?
37. Which is a secondary consumer?
38. Which are decomposers?
39. Which is a food web?
40. Which are bacteria?

33.	ANS:	B	DIF:	A	OBJ:	30-7
34.	ANS:	E	DIF:	A	OBJ:	30-7
35.	ANS:	D	DIF:	A	OBJ:	30-7
36.	ANS:	F	DIF:	A	OBJ:	30-7

37.	ANS:	C	DIF:	A	OBJ:	30-7
38.	ANS:	A	DIF:	A	OBJ:	30-7
39.	ANS:	G	DIF:	A	OBJ:	30-7
40.	ANS:	A	DIF:	A	OBJ:	30-7

SHORT ANSWER

Choice	Doer	Receiver
A		
B		
C		

Figure 30-2

1. Pick the choices in Figure 30-2 that would best show an example of mutualism. Explain why.

ANS: Choice C because the "doer" and "receiver" are both happy. The animal that "does" get food or shelter is helped, while the "receiver" also gets food or shelter and is also helped.

DIF: OBJ:

2. Pick the choice in Figure 30-2 that would best show an example of commensalism. Explain why.

ANS: Choice B because the "doer" is happy while the "receiver" is neither happy nor sad. The animal that "does" may get food or shelter and is helped, while the "receiver" is neither helped nor harmed.

DIF: OBJ:

3. Pick the choice in Figure 30-2 that would best show an example of parasitism. Explain why.

ANS: Choice A. The "doer" is happy while the "receiver" is unhappy. The animal that "does" gets food and is helped, while the "receiver" is used as food and is not helped.

DIF: OBJ:

4. How can a pack of wolves help each other by living together?

ANS: They may help one another to locate food or kill a large animal. A mate for breeding is close by.

DIF: A OBJ: 30-1

5. How can a flock of geese that lives together help each other?

   ANS: protection from predators, help in finding food, a mate for breeding is close by

   DIF: A   OBJ: 30-1

6. Give several limiting factors that could affect the human population.

   ANS: space, food, buildup of wastes, pollution of air

   DIF: A   OBJ: 30-3

7. Why can crowding among plants be a limiting factor?

   ANS: Root systems will have to share water and soil minerals, leaves may be shaded and cannot make food.

   DIF: A   OBJ: 30-3

8. Why do farmers remove weeds from their fields?

   ANS: Weeds compete with the farmer's crops for soil minerals and water.

   DIF: A   OBJ: 30-3

9. Describe the following for an earthworm and a cactus: a.) community where each may be found, b.) habitat for each, and c.) each one's niche.

   ANS: a.) earthworm-forest, cactus-desert; b.) earthworm-moist soil, cactus-sandy soil with little water; c.) earthworm-breaks up soil, cactus-makes food and releases oxygen into the air, holds soil in place

   DIF: A   OBJ: 30-4

10. Explain why the amount of available energy changes as one moves up a food chain.

    ANS: Energy is lost as heat at each level of a food chain. Thus, the amount of energy decreases from producer to secondary consumer.

    DIF: A   OBJ: 30-6

11. Explain why the number of organisms changes as one moves up a food chain.

    ANS: Less energy is available at each level so numbers decrease as one moves from producer to secondary consumer.

    DIF: A   OBJ: 30-6

12. Explain why a food chain must start with a producer.

    ANS: Producers are the only organisms in the food chain that can make food through photosynthesis.

    DIF: A   OBJ: 30-6

13. A friend borrows 5 sheets of your notebook paper. Explain what must be done to make this act an example of mutualism.

    ANS: Your friend either returns the paper or you borrow a pencil from your friend.

    DIF: A   OBJ: 30-8

14. A friend finds a $5 bill. Explain what must be done to make this act an example of commensalism.

    ANS: Your friend keeps the entire amount.

    DIF: A   OBJ: 30-9

15. Your friend borrows $5 from you. Explain what must be done to make this act an example of parasitism.

    ANS: Your friend never repays the money and/or continues to borrow until you run out of money.

    DIF: A   OBJ: 30-10

CHAPTER 31—ECOSYSTEMS AND BIOMES

TRUE/FALSE

1. Temperature and water are two nonliving factors that are NOT cycled.

   ANS: F   DIF: B   OBJ: 31-2

2. An ecosystem contains one specific community.

   ANS: F   DIF: B   OBJ: 31-1

3. Carbon dioxide is used by producers to make food.

   ANS: T   DIF: A   OBJ: 31-3

4. Nitrates are chemical compounds found in carbon dioxide.

   ANS: F   DIF: B   OBJ: 31-3

5. As a community goes through succession, no change occurs in the kinds of living things that make up the community.

   ANS: F   DIF: A   OBJ: 31-5

6. Oxygen is released by primary consumers during photosynthesis.

   ANS: F   DIF: A   OBJ: 31-3

7. All biomes have certain plants, animals, and climate.

   ANS: T   DIF: B   OBJ: 31-7

8. Pond communities can change to land communities over a period of time.

   ANS: T   DIF: B   OBJ: 31-5

9. The oxygen-carbon dioxide cycle does NOT take place in a water ecosystem.

   ANS: F   DIF: A   OBJ: 31-3

10. The nonliving parts of the nitrogen cycle are nitrogen and soil.

    ANS: T   DIF: B   OBJ: 31-3

11. Bushes grow after weeds in land communities.

    ANS: T   DIF: B   OBJ: 31-4

12. A desert can never be a climax community.

    ANS: F   DIF: A   OBJ: 31-4

13. The nitrogen cycle includes decomposers.

    ANS: T   DIF: B   OBJ: 31-3

14. As a land ecosystem goes through succession, no nutrients are added to the soil.

    ANS: F   DIF: A   OBJ: 31-4

15. A taiga is a biome.

    ANS: T   DIF: B   OBJ: 31-7

16. Some gases in the environment are used for photosynthesis.

    ANS: T   DIF: B   OBJ: 31-3

17. In dead organisms, the nitrates are changed into protein.

    ANS: F   DIF: B   OBJ: 31-3

18. It rains almost every day in the grasslands.

    ANS: F   DIF: A   OBJ: 31-6

19. Climate is the same in a biome every day of the year.

    ANS: F   DIF: B   OBJ: 31-6

MULTIPLE CHOICE

1. Plants get nitrogen mainly from ____.
   a. soil
   b. water
   c. air
   d. all parts of the environment

   ANS: A   DIF: A   OBJ: 31-3

2. Soil forms from ____.
   a. water
   b. nitrates
   c. decomposers
   d. broken down rocks

   ANS: D   DIF: B   OBJ: 31-3

3. In the water cycle, water is in the form of a _____ after it evaporates.
   a. gas
   b. solid
   c. liquid
   d. all three

   ANS: A   DIF: A   OBJ: 31-2

4. Living organisms use nitrogen to make _____.
   a. fat
   b. carbohydrates
   c. protein
   d. water

   ANS: C   DIF: B   OBJ: 31-3

5. When plants and animals die, the nitrogen in their bodies _____.
   a. enters the water cycle
   b. enters the oxygen cycle
   c. is returned to the soil
   d. is released into the air

   ANS: C   DIF: A   OBJ: 31-3

6. The main source of energy in an ecosystem is _____.
   a. an animal
   b. a plant
   c. the sun
   d. oxygen-carbon dioxide cycle

   ANS: C   DIF: B   OBJ: 31-1

7. When you study an ecosystem, you study how living things affect _____.
   a. other living things
   b. nonliving factors
   c. the environment
   d. a, b, and c

   ANS: D   DIF: A   OBJ: 31-1

8. Which gas is given off during respiration?
   a. oxygen
   b. nitrogen
   c. ozone
   d. carbon dioxide

   ANS: D   DIF: B   OBJ: 31-3

9. A forest ecosystem seems cool because _____.
   a. it is wetter
   b. it is drier
   c. there is no water cycle
   d. leaves block the sunlight

   ANS: D   DIF: A   OBJ: 31-6

10. What is the first type of animal that shows up after weeds start to grow in a community?
    a. primary consumer
    b. secondary consumer
    c. meat eater
    d. decomposer

    ANS: A   DIF: A   OBJ: 31-4

11. Water, air, temperature, and light are _____ parts of an ecosystem.
    a. living
    b. nonliving
    c. both living and nonliving
    d. consumer

    ANS: B   DIF: B   OBJ: 31-1

12. _____ is needed in photosynthesis.
    a. Nitrogen
    b. Oxygen
    c. Carbon dioxide
    d. Soil

    ANS: C   DIF: B   OBJ: 31-3

13. Living parts of an ecosystem include plants, animals, and _____.
    a. soil
    b. water
    c. nutrients
    d. decomposers

    ANS: D   DIF: B   OBJ: 31-1

14. An ecosystem study includes both _____ and _____ things in an area.
    a. green, nongreen
    b. living, nonliving
    c. living, producer
    d. producers, plant

    ANS: B   DIF: B   OBJ: 31-1

15. Water may evaporate into the air from _____.
    a. lakes
    b. animals
    c. plants
    d. all choices are correct

    ANS: D   DIF: B   OBJ: 31-2

16. The path that water takes through an ecosystem is a water _____.
    a. fall
    b. gas
    c. cycle
    d. plan

    ANS: C   DIF: B   OBJ: 31-2

17. Where may water be found?
    a. in plant cells
    b. underground
    c. both a and b
    d. neither a nor b

    ANS: C   DIF: B   OBJ: 31-2

18. Nutrients added to a community come from dead plants and animals as they _____.
    a. dry out
    b. decompose
    c. grow
    d. reproduce

    ANS: B   DIF: B   OBJ: 31-4

19. Succession is a series of changes in a community as it _____.
    a. ages
    b. increases in size
    c. decreases in size
    d. recycles

    ANS: A   DIF: B   OBJ: 31-4

20. A climax community is the _____ stage of succession.
    a. starting
    b. middle
    c. final
    d. poorest

    ANS: C   DIF: B   OBJ: 31-4

21. What kinds of green organisms are found in a new pond?
    a. tree and ferns
    b. algae
    c. moss and flowering plants
    d. pine trees

    ANS: B   DIF: B   OBJ: 31-5

22. What kinds of animals are found in a new pond?
    a. large fish
    b. frogs
    c. snails and small fish
    d. both a and b

    ANS: C   DIF: B   OBJ: 31-5

23. What kind of animals are found in an old pond?
    a. large fish
    b. frogs
    c. snails and small fish
    d. both a and b

    ANS: D   DIF: B   OBJ: 31-5

24. Rain or snow falling to Earth is _____.
    a. condensation
    b. evaporation
    c. precipitation
    d. transpiration

    ANS: C   DIF: B   OBJ: 31-6

25. Climate is determined by the amount of _____ taken over many years.
    a. water, rain, snow
    b. light, temperature, precipitation
    c. light, dark, twilight
    d. precipitation, evaporation, rain

    ANS: B   DIF: B   OBJ: 31-6

26. A biome usually covers _____.
    a. several counties
    b. several continents
    c. a city
    d. one community

    ANS: B   DIF: B   OBJ: 31-7

27. Each different kind of biome has _____ producers and consumers.
a. similar
b. different
c. too many
d. too few
ANS: B DIF: B OBJ: 31-7

28. The two types of water ecosystems are _____ and _____ water.
a. fresh, stream
b. lake, pond
c. salt, ocean
d. fresh, salt
ANS: D DIF: B OBJ: 31-7

29. The largest ecosystem on Earth is the _____.
a. desert
b. forest
c. ocean
d. coral reef
ANS: C DIF: B OBJ: 31-7

30. You would expect to see _____ if living near a temperate forest biome.
a. mink and moose
b. deer and bear
c. tree frogs and monkeys
d. musk oxen and caribou
ANS: B DIF: B OBJ: 31-7

31. A biome with a very cold climate would be a _____.
a. tropical rain forest
b. desert
c. tundra
d. grassland
ANS: C DIF: B OBJ: 31-7

MATCHING

Choose the phrase from the following list that best matches each statement below.
a. living part
b. nonliving part
c. both living and nonliving parts

1. what makes up an ecosystem
2. producers
3. algae and fungi
4. soil nutrients
5. hours of sunlight
6. amount of sunlight
7. amount of rainfall
8. consumers

1. ANS: C DIF: A OBJ: 31-1
2. ANS: A DIF: A OBJ: 31-1
3. ANS: A DIF: A OBJ: 31-1
4. ANS: B DIF: A OBJ: 31-1
5. ANS: B DIF: A OBJ: 31-1
6. ANS: B DIF: A OBJ: 31-1
7. ANS: B DIF: A OBJ: 31-1
8. ANS: A DIF: A OBJ: 31-1

Choose the biome from the following list that best matches each statement below.
a. tundra
b. taiga
c. temperate forest
d. tropical rain forest
e. grassland
f. desert

9. cacti and small bushes
10. hickory and maple trees
11. orchids and palm trees
12. spruce and firs
13. lichens and moss
14. antelope, gophers, and prairie dogs
15. lizards, snakes, and scorpions
16. moose, weasel, and mink
17. Temperatures stay at about 25 degrees Celsius all year long.
18. Temperatures range from -25 to 38 degrees Celsius.
19. over 200 centimeters of rainfall each year

9. ANS: F DIF: A OBJ: 31-7
10. ANS: C DIF: A OBJ: 31-7
11. ANS: D DIF: A OBJ: 31-7
12. ANS: B DIF: A OBJ: 31-7
13. ANS: A DIF: A OBJ: 31-7
14. ANS: E DIF: A OBJ: 31-7
15. ANS: F DIF: A OBJ: 31-7
16. ANS: B DIF: A OBJ: 31-7
17. ANS: D DIF: A OBJ: 31-7
18. ANS: C DIF: A OBJ: 31-7
19. ANS: D DIF: A OBJ: 31-7

Examine Figure 31-1. Choose the letter of the diagram that best matches each statement below.

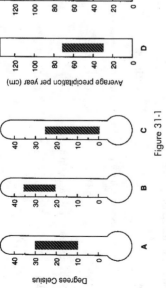

Figure 31-1

20. temperature range of 0 to 25 degrees Celsius
21. highest temperature shown
22. lowest temperature shown
23. temperature range of 10 to 30 degrees Celsius
24. precipitation each year of between 40 and 60 centimeters
25. highest amount of precipitation each year

20. ANS: C   DIF: A   OBJ: 31-6
21. ANS: B   DIF: A   OBJ: 31-6
22. ANS: C   DIF: A   OBJ: 31-6
23. ANS: A   DIF: A   OBJ: 31-6
24. ANS: E   DIF: A   OBJ: 31-6
25. ANS: D   DIF: A   OBJ: 31-6

PROBLEM

1. The following statements describe the stages of land succession. Arrange the steps in correct order from 1 to 5 by numbering each statement.
   a. _____ A forest is present.
   b. _____ Bare soil is present.
   c. _____ First primary consumer appears.
   d. _____ Bushes and small trees appear.
   e. _____ Weeds begin to appear.

ANS: 5, 1, 3, 4, 2   DIF: A   OBJ: 31-4

2. The following statements describe the stages of pond succession. Arrange the steps in correct order from 1 to 5 by numbering each statement.
   a. _____ The pond is so shallow that no fish can live in the pond.
   b. _____ Dead organisms begin piling up on the pond bottom.
   c. _____ The pond becomes more shallow and many kinds of organisms live in the pond.
   d. _____ The pond is very deep and few organisms live in the pond.
   e. _____ Dry land is present where the pond once was.

ANS: 4, 2, 3, 1, 5   DIF: A   OBJ: 31-5

3. The following statements describe the steps in the nitrogen cycle. Arrange the steps in correct order from 1 to 5 by numbering each statement.
   a. _____ Protein from dead organisms is changed into nitrates.
   b. _____ Plants take up nitrates.
   c. _____ Dead organisms are attacked by fungi and bacteria.
   d. _____ Animals eat plants and use nitrogen from plants to make protein.
   e. _____ Nitrates stay in the soil.

ANS: 2, 4, 1, 5, 3   DIF: A   OBJ: 31-3

4. The following statements describe the steps in the water cycle. Arrange the steps in correct order from 1 to 4 by numbering each statement.
   a. _____ Water on the ground is taken up by plants and animals.
   b. _____ Plants and animals lose water which evaporates into the air. Water also evaporates into the air from oceans, rivers, and lakes.
   c. _____ Water falls to Earth as rain.
   d. _____ Rain soaks into soil and then flows into oceans, rivers, and lakes as groundwater.

ANS: 2, 4, 1, 3   DIF: A   OBJ: 31-2

CHAPTER 32—SOLVING ECOLOGICAL PROBLEMS

TRUE/FALSE

1. You would expect to find more PCBs in fish-eating birds than in fish.

ANS: T   DIF: A   OBJ: 32-5

2. The ozone layer causes harmful radiation to reach Earth.

ANS: F   DIF: A   OBJ: 32-4

3. Both animals and plants may become endangered.

ANS: T   DIF: B   OBJ: 32-1

4. The greenhouse effect may cause temperatures on Earth to rise slowly.

ANS: T   DIF: A   OBJ: 32-4

5. Ladybird beetles are natural enemies of aphids.

ANS: T   DIF: B   OBJ: 32-7

6. Acid rain destroys forests and crops only.

ANS: F   DIF: A   OBJ: 32-4

7. Lead and oxygen are heavy metals.

ANS: F   DIF: B   OBJ: 32-5

8. Not all chemicals are biodegradable.

ANS: T   DIF: A   OBJ: 32-5

9. Some chemicals cause cancer.

ANS: T   DIF: A   OBJ: 32-5

10. Fertilizer moves through the food chain as a harmful substance.

ANS: F   DIF: A   OBJ: 32-2

11. Nutrients cause rapid aging in a lake.

ANS: T   DIF: A   OBJ: 32-2

12. Recycling aluminum cans does not help to conserve resources.

ANS: F   DIF: A   OBJ: 32-6

13. Turning off lights when not needed can help reduce pollution.

ANS: T   DIF: A   OBJ: 32-7

14. Particles in smoke can block out the sun.

ANS: T   DIF: A   OBJ: 32-4

15. Radon is a gas found in the ground that gives off radiation.

ANS: T   DIF: B   OBJ: 32-4

16. Fungi are being used to kill gypsy moths.

ANS: F   DIF: B   OBJ: 32-7

17. Rain forests are being destroyed or changed to farmland in parts of the world.

ANS: T   DIF: B   OBJ: 32-1

18. Buried toxic wastes can pollute nearby water supplies.

ANS: T   DIF: B   OBJ: 32-5

19. Rain is more acidic in the northwest United States than in the eastern states.

ANS: F   DIF: A   OBJ: 32-4

20. Acid rain forms in the air when water combines with sulfur dioxide.

ANS: T   DIF: A   OBJ: 32-4

21. Fossil fuels are the remains of organisms that lived millions of years ago.

ANS: T   DIF: B   OBJ: 32-3

22. Fossil fuels are renewable.

ANS: F   DIF: B   OBJ: 32-3

23. The supply of fossil fuels remains constant.

ANS: F   DIF: B   OBJ: 32-3

24. Fossil fuels are used mainly for anything that needs energy.

ANS: T   DIF: B   OBJ: 32-3

MULTIPLE CHOICE

1. Acid rain has a pH below _____.
   a. 4.5
   b. 5.5
   c. 7
   d. 10

   ANS: B   DIF: B   OBJ: 32-4

2. The reusing of resources is _____.
   a. trash collection
   b. recycling
   c. litter
   d. landfills

   ANS: B   DIF: B   OBJ: 32-7

3. Which of the following is NOT a natural resource?
   a. trees
   b. water
   c. air
   d. television

   ANS: D   DIF: A   OBJ: 32-1

4. The greenhouse effect is caused by large amounts of _____ in the air.
   a. oxygen
   b. carbon dioxide
   c. water
   d. ozone

   ANS: B   DIF: B   OBJ: 32-4

5. Which of the following is NOT a fossil fuel?
   a. oil
   b. coal
   c. wood
   d. natural gas

   ANS: C   DIF: B   OBJ: 32-3

6. Smog is a combination of _____.
   a. smoke and fog
   b. haze and water vapor
   c. smoke and carbon dioxide
   d. smoke and oxygen

   ANS: A   DIF: A   OBJ: 32-4

7. Many lakes in Minnesota and New York are dead because of _____.
   a. DDT
   b. too much rain
   c. acid rain
   d. carbon monoxide

   ANS: C   DIF: A   OBJ: 32-4

8. _____ quickly brings about soil erosion when bare soil dries out.
   a. Animals
   b. Plants
   c. Wind
   d. Protists

   ANS: C   DIF: B   OBJ: 32-2

9. When children eat old paint, they can become sick from the _____ in the paint.
   a. nitrogen
   b. lead
   c. iron
   d. oxygen

   ANS: B   DIF: B   OBJ: 32-5

10. Burning coal produces acid rain because coal contains _____.
    a. lead
    b. sulfur
    c. oxygen
    d. hydrogen

    ANS: B   DIF: A   OBJ: 32-4

11. A toxic waste produced in making paint and ink is _____.
    a. DDT
    b. mercury
    c. PCB
    d. carbon monoxide

    ANS: C   DIF: B   OBJ: 32-5

12. A gas in polluted air that can harm humans is ____.
   a. oxygen
   b. ozone
   c. sulfur dioxide
   d. mercury

   ANS: C   DIF: B   OBJ: 32-4

13. Materials that settle on the bottom of a pond are ____.
   a. pollutants
   b. sediments
   c. erosion
   d. nutrients

   ANS: B   DIF: B   OBJ: 32-2

14. ____ is the wearing away of soil by water or wind.
   a. Pollution
   b. Resources
   c. Erosion
   d. Extinction

   ANS: C   DIF: B   OBJ: 32-2

15. Plants reduce soil loss by having their ____ hold soil in place.
   a. stems
   b. resources
   c. nutrients
   d. roots

   ANS: D   DIF: B   OBJ: 32-2

16. Extra nutrients in soil come from nearby ____ and untreated ____.
   a. factories, sewage
   b. farms, sewage
   c. homes, plant parts
   d. factories, plastics

   ANS: B   DIF: B   OBJ: 32-2

17. Water is the most ____ resource on Earth and it is also ____.
   a. wasted, polluted
   b. wasted, expensive
   c. abundant, renewable
   d. abundant, inexpensive

   ANS: C   DIF: B   OBJ: 32-2

32-5

18. A natural predator helps to reduce the need for ____.
   a. pesticides
   b. bacteria
   c. power plants
   d. aphids

   ANS: A   DIF: B   OBJ: 32-7

19. Alternate energy forms for electricity may include use of ____ power.
   a. erosion
   b. chemical
   c. solar
   d. recyclable

   ANS: C   DIF: B   OBJ: 32-7

20. Gypsy moths are one cause of the death of ____.
   a. humans
   b. aphids
   c. ladybird beetles
   d. oak trees

   ANS: D   DIF: B   OBJ: 32-7

21. An endangered species ____ becomes extinct.
   a. always
   b. sometimes
   c. never

   ANS: B   DIF: B   OBJ: 32-1

22. Car engines produce ____ pollutant gases.
   a. harmful
   b. harmless
   c. explosive

   ANS: A   DIF: B   OBJ: 32-4

23. In a refuge, an animal is ____.
   a. killed
   b. protected
   c. endangered

   ANS: B   DIF: B   OBJ: 32-6

24. If snow has a pH of 4.5, it is ____.
   a. an acid
   b. neutral
   c. a base

   ANS: A   DIF: A   OBJ: 32-4

32-6

25. A threatened living thing is close to becoming _____.
a. extinct
b. endangered
c. replaced

ANS: B   DIF: B   OBJ: 32-1

26. Renewable resources _____ replaced.
a. can be
b. cannot be
c. are too expensive to be

ANS: A   DIF: B   OBJ: 32-1

27. Animals forced from where they live must find new _____.
a. mates
b. resources
c. habitats

ANS: C   DIF: B   OBJ: 32-1

28. Plants _____ move to new areas when their habitat is destroyed.
a. sometimes
b. can
c. cannot

ANS: C   DIF: B   OBJ: 32-1

29. Soil erosion is reduced when crops are planted _____ the slope of land.
a. across
b. up and down
c. diagonally on

ANS: A   DIF: A   OBJ: 32-6

30. Water can be reused if _____ are first removed.
a. tastes
b. wastes
c. minerals

ANS: B   DIF: A   OBJ: 32-6

31. The Endangered Species Act protects the _____ of any endangered species.
a. habitat
b. mates
c. toxic effect

ANS: A   DIF: A   OBJ: 32-6

32. The government as well as _____ must work together to conserve resources.
a. you
b. foreign countries
c. animals

ANS: A   DIF: A   OBJ: 32-6

MATCHING

Choose the type of pollution from the following list that best matches each statement below.

a. air pollution
b. land pollution
c. water pollution

1. smog
2. sulfur dioxide
3. burning coal to produce energy
4. may make fish harmful for humans to eat
5. heavy metals
6. soot
7. may irritate the eyes, nose, lungs, and throat
8. plastic waste
9. gasoline engines
10. PCB
11. mercury
12. dump site
13. pesticides
14. untreated sewage
15. fertilizer
16. coal dust

1. ANS: A   DIF: A   OBJ: 32-4
2. ANS: A   DIF: A   OBJ: 32-4
3. ANS: A   DIF: A   OBJ: 32-4
4. ANS: C   DIF: A   OBJ: 32-5
5. ANS: C   DIF: A   OBJ: 32-5
6. ANS: A   DIF: A   OBJ: 32-4
7. ANS: A   DIF: A   OBJ: 32-4
8. ANS: B   DIF: A   OBJ: 32-2
9. ANS: A   DIF: A   OBJ: 32-4
10. ANS: C   DIF: A   OBJ: 32-5
11. ANS: C   DIF: A   OBJ: 32-5
12. ANS: B   DIF: A   OBJ: 32-2
13. ANS: C   DIF: A   OBJ: 32-5
14. ANS: C   DIF: A   OBJ: 32-5
15. ANS: C   DIF: A   OBJ: 32-5
16. ANS: A   DIF: A   OBJ: 32-4

SHORT ANSWER

1. Why can't the supply of fossil fuels be increased?

   ANS: They take long periods of time to form under the ground.

   DIF: A   OBJ: 32-3

2. Why does our need for fossil fuels continue to rise?

   ANS: The human population continues to grow and more energy is needed by these people.

   DIF: A   OBJ: 32-3

3. What can be done to conserve our supply of fossil fuels?

   ANS: New energy sources must be found. Governments must pass laws that will reduce our use of these fuels. Humans must learn to get along with less energy use.

   DIF: A   OBJ: 32-3

4. Explain the meaning of the term biodegradable and give an example of a chemical that is not biodegradable.

   ANS: Something is biodegradable if it can be broken down by microbes into harmless chemicals that can be used by other living things. Pesticides such as DDT, some wastes such as heavy metals, and PCBs are not biodegradable.

   DIF: A   OBJ: 32-5

5. Why does the amount of a chemical that is not biodegradable increase in animals at every step of a food chain?

   ANS: Most living things cannot excrete chemicals that are not biodegradable. At every step up in the food chain, the amount of these chemicals increases.

   DIF: A   OBJ: 32-5

6. How can rain be made acid?

   ANS: Water in air will mix with pollutants such as sulfur dioxide to form acids.

   DIF: A   OBJ: 32-5

7. Why is acid rain more of a problem in eastern Canada and the eastern United States?

   ANS: Most of the countries' industry is in the east, and therefore most of the pollutants are released into the air in the eastern part of these countries. Winds also carry acid rain from west and central areas toward the east.

   DIF: A   OBJ: 32-5

8. Describe several things that you can do to conserve water.

   ANS: turning off the water when not directly needed during washing and brushing of teeth, reducing toilet flushing, taking shorter showers, reducing amount and frequency of lawn watering, reducing amount and frequency of water used in car washing

   DIF: A   OBJ: 32-6

9. What are two ways in which animals and plants are becoming threatened or endangered?

   ANS: illegal hunting, trapping, or selling; illegal removal of plants; destruction of habitats for farmland

   DIF: A   OBJ: 32-1

10. Explain each of the following conditions: threatened, endangered, extinct.

    ANS: threatened-a species is still not endangered but may be getting close to that category; endangered-numbers are further reduced so that the species is close to being extinct; extinct-no living members of a species are left

    DIF: A   OBJ: 32-1

11. Give three reasons why plants do not grow well in subsoil.

    ANS: Subsoil is packed down, nutrients are not available, and little oxygen is found.

    DIF: A   OBJ: 32-2

12. Explain how humans are making lakes age faster.

    ANS: Humans are allowing fertilizers and untreated sewage to enter lakes. These fertilizers and untreated sewage contain nutrients that speed up growth of lake plants and thus speed up the aging of the lakes.

    DIF: A   OBJ: 32-2

UNIT 1—KINDS OF LIFE

MULTIPLE CHOICE

1. The SI unit of length is the _____.
   a. meter
   b. liter
   c. gram
   d. newton

   ANS: A   DIF: A   OBJ: 1-5

2. Changes that occur during an experiment are compared with a _____.
   a. variable
   b. control
   c. hypothesis
   d. conclusion

   ANS: B   DIF: A   OBJ: 1-7

3. At the end of an experiment, a scientist makes a(n) _____.
   a. hypothesis
   b. observation
   c. problem
   d. conclusion

   ANS: D   DIF: A   OBJ: 1-7

4. A microscope that can magnify up to 500 000 times is the _____.
   a. light microscope
   b. electron microscope
   c. stereomicroscope
   d. three-dimensional microscope

   ANS: B   DIF: A   OBJ: 1-3

5. A liter is used to measure _____.
   a. length
   b. volume
   c. mass
   d. weight

   ANS: B   DIF: A   OBJ: 1-5

6. How much matter is in something is its _____.
   a. weight
   b. mass
   c. volume
   d. length

   ANS: B   DIF: A   OBJ: 1-4

7. A statement that can be tested is called a(n) _____.
   a. experiment
   b. observation
   c. variable
   d. hypothesis

   ANS: D   DIF: A   OBJ: 1-7

8. The use of discoveries in science to solve everyday problems is _____.
   a. research
   b. experimentation
   c. technology
   d. industry

   ANS: C   DIF: A   OBJ: 1-9

9. Today most scientists classify living things into _____.
   a. five kingdoms
   b. five phyla
   c. one kingdom
   d. one family

   ANS: A   DIF: A   OBJ: 3-5

10. The recorded measurements taken during an experiment are _____.
    a. conclusions
    b. data
    c. variables
    d. controls

    ANS: B   DIF: A   OBJ: 1-7

11. A group of similar cells carrying out a specific job is a(n) _____.
    a. organ
    b. tissue
    c. organ system
    d. organism

    ANS: B   DIF: A   OBJ: 2-8

12. Living things get energy from food in the process of _____.
    a. osmosis
    b. diffusion
    c. photosynthesis
    d. cellular respiration

    ANS: D   DIF: A   OBJ: 2-1

13. All living things are made of small units called _____.
    a. ribosomes
    b. cells
    c. vacuoles
    d. mitochondria

    ANS: B   DIF: A   OBJ: 2-3

14. Osmosis is the movement of _____ into and out of cells.
    a. chemicals
    b. oxygen
    c. water
    d. cytoplasm

    ANS: C   DIF: A   OBJ: 2-7

15. The movement of a substance from where there is a large amount to where there is a small amount is _____.
    a. diffusion
    b. osmosis
    c. respiration
    d. photosynthesis

    ANS: A   DIF: A   OBJ: 2-6

16. The cell part that controls cell activities is the _____.
    a. nucleolus
    b. nucleus
    c. cytoplasm
    d. cell membrane

    ANS: B   DIF: A   OBJ: 2-5

17. Cell parts with information that determine what traits a living thing will have are _____.
    a. vacuoles
    b. mitochondria
    c. chromosomes
    d. ribosomes

    ANS: C   DIF: A   OBJ: 2-5

18. Most of the cell's chemical reactions take place in the _____.
    a. nucleus
    b. vacuole
    c. cytoplasm
    d. centriole

    ANS: C   DIF: A   OBJ: 2-5

19. The part of a plant cell that gives support and shape is the _____.
    a. cell membrane
    b. chloroplast
    c. cytoplasm
    d. cell wall

    ANS: D   DIF: A   OBJ: 2-5

20. Cell parts that contain chlorophyll and trap energy from the sun are _____.
    a. mitochondria
    b. chloroplasts
    c. ribosomes
    d. vacuoles

    ANS: B   DIF: A   OBJ: 2-5

21. Body organs are made of many _____ working together.
    a. tissues
    b. organs
    c. systems
    d. organisms

    ANS: A   DIF: A   OBJ: 2-8

22. The word classify means to _____.
    a. group
    b. write
    c. count
    d. find things

    ANS: A   DIF: A   OBJ: 3-2

23. The first scientist to classify living things was _____.
    a. Hooke
    b. Brown
    c. Aristotle
    d. Linnaeus

    ANS: C   DIF: A   OBJ: 3-3

24. Of the following, Felis leo is most closely related to _____.
    a. Rana pipiens
    b. Felis domesticus
    c. Xenopus laevis
    d. Homo sapiens

    ANS: B   DIF: A   OBJ: 3-7

MULTIPLE CHOICE

1. Viruses consist of a protein coat around a _____ .
   a. cell
   b. nucleus
   c. chromosome-like part
   d. chloroplast

   ANS: C   DIF: A   OBJ: 4-1

2. The common cold is caused by _____ .
   a. bacteria
   b. blue-green bacteria
   c. viruses
   d. endospores

   ANS: C   DIF: A   OBJ: 4-3

3. Viruses reproduce only when they are _____ .
   a. very old
   b. on dead cells
   c. on plants
   d. in a living host

   ANS: D   DIF: A   OBJ: 4-2

4. Chemicals that kill bacteria on the skin are _____ .
   a. saprophytes
   b. disinfectants
   c. antiseptics
   d. vaccines

   ANS: C   DIF: A   OBJ: 4-4

5. Bacterial cells do not contain a _____ .
   a. cell membrane
   b. nucleus
   c. cell wall
   d. chromosome

   ANS: B   DIF: A   OBJ: 4-4

6. Bacteria that use dead organisms for food are _____ .
   a. saprophytes
   b. communicable
   c. parasites
   d. endospores

   ANS: A   DIF: A   OBJ: 4-4

25. Linnaeus based his classification system on _____ .
    a. specific traits
    b. size
    c. where organisms live
    d. number of cells

    ANS: A   DIF: A   OBJ: 3-4

26. The largest groups into which living things are classified are _____ .
    a. families
    b. species
    c. orders
    d. kingdoms

    ANS: D   DIF: A   OBJ: 3-5

27. To determine how to classify organisms, modern biologists may use _____ .
    a. structure and origin of body parts
    b. body chemistry
    c. common ancestors
    d. a, b, and c are all correct

    ANS: D   DIF: A   OBJ: 3-6

7. When human cells are first attacked by a virus, the cells may produce _____.
   a. a vaccine
   b. interferon
   c. an antibody
   d. an antibiotic
   ANS: B   DIF: A   OBJ: 4-3

8. To determine whether a disease is caused by a certain bacterium, scientists use _____.
   a. antiseptics
   b. antibiotics
   c. Koch's postulates
   d. vaccines
   ANS: C   DIF: A   OBJ: 4-5

9. One-celled monerans that contain chlorophyll and can make their own food are _____.
   a. viruses
   b. bacteria
   c. protists
   d. blue-green bacteria
   ANS: D   DIF: A   OBJ: 4-6

10. A mushroom is an example of a _____.
   a. sporangium fungus
   b. club fungus
   c. sac fungus
   d. lichen
   ANS: B   DIF: A   OBJ: 5-4

11. Which of the following is NOT a member of the protist kingdom?
   a. bacterium
   b. slime mold
   c. paramecium
   d. amoeba
   ANS: A   DIF: A   OBJ: 5-3

12. A living arrangement in which both living things benefit is _____.
   a. neighbors
   b. mutualism
   c. parasitism
   d. saprophytes
   ANS: B   DIF: A   OBJ: 5-5

13. A paramecium uses its _____ to move through water.
   a. flagella
   b. vacuole
   c. cilia
   d. false feet
   ANS: C   DIF: A   OBJ: 5-2

14. Seed plants are divided into two groups: _____.
   a. conifers and flowering plants
   b. mosses and liverworts
   c. algae and ferns
   d. ferns and mosses
   ANS: A   DIF: A   OBJ: 6-6

15. Plantlike organisms that live in fresh and salt water, in moist soil, and on tree bark are _____.
   a. mosses
   b. algae
   c. liverworts
   d. ferns
   ANS: B   DIF: A   OBJ: 5-2

16. Plants are grouped according to similar _____.
   a. sizes
   b. shapes
   c. cell parts
   d. traits
   ANS: D   DIF: A   OBJ: 6-6

17. Fir and pine trees are classified as _____.
   a. conifers
   b. flowering plants
   c. shrubs
   d. mosses
   ANS: A   DIF: A   OBJ: 6-6

18. The most complex worms are the _____.
   a. flatworms
   b. roundworms
   c. segmented worms
   d. hookworms
   ANS: C   DIF: A   OBJ: 7-5

19. The phylum with more animal types than any other is the _____.
    a. sponges
    b. stinging-cell animals
    c. jointed-leg animals
    d. chordates

    ANS: C   DIF: A   OBJ: 8-1

20. Hookworms are parasitic _____.
    a. segmented worms
    b. roundworms
    c. flatworms
    d. leeches

    ANS: B   DIF: A   OBJ: 7-5

21. The body of a sponge is made up of _____ layers of cells.
    a. two
    b. three
    c. four
    d. five

    ANS: A   DIF: A   OBJ: 7-3

22. The armlike parts that surround the mouth of a jellyfish are _____.
    a. stinging cells
    b. discs
    c. tentacles
    d. radulas

    ANS: C   DIF: A   OBJ: 7-4

23. The shell of a soft-bodied animal is made by the _____.
    a. radula
    b. foot
    c. tentacle
    d. mantle

    ANS: D   DIF: A   OBJ: 7-7

24. Tapeworms form _____ in the muscles of their hosts.
    a. eggs
    b. body sections
    c. cysts
    d. discs

    ANS: C   DIF: A   OBJ: 7-6

25. Sharks and rays are _____.
    a. jawless fish
    b. cartilage fish
    c. bony fish
    d. soft-bodied animals

    ANS: B   DIF: A   OBJ: 8-4

26. There are more kinds of _____ than all other animals combined.
    a. insects
    b. millipedes
    c. spiders
    d. scorpions

    ANS: A   DIF: A   OBJ: 8-2

UNIT 3—BODY SYSTEMS--MAINTAINING LIFE

MULTIPLE CHOICE

1. Energy present in nutrients is measured in _____.
   - a. Celsius
   - b. Calories
   - c. RDA
   - d. minerals

   ANS: B   DIF: A   OBJ: 9-5

2. A nutrient that is NOT stored in the body but supplies energy is _____.
   - a. fat
   - b. protein
   - c. water
   - d. carbohydrate

   ANS: D   DIF: A   OBJ: 9-2

3. Vitamins and minerals are needed by the body in _____.
   - a. large amounts
   - b. kilograms
   - c. small amounts

   ANS: C   DIF: A   OBJ: 9-1

4. A person receives 50 percent of the RDA for vitamin C. This means that _____.
   - a. no more of this vitamin is needed
   - b. too much vitamin C has been eaten
   - c. there is a 50 percent chance of illness
   - d. 50 percent more is needed for that day

   ANS: D   DIF: A   OBJ: 9-3

5. Taking in more Calories than one uses usually results in a person's _____.
   - a. losing weight
   - b. becoming ill
   - c. gaining weight
   - d. sleeping well

   ANS: C   DIF: A   OBJ: 9-4

6. Chemicals that aid in the digestion of food are _____.
   - a. fats
   - b. nutrients
   - c. enzymes
   - d. starches

   ANS: C   DIF: A   OBJ: 10-3

7. The main role of the liver and the gallbladder in digestion is to help _____.
   - a. protein digestion
   - b. absorption
   - c. make enzymes
   - d. fat digestion

   ANS: D   DIF: A   OBJ: 10-4

8. Which organ will food pass through after leaving the stomach?
   - a. esophagus
   - b. small intestine
   - c. liver
   - d. large intestine

   ANS: B   DIF: A   OBJ: 10-4

9. Villi are located in the _____.
   - a. small intestine
   - b. large intestine
   - c. epiglottis

   ANS: A   DIF: A   OBJ: 10-5

10. Which organ helps with the digestion of fat, protein, and carbohydrate?
    - a. salivary glands
    - b. pancreas
    - c. liver
    - d. large intestine

    ANS: B   DIF: A   OBJ: 10-4

11. Valves between the right atrium and the right ventricle are called the _____ valves.
    - a. semilunar
    - b. tricuspid
    - c. bicuspid
    - d. pulmonary

    ANS: B   DIF: A   OBJ: 11-3

12. The right side of the heart pumps blood only to the _____.
    - a. lungs
    - b. body
    - c. brain
    - d. liver

    ANS: A   DIF: A   OBJ: 11-5

13. The left side of the heart pumps blood that has much _____ and little _____.
   a. oxygen/carbon dioxide
   b. carbon dioxide/oxygen
   c. water/food
   d. food/vitamins

   ANS: A   DIF: A   OBJ: 11-5

14. A heart attack may occur when _____ are blocked.
   a. pulmonary arteries
   b. pulmonary veins
   c. capillaries
   d. coronary vessels

   ANS: D   DIF: A   OBJ: 11-10

15. What is delivered to all body cells by plasma?
   a. antigens
   b. carbon dioxide
   c. food
   d. oxygen

   ANS: C   DIF: A   OBJ: 12-1

16. The blood cells that deliver oxygen to body cells are _____.
   a. white blood cells
   b. red blood cells
   c. platelets
   d. cholesterol

   ANS: B   DIF: A   OBJ: 12-4

17. The number 8000 in a small drop of blood best describes the number of _____.
   a. platelets
   b. veins
   c. red blood cells
   d. white blood cells

   ANS: D   DIF: A   OBJ: 12-3

18. The red cell proteins in blood type A match the plasma proteins in blood type _____.
   a. A
   b. B and O
   c. B
   d. O

   ANS: B   DIF: A   OBJ: 12-6

19. Antibodies are made by the body's _____.
   a. urinary system
   b. digestive system
   c. immune system
   d. skin

   ANS: C   DIF: A   OBJ: 12-8

20. Alveoli are small sacs that make up the _____.
   a. liver
   b. small intestine
   c. diaphragm
   d. lungs

   ANS: D   DIF: A   OBJ: 13-4

21. The _____ prevents food from entering the trachea.
   a. bronchus
   b. nasal chamber
   c. diaphragm
   d. epiglottis

   ANS: D   DIF: A   OBJ: 13-4

22. As you breathe in, the diaphragm will be _____.
   a. relaxed
   b. contracted
   c. pushing up
   d. unable to work

   ANS: B   DIF: A   OBJ: 13-6

23. The small filtering unit of the kidney is the _____.
   a. neuron
   b. bladder
   c. nephron
   d. ureter

   ANS: C   DIF: A   OBJ: 13-11

24. Urine is a combination of _____.
   a. water and salt
   b. urea
   c. neither a nor b
   d. both a and b

   ANS: D   DIF: A   OBJ: 13-11

MULTIPLE CHOICE

1. A single nerve cell is called a _____.
   a. brain
   b. neuron
   c. spinal cord
   d. nephron

   ANS: B   DIF: A   OBJ: 15-3

2. Axon ends _____ messages while dendrite ends _____ messages.
   a. destroy/form
   b. receive/send
   c. send/receive
   d. block/form

   ANS: C   DIF: A   OBJ: 15-3

3. Blood pressure and heartbeat are controlled by your brain's _____.
   a. cerebrum
   b. cerebellum
   c. lobes
   d. medulla

   ANS: D   DIF: A   OBJ: 15-4

4. An action that you can control is said to be _____.
   a. very slow
   b. very fast
   c. a reflex
   d. voluntary

   ANS: D   DIF: A   OBJ: 15-4

5. A reflex may or may not use the _____.
   a. spinal cord
   b. skin's neurons
   c. brain
   d. body's muscles

   ANS: C   DIF: A   OBJ: 15-5

6. The endocrine glands make _____.
   a. hormones
   b. enzymes
   c. water
   d. impulses

   ANS: A   DIF: A   OBJ: 15-6

25. The muscle type that forms the stomach and blood vessels is _____.
   a. cardiac
   b. skeletal
   c. smooth
   d. voluntary

   ANS: C   DIF: A   OBJ: 14-4

26. When a muscle contracts, it _____.
   a. stretches
   b. lengthens
   c. shortens
   d. hurts

   ANS: C   DIF: A   OBJ: 14-5

27. The part of a bone that has many empty spaces is _____.
   a. marrow
   b. spongy bone
   c. joints
   d. cartilage

   ANS: B   DIF: A   OBJ: 14-2

7. Thyroxine is formed by the body's _____.
   a. pituitary gland
   b. thyroid gland
   c. adrenal gland
   d. pancreas

   ANS: B   DIF: A   OBJ: 15-7

8. Diabetes mellitus results when the pancreas cannot make enough _____.
   a. thyroxine
   b. insulin
   c. hormone
   d. glucose

   ANS: B   DIF: A   OBJ: 15-9

9. The human eye can detect _____ with cones.
   a. light
   b. color
   c. black and white
   d. dark

   ANS: B   DIF: A   OBJ: 16-3

10. The main job of the retina of your eye is to _____.
   a. detect light
   b. adjust for distance viewing
   c. protect
   d. focus

   ANS: A   DIF: A   OBJ: 16-3

11. The nerve carrying messages from eye to brain is the _____.
   a. auditory nerve
   b. optic nerve
   c. neuron nerve
   d. spinal cord

   ANS: B   DIF: A   OBJ: 16-3

12. Your three ear bones are part of the _____.
   a. outer ear
   b. middle ear
   c. inner ear
   d. cochlea

   ANS: B   DIF: A   OBJ: 16-5

13. The retina of your eye could best be compared to the _____ of your ear.
   a. cochlea
   b. eardrum
   c. oval window
   d. bones

   ANS: A   DIF: A   OBJ: 16-3

14. Taste buds detect _____.
   a. sounds
   b. molecules
   c. pressures
   d. colors

   ANS: B   DIF: A   OBJ: 16-4

15. Cocaine is dangerous because it can speed up and then stop _____.
   a. muscle action
   b. withdrawal
   c. heartbeat
   d. behavior

   ANS: C   DIF: A   OBJ: 18-9

16. The dermis and epidermis are parts of the _____.
   a. skin
   b. small intestine
   c. muscles
   d. cochlea

   ANS: A   DIF: A   OBJ: 16-4

17. A response in behavior is how an animal _____.
   a. detects a message
   b. reacts
   c. sleeps
   d. breathes

   ANS: B   DIF: A   OBJ: 17-1

18. A behavior that one is born with and does not have to be taught is _____.
   a. learned
   b. wrong
   c. innate
   d. a reward

   ANS: C   DIF: A   OBJ: 17-2

19. The chirping of crickets and the croaking of frogs are behaviors that help with _____.
    a. gathering food
    b. protection
    c. migration
    d. finding a mate

    ANS: D   DIF: A   OBJ: 17-4

20. Animals that give parental care usually produce _____ offspring than those that do not give parental care.
    a. more
    b. one more
    c. fewer
    d. one less

    ANS: C   DIF: A   OBJ: 17-6

21. Penguins that find their way home usually use _____ for direction.
    a. the moon
    b. a map
    c. the sun
    d. humans

    ANS: C   DIF: A   OBJ: 17-5

22. Silk moths give off a pheromone that helps them attract _____.
    a. silk
    b. bees
    c. males
    d. females

    ANS: C   DIF: A   OBJ: 17-5

23. Which of the following is a behavior that helps in protection?
    a. being a social insect
    b. forming a ring around young
    c. both a and b
    d. neither a nor b

    ANS: C   DIF: A   OBJ: 17-5

24. If a person is dependent on a drug and stops using it, _____ results.
    a. drug abuse
    b. withdrawal
    c. drug misuse
    d. overdose

    ANS: B   DIF: A   OBJ: 18-9

25. Over-the-counter drugs do NOT need a _____.
    a. neuron
    b. tolerance
    c. side effect
    d. prescription

    ANS: D   DIF: A   OBJ: 18-1

26. An overdose results when the kidneys get rid of a drug _____.
    a. too quickly
    b. too slowly
    c. both a and b
    d. neither a nor b

    ANS: B   DIF: A   OBJ: 18-2

27. A stimulant drug will cause body activity to _____.
    a. slow
    b. speed up
    c. sleep
    d. feel less pain

    ANS: B   DIF: A   OBJ: 18-4

28. Depressants will often block messages from moving across the _____.
    a. dendrite
    b. neuron
    c. brain
    d. synapse

    ANS: D   DIF: A   OBJ: 18-4

UNIT 5—PLANT SYSTEMS AND FUNCTIONS

MULTIPLE CHOICE

1. Thigmotropism is a response to _____.
   a. contact
   b. gravity
   c. light
   d. water

   ANS: A   DIF: A   OBJ: 21-3

2. Which is NOT a job of stems?
   a. transport of water
   b. transport of food
   c. support of leaves
   d. anchorage

   ANS: D   DIF: A   OBJ: 20-4

3. Soil is hard when the soil particles are _____.
   a. packed closely together
   b. packed loosely
   c. different sizes
   d. large

   ANS: A   DIF: A   OBJ: 21-5

4. Root hairs are part of which cell layer?
   a. xylem
   b. cortex
   c. epidermis
   d. phloem

   ANS: C   DIF: A   OBJ: 20-10

5. Plants use minerals for making chlorophyll and _____.
   a. energy
   b. carbon dioxide
   c. water
   d. cell walls

   ANS: D   DIF: A   OBJ: 21-5

6. Most photosynthesis takes place in which cells of a leaf?
   a. palisade
   b. xylem
   c. epidermis
   d. phloem

   ANS: A   DIF: A   OBJ: 19-2

7. Cortex cells _____.
   a. produce food
   b. store food
   c. carry water
   d. produce xylem and phloem

   ANS: B   DIF: A   OBJ: 20-5

8. Environmental factors needed by a plant for proper growth are _____.
   a. tropisms
   b. raw materials
   c. responses
   d. growth requirements

   ANS: D   DIF: A   OBJ: 21-5

9. Tropisms in plants _____.
   a. occur at night only
   b. involve movement
   c. occur during day only
   d. involve roots only

   ANS: B   DIF: A   OBJ: 21-3

10. Cambium cells _____.
    a. grow new root hairs
    b. make xylem and phloem
    c. form a protective layer
    d. make food for stems

    ANS: B   DIF: A   OBJ: 20-2

11. The size of the stoma is changed by _____.
    a. epidermis
    b. waxy layer
    c. guard cells
    d. palisade cells

    ANS: C   DIF: A   OBJ: 19-2

12. The function of xylem in a woody stem is to _____.
    a. make food
    b. carry water
    c. carry food
    d. protect all cells

    ANS: B   DIF: A   OBJ: 20-4

13. Hormones do NOT control which of the following?
   a. shape of roots
   b. flowering
   c. growth
   d. side branching
   ANS: A   DIF: A   OBJ: 21-1

14. Plants grown in less light than normal have stems that are _____.
   a. tall and green
   b. woody and green
   c. tall and pale green
   d. woody and yellow
   ANS: C   DIF: A   OBJ: 21-5

15. Gravitropism is a response to _____.
   a. light
   b. gravity
   c. contact
   d. water
   ANS: B   DIF: A   OBJ: 21-3

16. Long-day plants bloom during _____.
   a. summer
   b. autumn
   c. both a and b
   d. all year
   ANS: A   DIF: A   OBJ: 21-2

17. An example of a plant with a taproot is _____.
   a. dandelion
   b. carrot
   c. grass
   d. both a and b
   ANS: D   DIF: A   OBJ: 20-7

18. Leaves change color in autumn because of the breakdown of _____.
   a. chlorophyll
   b. xylem
   c. sugar
   d. cells
   ANS: A   DIF: A   OBJ: 19-9

19. Plants that have a one-year life cycle are _____.
   a. perennials
   b. annuals
   c. biennials
   d. triennials
   ANS: B   DIF: A   OBJ: 21-4

20. The function of phloem is to transport _____.
   a. food
   b. water
   c. oxygen
   d. minerals
   ANS: A   DIF: A   OBJ: 20-4

21. Chlorophyll in a leaf _____.
   a. traps light energy
   b. collects water
   c. traps carbon dioxide
   d. uses oxygen to make food
   ANS: A   DIF: A   OBJ: 19-4

22. Which of the following is NOT a tropism in a plant?
   a. roots growing down
   b. stems winding round other objects
   c. bending toward light
   d. flowers dying
   ANS: D   DIF: A   OBJ: 21-3

23. Most water enters a plant through the _____.
   a. phloem cells
   b. xylem cells
   c. root hairs
   d. cortex cells
   ANS: C   DIF: A   OBJ: 20-10

24. Root hairs absorb which of the following?
   a. food
   b. water
   c. light
   d. energy
   ANS: B   DIF: A   OBJ: 20-10

MULTIPLE CHOICE

1. Your body can repair itself and grow by using the cell process ____.
   a. meiosis
   b. reproduction
   c. mitosis
   d. respiration

   ANS: C   DIF: A   OBJ: 22-1

2. When a cell reproduces by mitosis, it always forms ____.
   a. one cell
   b. two cells
   c. sex cells
   d. cancer

   ANS: B   DIF: A   OBJ: 22-1

3. In step 1 of mitosis, sister chromatids ____.
   a. divide
   b. disappear
   c. copy themselves
   d. shorten

   ANS: D   DIF: A   OBJ: 22-3

4. What cell type is formed as a result of meiosis?
   a. body cells
   b. liver cells
   c. sex cells
   d. skin cells

   ANS: C   DIF: A   OBJ: 22-4

5. During meiosis, the chromosome number of a cell ____.
   a. is reduced
   b. is increased
   c. remains the same
   d. doubles

   ANS: A   DIF: A   OBJ: 22-4

6. Polar bodies form during the making of ____.
   a. sperm cells
   b. liver cells
   c. cancer cells
   d. egg cells

   ANS: D   DIF: A   OBJ: 22-6

---

25. Which of the following leaf parts is NOT made of cells?
    a. palisade
    b. phloem
    c. stoma
    d. epidermis

    ANS: C   DIF: A   OBJ: 19-2

7. An egg and sperm each give a new embryo _____ of its new chromosomes.
   a. 3/4
   b. 4/5
   c. 1/2
   d. 2/3

   ANS: C   DIF: A   OBJ: 22-6

8. Cell reproduction at an abnormally fast rate is called _____.
   a. meiosis
   b. growth
   c. cancer
   d. aging

   ANS: C   DIF: A   OBJ: 22-8

9. Plants that reproduce by asexual reproduction are using _____.
   a. mitosis
   b. one parent
   c. two parents
   d. both a and b

   ANS: D   DIF: A   OBJ: 23-9

10. Bulbs and tubers are _____.
    a. roots
    b. leaves
    c. flowers
    d. stems

    ANS: D   DIF: A   OBJ: 23-3

11. The flower part that is male is the _____.
    a. pistil
    b. ovary
    c. stamen
    d. sepal

    ANS: C   DIF: A   OBJ: 23-4

12. The saclike part at the top of a stamen produces _____.
    a. eggs
    b. ovules
    c. pollen
    d. sperm

    ANS: C   DIF: A   OBJ: 23-4

13. Unlike an adult frog, a tadpole has _____.
    a. legs
    b. a tail
    c. no mouth
    d. fins

    ANS: B   DIF: A   OBJ: 25-6

14. A bud is formed on a hydra by the process of _____.
    a. meiosis
    b. mitosis
    c. regeneration
    d. fertilization

    ANS: B   DIF: A   OBJ: 24-2

15. By the end of the first month of development, you already had all the following EXCEPT _____.
    a. heart
    b. sex organs
    c. brain
    d. stomach

    ANS: B   DIF: A   OBJ: 25-3

16. Chicken eggs carry their stored food in the form of _____.
    a. yolk and albumen
    b. an umbilical cord
    c. the placenta
    d. eggshells

    ANS: A   DIF: A   OBJ: 25-5

17. A human male forms _____ sperm from each original cell.
    a. one
    b. two
    c. four
    d. eight

    ANS: C   DIF: A   OBJ: 22-6

18. Budding and regeneration are forms of _____ reproduction.
    a. sexual
    b. slow
    c. asexual
    d. internal

    ANS: C   DIF: A   OBJ: 24-2

25. A fertilized egg will divide many times from one cell to many cells. This is called _____.
    a. menstruation
    b. cleavage
    c. development
    d. metamorphosis

    ANS: B   DIF: A   OBJ: 25-1

26. Which of the following is NOT provided through the placenta?
    a. complete protection for the fetus
    b. food
    c. oxygen
    d. pathway for wastes

    ANS: A   DIF: A   OBJ: 25-2

27. Your navel is all that remains of your _____.
    a. umbilical cord
    b. placenta
    c. amniotic sac
    d. yolk

    ANS: A   DIF: A   OBJ: 25-3

28. You were first called a(n) _____ and then a _____ after three months of development.
    a. nymph/fetus
    b. larva/nymph
    c. embryo/fetus
    d. nymph/larva

    ANS: C   DIF: A   OBJ: 25-3

19. Animals that carry out external fertilization include _____.
    a. humans
    b. cats
    c. birds
    d. frogs

    ANS: D   DIF: A   OBJ: 24-4

20. In males, _____ form _____ cells.
    a. ovaries/sperm
    b. testes/eggs
    c. testes/sperm
    d. ovaries/eggs

    ANS: C   DIF: A   OBJ: 22-6

21. Oviducts carry egg cells toward the _____.
    a. ovaries
    b. ureters
    c. penis
    d. uterus

    ANS: D   DIF: A   OBJ: 24-6

22. During the menstrual cycle, an ovary releases an egg at about day _____.
    a. 1
    b. 32
    c. 28
    d. 14

    ANS: D   DIF: A   OBJ: 24-7

23. If an egg is fertilized, it will remain in the _____ for development.
    a. vagina
    b. uterus
    c. oviduct
    d. ovary

    ANS: B   DIF: A   OBJ: 24-6

24. The hormone that is connected with menstruation and the menstrual cycle is _____.
    a. estrous
    b. thyroxine
    c. estrogen
    d. insulin

    ANS: C   DIF: A   OBJ: 24-7

UNIT 7—TRAITS OF LIVING THINGS

MULTIPLE CHOICE

1. Mendel noticed that short plants mated to short plants produced _____ plants.
   a. all short
   b. all tall
   c. tall and short
   d. mostly short

   ANS: A   DIF: A   OBJ: 26-6

2. A mutation is a change in the _____ of an organism.
   a. color
   b. DNA code
   c. environment
   d. birthrate

   ANS: B   DIF: A   OBJ: 28-4

3. DNA in identical twins is _____.
   a. different
   b. the same
   c. changed slightly
   d. changed greatly

   ANS: B   DIF: A   OBJ: 28-5

4. A genetic disorder in which a person's blood does not clot is _____.
   a. type Q blood
   b. hemophilia
   c. pneumonia
   d. cystic fibrosis

   ANS: B   DIF: A   OBJ: 27-6

5. A trait that is inherited on sex chromosomes is _____.
   a. eye color
   b. dyslexia
   c. cystic fibrosis
   d. hemophilia

   ANS: D   DIF: A   OBJ: 27-6

6. When a cell divides, DNA copies itself, producing two new cells with _____.
   a. no chromosomes
   b. identical genes
   c. extra chromosomes
   d. half the number of chromosomes

   ANS: B   DIF: A   OBJ: 28-3

7. Which of the following is pure dominant?
   a. Mn
   b. MM
   c. Ff
   d. mm

   ANS: B   DIF: A   OBJ: 26-2

8. A trait that shows lack of dominance is _____.
   a. color blindness
   b. PKU
   c. hemophilia
   d. sickle-cell anemia

   ANS: D   DIF: A   OBJ: 27-4

9. The number of different nitrogen bases in DNA is _____.
   a. two
   b. four
   c. six
   d. eight

   ANS: B   DIF: A   OBJ: 28-1

10. The shape of a DNA molecule is _____.
    a. straight
    b. circular
    c. flat
    d. spiral

    ANS: D   DIF: A   OBJ: 28-1

11. In a DNA molecule, base A joins with base _____.
    a. A
    b. C
    c. T
    d. G

    ANS: C   DIF: A   OBJ: 28-1

12. When both parents are heterozygous for cystic fibrosis, expected offspring will be _____.
    a. 1/4 with cystic fibrosis
    b. 1/2 with cystic fibrosis
    c. 3/4 with cystic fibrosis
    d. all with cystic fibrosis

    ANS: A   DIF: A   OBJ: 27-7

13. Autosomes are chromosomes that _____.
   a. are X and Y
   b. do not determine sex
   c. determine sex
   d. are found in sex cells only

   ANS: B   DIF: A   OBJ: 27-3

14. PKU is a disorder that can harm which organ of the body?
   a. eyes
   b. blood vessels
   c. heart
   d. brain

   ANS: D   DIF: A   OBJ: 27-6

15. Any trait that makes an organism better able to survive in its surroundings is a(n) _____.
   a. adaptation
   b. fossil
   c. mutation
   d. chromosome

   ANS: A   DIF: A   OBJ: 29-1

16. A person with type O blood can pass on genes _____.
   a. BO
   b. AO
   c. BB
   d. OO

   ANS: D   DIF: A   OBJ: 27-5

17. A person with blood type A has genes _____.
   a. OO
   b. BO
   c. AO or AA
   d. AO or AB

   ANS: C   DIF: A   OBJ: 27-5

18. DNA controls the _____ of living things.
   a. number
   b. traits
   c. behavior
   d. environment

   ANS: B   DIF: A   OBJ: 28-2

19. Besides _____ bases, DNA contains sugar and acid.
   a. fat
   b. oxygen
   c. nitrogen
   d. carbohydrate

   ANS: C   DIF: A   OBJ: 28-1

20. DNA forms the code for making _____ on ribosomes.
   a. proteins
   b. genes
   c. fats
   d. chromosomes

   ANS: A   DIF: A   OBJ: 28-3

21. Evidence that life existed in the past is called a _____.
   a. mutation
   b. fossil
   c. variation
   d. selection

   ANS: B   DIF: A   OBJ: 29-5

22. Animals that are most fit for their surroundings usually _____.
   a. are killed
   b. survive
   c. do not reproduce
   d. kill other animals

   ANS: B   DIF: A   OBJ: 29-1

23. If both parents are color-blind, the chance of their children being color-blind is _____.
   a. 1/4
   b. 2/4
   c. 3/4
   d. 4/4

   ANS: D   DIF: A   OBJ: 27-5

24. Which is true about an X chromosome when compared to a Y chromosome?
   a. X is longer than Y
   b. X has fewer genes than Y
   c. X is shorter than Y
   d. X has same number of genes as Y

   ANS: A   DIF: A   OBJ: 27-3

MULTIPLE CHOICE

1. Prey population usually decreases as a predator population _____.
   a. increases
   b. decreases
   c. emigrates
   d. stays the same

   ANS: A   DIF: A   OBJ: 30-10

2. There are fewer organisms at the top of an energy pyramid because _____.
   a. they have less space
   b. less energy is available to them
   c. they are small organisms
   d. more energy is available to them

   ANS: B   DIF: A   OBJ: 30-6

3. Predator-prey relationships _____.
   a. are limiting factors
   b. are all commensalism
   c. affect only prey populations
   d. affect only predator populations

   ANS: A   DIF: A   OBJ: 30-10

4. Which is NOT a kind of particle in the air we breathe?
   a. soot
   b. dust
   c. carbon dioxide
   d. smoke

   ANS: C   DIF: A   OBJ: 32-4

5. A metal that makes children sick if they eat old paint is _____.
   a. nitrogen
   b. lead
   c. iron
   d. mercury

   ANS: B   DIF: A   OBJ: 32-5

6. In an ecosystem, you study how living parts and _____ work together.
   a. plants
   b. animals
   c. both a and b
   d. nonliving parts

   ANS: D   DIF: A   OBJ: 31-1

---

25. Each human sperm or egg has how many chromosomes?
    a. 23
    b. 46
    c. 92
    d. 43

    ANS: A   DIF: A   OBJ: 27-1

26. A heterozygous individual contains which of the following genes for a trait?
    a. two dominant genes
    b. two recessive genes
    c. one dominant/one recessive gene
    d. two dominant/two recessive genes

    ANS: C   DIF: A   OBJ: 26-2

27. The correct genes for a father who is color blind would be _____.
    a. CC
    b. cc
    c. CY
    d. cY

    ANS: D   DIF: A   OBJ: 27-5

7. _____ is needed for photosynthesis.
   a. Nitrogen
   b. Oxygen
   c. Carbon dioxide
   d. Soil

   ANS: C   DIF: A   OBJ: 31-3

8. Which level of a food chain has the most energy available?
   a. secondary consumers
   b. primary consumers
   c. animals
   d. producers

   ANS: D   DIF: A   OBJ: 30-6

9. North America includes which of the following?
   a. three communities
   b. six climax communities
   c. several biomes
   d. a few populations

   ANS: C   DIF: A   OBJ: 31-7

10. Acid forms in the air when _____ join(s) with water.
    a. dust particles
    b. smoke particles
    c. sulfur dioxide
    d. oxygen

    ANS: C   DIF: A   OBJ: 32-4

11. Very fine floating soil particles that settle on the bottom of a stream are _____.
    a. sediment
    b. gravel
    c. pollutants
    d. biodegradable

    ANS: A   DIF: A   OBJ: 32-2

12. Food is made in a community by _____.
    a. all consumers
    b. decomposers
    c. primary consumers
    d. producers

    ANS: D   DIF: A   OBJ: 30-5

13. In an ecosystem, living things are affected by nonliving things such as _____.
    a. soil and sunlight
    b. consumers
    c. decomposers
    d. producers

    ANS: A   DIF: A   OBJ: 31-1

14. As a pond goes through succession it becomes _____.
    a. larger
    b. more shallow
    c. deeper
    d. cleaner

    ANS: B   DIF: A   OBJ: 31-5

15. Which of the following is being destroyed and changed to farmland?
    a. desert
    b. swamps
    c. tundra
    d. rain forest

    ANS: D   DIF: A   OBJ: 32-1

16. Certain chemicals found in spray cans destroy Earth's _____ layer.
    a. carbon dioxide
    b. nitrogen
    c. smog
    d. ozone

    ANS: D   DIF: A   OBJ: 32-4

17. In the water cycle, water is in the form of a _____ after it evaporates.
    a. gas
    b. solid
    c. liquid
    d. liquid and solid

    ANS: A   DIF: A   OBJ: 31-2

18. A chemical that causes weak shells in birds' eggs is _____.
    a. PCB
    b. DDT
    c. mercury
    d. fertilizer

    ANS: B   DIF: A   OBJ: 32-5

19. One way to conserve wildlife is to set up _____.
   a. recycling centers
   b. reservoirs
   c. refuges
   d. landfills

   ANS: C   DIF: A   OBJ: 32-6

20. Which is NOT a water pollution problem?
   a. smog
   b. PCBs
   c. pesticides
   d. toxic chemicals

   ANS: A   DIF: A   OBJ: 32-5

21. Deer and mice are examples of _____.
   a. producers
   b. primary consumers
   c. secondary consumers
   d. decomposers

   ANS: B   DIF: A   OBJ: 30-5

22. What kind of animal shows up after weeds start to grow in a community?
   a. primary consumer
   b. secondary consumer
   c. meat eater
   d. both a and b

   ANS: A   DIF: A   OBJ: 31-4

23. Climate does NOT include _____.
   a. snow
   b. rain
   c. temperature
   d. soil

   ANS: D   DIF: A   OBJ: 31-6

24. An area with a distinct climate and specific organisms is a _____.
   a. biome
   b. community
   c. climax community
   d. pond community

   ANS: A   DIF: A   OBJ: 31-7

25. A gas that is dangerous because it gives off radiation is _____.
   a. carbon monoxide
   b. neon
   c. ozone
   d. radon

   ANS: D   DIF: A   OBJ: 32-4

26. A biodegradable substance is one that _____.
   a. causes pollution
   b. breaks down
   c. stays in ecosystems
   d. moves through food chains

   ANS: B   DIF: A   OBJ: 32-7

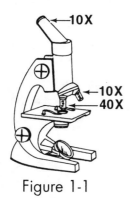

Figure 1-1

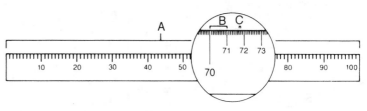

Figure 1-2

Cell 1

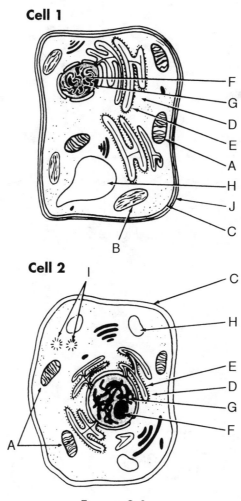

Figure 2-1

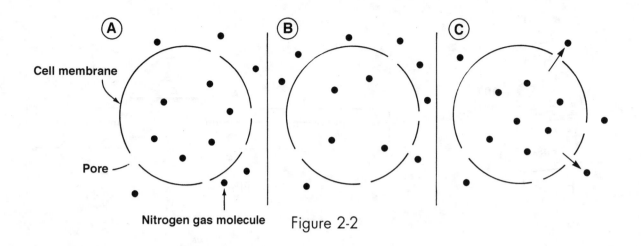

Cell membrane

Pore

Nitrogen gas molecule

Figure 2-2

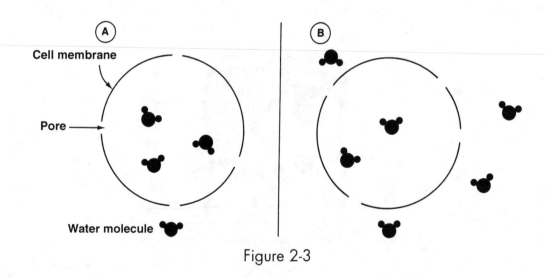

Cell membrane

Pore

Water molecule

Figure 2-3

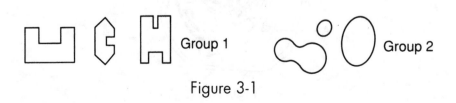

Group 1   Group 2

Figure 3-1

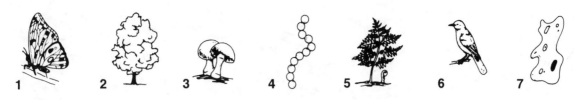

Figure 3-2

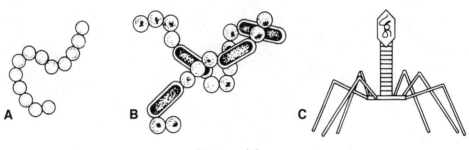

A   B   C

Figure 4-1

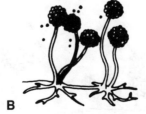

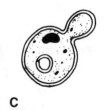

A   B   C

Figure 5-1

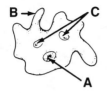
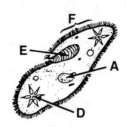

Figure 5-2

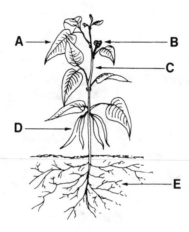

Figure 6-1

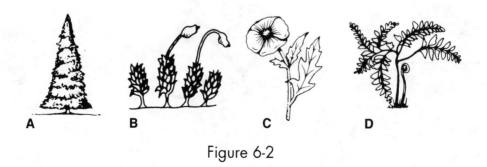

Figure 6-2

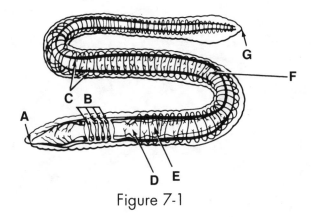

Figure 7-1

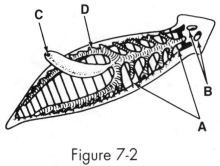

Figure 7-2

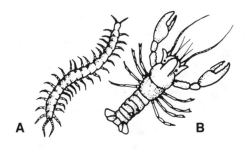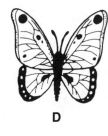

Figure 8-1

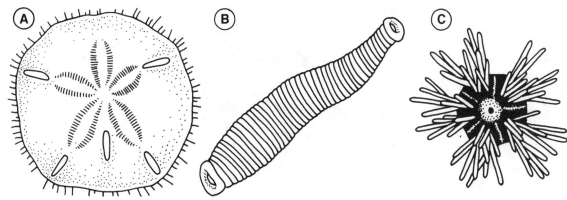

Figure 8-2

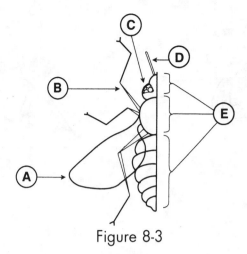

Figure 8-3

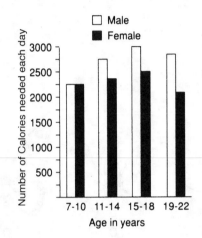

Figure 9-1

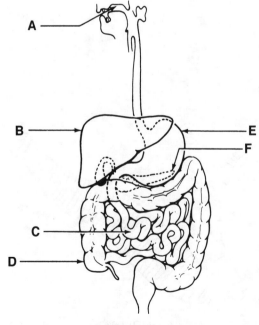

Figure 10-1

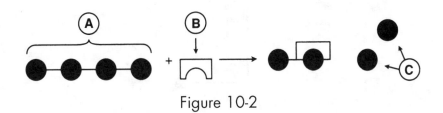

Figure 10-2

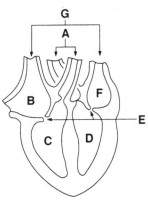

Figure 11-1

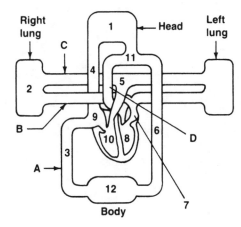

Figure 11-2

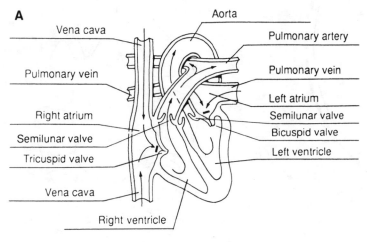

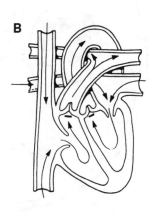

Figure 11-3

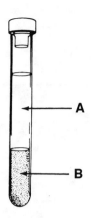

Figure 12-1

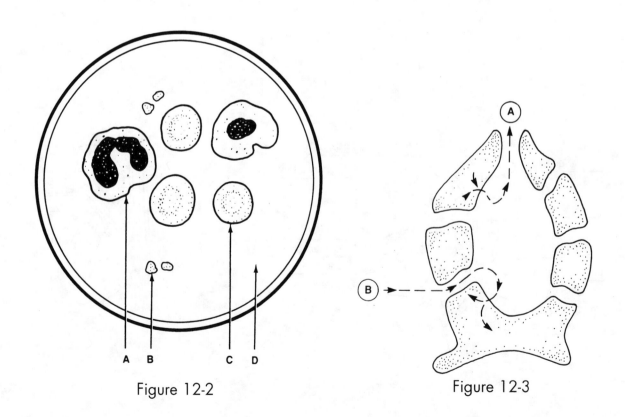

Figure 12-2

Figure 12-3

Blood type	Red cell protein present	Plasma protein present
A	Red cell Protein	
B		
AB		None
O		

Figure 12-4

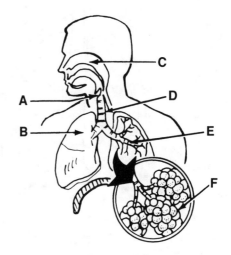

Figure 13-1

$$O_2 \ + \ C_6H_{12}O_6 \ \xrightarrow{\ \ A\ \ } \ CO_2 \ + \ H_2O$$

Figure 13-2

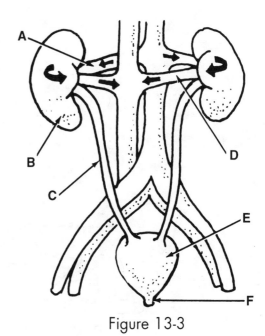

Figure 13-3

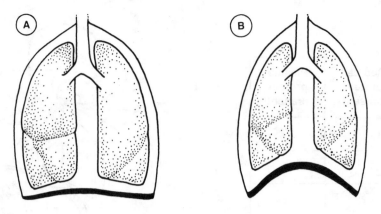

Figure 13-4

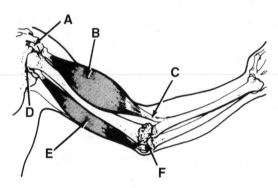

Figure 14-1

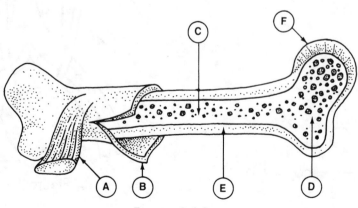

Figure 14-2

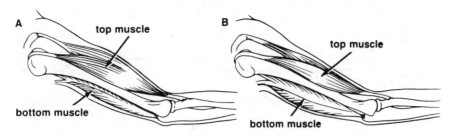

A top muscle

bottom muscle

B top muscle

bottom muscle

Figure 14-3

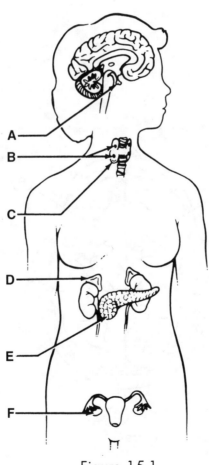

A

B

C

D

E

F

Figure 15-1

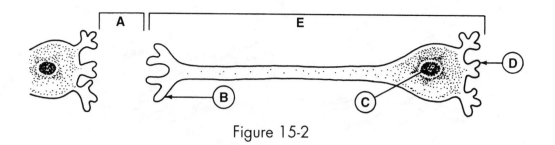

Figure 15-2

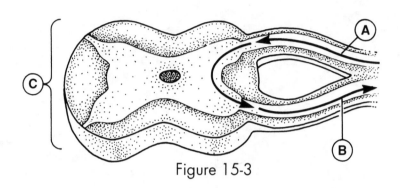

Figure 15-3

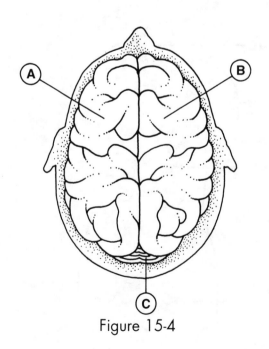

Figure 15-4

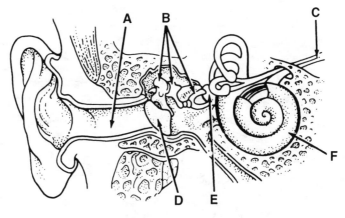

Figure 16-1

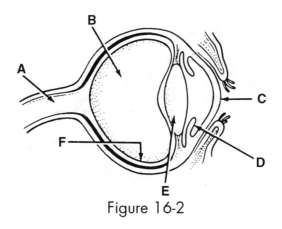

Figure 16-2

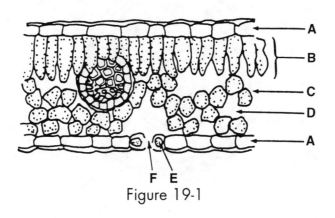

Figure 19-1

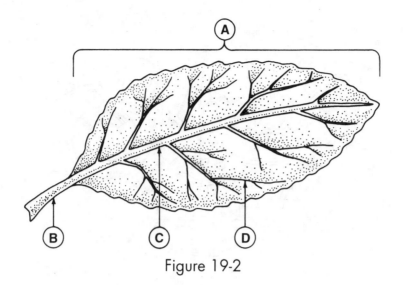

Figure 19-2

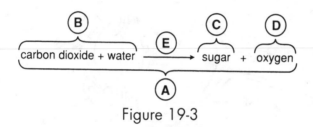

Figure 19-3

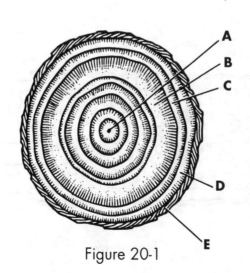

Figure 20-1

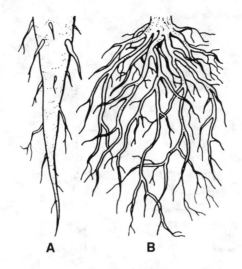

A   B

Figure 20-2

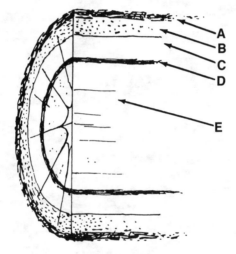

A
B
C
D

E

Figure 20-3

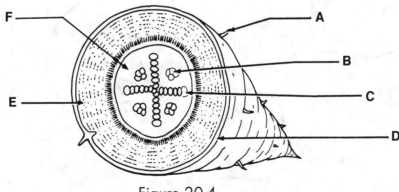

F

A

B

E

C

D

Figure 20-4

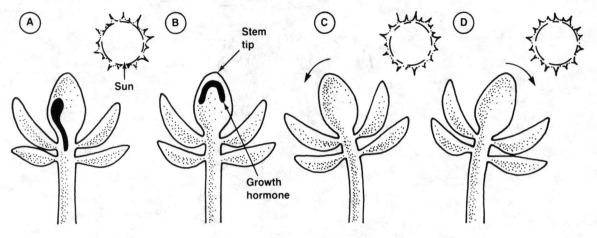

Figure 21-1

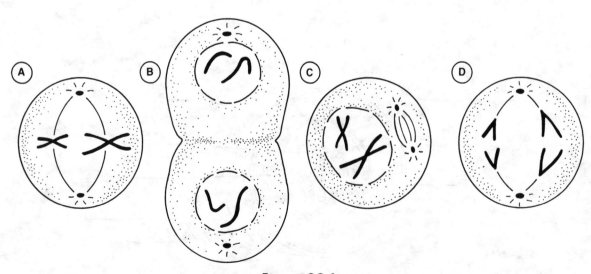

Figure 22-1

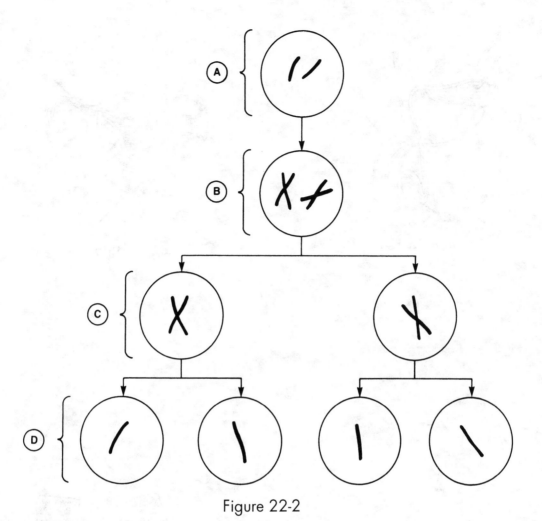

Figure 22-2

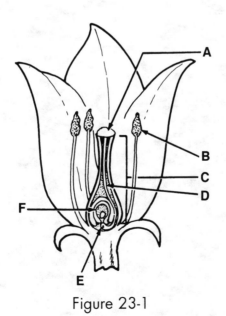

Figure 23-1

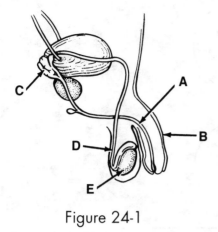

Figure 24-1

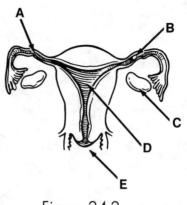

Figure 24-2

Figure 24-3

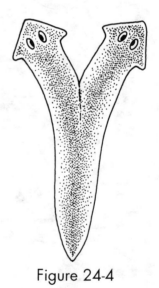

Figure 24-4

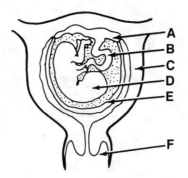

Figure 25-1

T = tall pea plant t = short pea plant

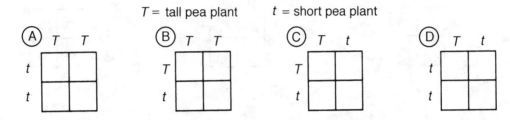

Figure 26-1

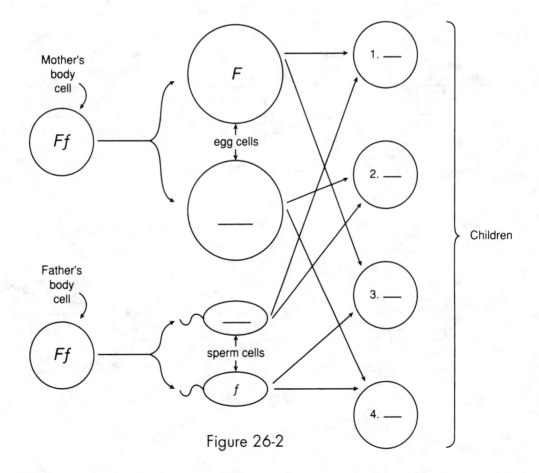

Figure 26-2

(a)

	D	d
D	DD	Dd
D	DD	Dd

(b)

	D	d
d	dd	dd
d	Dd	dd

(c)

	d	d
d	Dd	dd
d	Dd	dd

Figure 27-1

(a)

	X	Y
X	XX	XY
X	XX	XY

(b)

	X	Y
X	XX	XY
X	XX	XX

(c)

	X	Y
X	XX	XX
X	XY	XY

Figure 27-2

(a)

	f	f
F	Ff	Ff
f	FF	ff

(b)

	F	f
f	Ff	ff
f	Ff	ff

(c)

	F	f
F	FF	FF
f	Ff	ff

Figure 27-3

(a)

	S	S
s	Ss	Ss
s	ss	Ss

(b)

	S	s
s	Ss	Ss
s	Ss	ss

(c)

	S	s
S	SS	Ss
s	Ss	ss

Figure 27-4

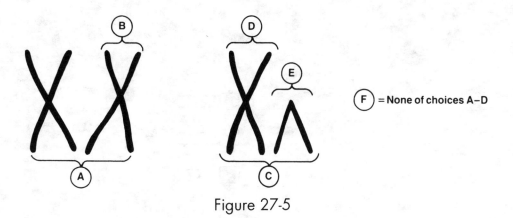

(F) = None of choices A–D

Figure 27-5

Blood Types

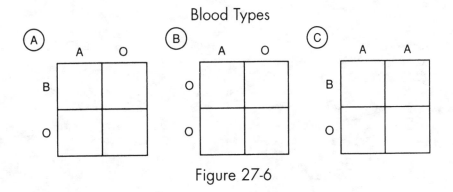

Figure 27-6

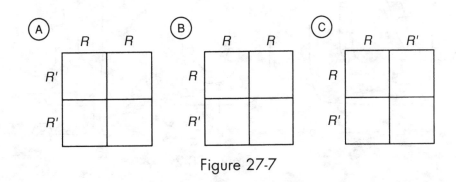

Figure 27-7

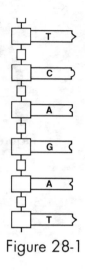

Figure 28-1

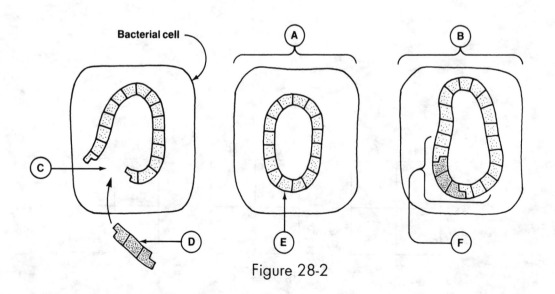

Figure 28-2

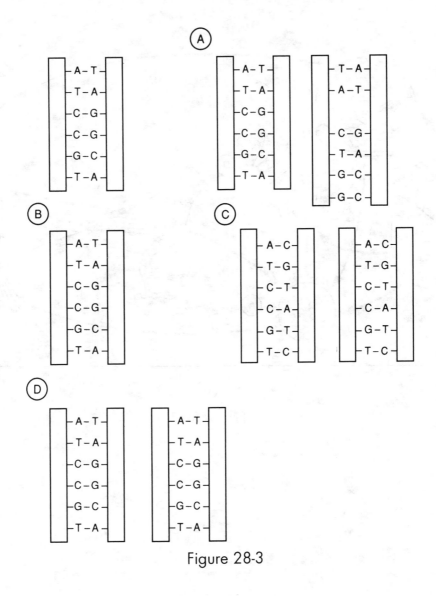

Figure 28-3

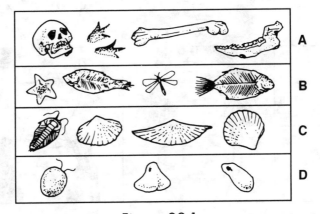

Figure 29-1

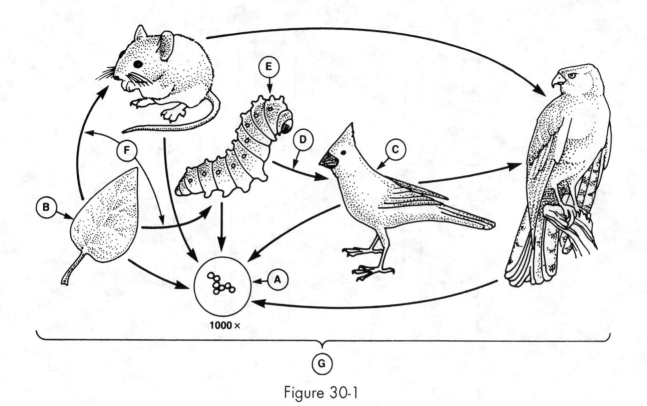

Figure 30-1

Choice	Doer	Receiver
A		
B		
C		

Figure 30-2

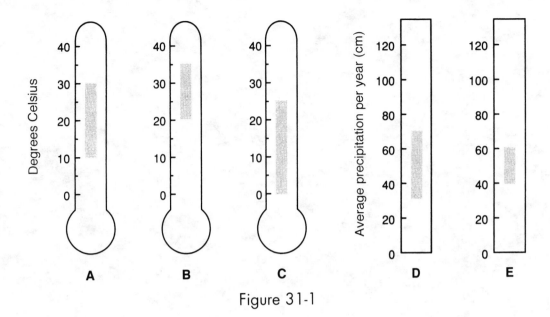

Figure 31-1